PPLN: 1273   WAVE: 001   PICK CTL #:0611527O
INU: P930138573785   TYPE: FPK   CHECK DGT: A1
PARCEL #: 0465991¡   CARTON TYPE: FPK

QTY	ISBN	TITLE	ED FM
1	0136123260	DIGITAL NEURAL NETWORKS	

LOCATION
FPK

SENT WITH THE COMPLIMENTS OF YOUR PH REPRESENTATIVE
SCOTT BARR   105 SILLEN PLANTATION
                             STEVENSVILLE   MD 21666
TELEPHONE (410) 643-3701
SHIP VIA UPS

Digital
Neural
Networks

**PRENTICE HALL INFORMATION
AND SYSTEM SCIENCES SERIES**
Thomas Kailath, Editor

Digital
Neural
Networks

S. Y. Kung

Department of Electrical Engineering
Princeton University

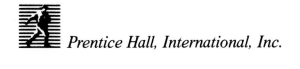
Prentice Hall, International, Inc.

0-13-617150-8

This edition may be sold only in those countries to which
it is consigned by Prentice-Hall International. It is not to
be re-exported and it is not for sale in the U.S.A., Mexico,
or Canada.

 ©1993 by PTR PRENTICE-HALL, INC.
A Simon & Schuster Company
Englewood Cliffs, N.J. 07632

Printed in the United States of America

10   9   8   7   6   5   4   3   2   1

ISBN 0-13-617150-8

Prentice-Hall International (UK) Limited, *London*
Prentice-Hall of Australia Pty. Limited, *Sydney*
Prentice-Hall Canada Inc., *Toronto*
Prentice-Hall Hispanoamericana, S.A., *Mexico*
Prentice-Hall of India Private Limited, *New Delhi*
Prentice-Hall of Japan, Inc., *Tokyo*
Simon & Schuster Asia Pte. Ltd., *Singapore*
Editora Prentice-Hall do Brasil, Ltda., *Rio de Janeiro*
Prentice-Hall Inc., *Englewood Cliffs, New Jersey*

To Se-Wei, Li, Charles,

and my parents

Contents

PART II   UNSUPERVISED MODELS _____

PART III   SUPERVISED MODELS ⸺⸺⸺⸺⸺⸺⸺

PART IV   TEMPORAL MODELS

PART V   ADVANCED TOPICS ─────────────────────────

PART VI   IMPLEMENTATION

10   Architecture and Implementation   337

Preface

Unification. — Confucius, 551-479 B.C

The field of *digital neural networks* brings together scientists who study how the brain works and engineers who build highly parallel and intelligent supercomputers. The main objective of this book is to provide a synergistic and systematic exploration of several fundamental issues on *digital neural networks.* The word *digital* refers to *discrete-time* digital processing systems. The term *neural networks* embodies information processing systems using a combination of *nonlinear, adaptive, network,* and *parallel processing* technologies. Digital neural networks provide a natural link between the rapid advance of (VLSI) microelectronics and parallel processing technology and the increasing need for intelligent processing techniques. This represents a truly interdisciplinary research field which will ultimately lead to the future intelligent processing systems.

Many excellent reference books on neural networks exist; some place emphasis on the biological view, and others take a physics perspective. In contrast, this book is intended to be a textbook prepared for the discipline of information science and electrical engineering.

The book contains six parts:

- **Part I: Introduction** (Chapter 1);

- **Part II: Unsupervised Models** — associative memory (Chapter 2) and competitive learning networks (Chapter 3);

- **Part III: Supervised Models** — decision and approximation/optimization based neural networks (Chapters 4 & 5);

- **Part IV: Temporal Models** — deterministic and stochastic temporal networks (Chapters 6 & 7);

- **Part V: Advanced Topics** — principal component neural networks (Chapter 8) and stochastic annealing networks (Chapter 9);

- **Part VI: Implementation** (Chapter 10).

The following road map serves as a guide for teaching or reading.

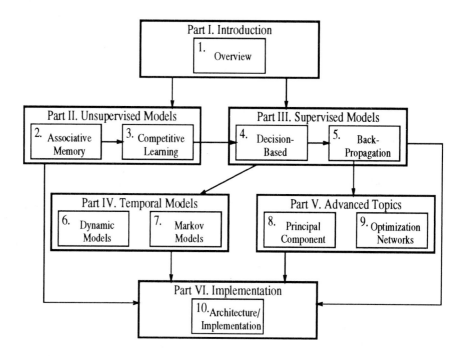

The topics covered in Chapters 1 - 5 and Chapter 9 follow a rather orthodox neural network presentation, while the topics addressed in Chapters 6 through 8 are somewhat unorthodox in that they stem from the conventional signal processing and system theoretical perspectives. Chapter 10 provides a methodology for mapping neural models to parallel architecture and implementation.

Some unique features of the book:

- It aims at a coherent treatment which links the orthodox and unorthodox approaches to neural models. For this, we introduce what can be called *neural network system theory,* which unifies many diversified neural models.

- It employs an application-driven perspective, particularly signal/image processing and pattern recognition applications. Moreover, it goes on to present an integrated study of the application, algorithm, and architecture aspects of neural networks.

- It provides a working knowledge of various neural models, including theoretical basis, potential applications, and digital implementations. With this cross-disciplinary background, the reader would be better equipped to tackle research and application projects related to neural information processing.

This book is intended to be a textbook for a one-semester graduate or undergraduate course. (It is assumed that the reader has the basic background of advanced calculus, linear system theory, and signal processing. Otherwise, some mathematical treatments in some sections may be too advanced for uninitiated students.) Lectures for an undergraduate or graduate class can be organized from the following recommended sections:

- Chapters 1 - 7, (except Section 5.4)

- Sections 8.2, 8.3, 9.2, and 10.2.

ACKNOWLEDGMENTS

Without enthusiastic support and encouragement from so many friends, it would be impossible to attempt a book on such a dynamic and diversified subject. First, my thanks go to the researchers who have contributed to this rich research literature of neural networks. Their works have provided the foundation for the book. Also, I must apologize for having overlooked many critical topics and references in bibliographical research due to time constraints.

This book is an outgrowth of many semesters' lectures on the subject. I am very much indebted to many of my in-class students for their invaluable questions and contributions on examples and exercises. The advanced part of the book is largely extracted from several Ph. D. dissertations under my supervision. I wish to thank all of them: Drs. Kostas Diamantaras, Mark Goudreau, Jen-Neng Hwang, Wei-Dong Mao, John Vlontzos, and especially Mr. Wei-Hsin Chou and Mr. Jin-Shiuh Taur. They deserve to be named co-authors of the book.

I have benefited greatly the frequent and enlightening exchange and collaboration with many of my colleagues. To name a few: Drs. Alice Chiang, Frank Fallside, Lee Giles, Robert Hecht-Nielsen, Yuhen Hu, Fred Juang, Teuvo Kohonen, Gary Kuhn, H.C. Lee, Lenart Ljung, Christoph von der Malsburg, Alastair McAulay, John Moody, Ulrich Ramacher, and John Sorensen. Their enthusiastic participation in this project has made this prolonged process more bearable and indeed very enjoyable and rewarding. My deep gratitude goes to the reviewers for their critical and constructive suggestions on many drafts of the book. They are Drs. Joshua Alspector, Brad Dickinson, Tony Kuh, Guanghan Xu, Mr. Jerry Murphy, and other anonymous reviewers. My sincere appreciation goes to my professor and the series editor, Professor Tom Kailath, for many years of inspiration and friendship.

I have been very fortunate to work with Ms. Karen Gettman and Ms. Kim Gueterman at Prentice Hall, who have provided very professional assistance throughout this project. I am grateful to the Department of Electrical Engineering, Princeton University, for making available a very scholarly environment for both teaching and research. I also want to thank the secretarial staff for their tireless and cheerful assistance during this long process: Susan Gafgen, Kim Hegelbach, Emmalee Morrison, and Lynn O'Shaughnessy. Finally, I am pleased to acknowledge that some work presented in this book was supported in part by Grants and Contracts from National Science Foundation, Air Force Office of Scientific Research, and Defense Advanced Research Project Agency.

Princeton, New Jersey   **S.Y. Kung**

Digital
Neural
Networks

PART I: INTRODUCTION

Chapter 1

Overview

1.1 Introduction

Neural networks have become a very popular field of research in cognitive science, neurobiology, computer engineering/science, signal processing, optics, and physics. They represent a very broad range of neural processing models. The purpose of this book is to provide an integrated and cohesive exploration of the fundamental issues on *digital neural networks*. The word "digital" refers to "discrete-time" processing. In terms of data format, it may involve discrete-value or continuous-value signals. The term "neural networks" is characterized by a combined adaptive network and parallel processing technologies. Therefore, the field requires a coherent study and understanding of multi-disciplinary issues, including application-needs, neural models, and parallel processing.

An artificial neural network is an abstract simulation of a real nervous system that contains a collection of *neuron units* communicating with each other via *axon connections*. Such a model bears a strong resemblance to axons and dendrites in a nervous system. Due to its self-organizing and adaptive nature, the model potentially offers a new parallel processing paradigm that could be more robust and user-friendly than the traditional approaches.

The first fundamental modeling of neural nets was proposed in 1943 by McCulloch and Pitts in terms of a computational model of "nervous activity". The McCulloch-Pitts neuron is a binary device and each neuron has a fixed threshold, thus performing simple threshold logic. The McCulloch-Pitts model lead the works of John von Neumann, Marvin Minsky, Frank Rosenblatt, and many others. Hebb postulated, in his classical book *The Organization of Behavior*, that the neurons were appropriately interconnected by self-organization and that "an existing pathway strengthens the connections between the neurons." He proposed that the connectivity of the brain is continually changing as an organism learns differing functional tasks, and that cell assemblies are created by such changes [55]. By embedding a vast number of simple neurons in an interacting nervous system, it is possible to provide computational power for very sophisticated information processing [16]. The neural models can be divided into two categories:

1. The first is the *biological type*. It encompasses networks mimicking biological neural systems such as audio (cochlea) functions or early vision (retina) functions.

2. The other type is *application-driven*. It depends less on the faithfulness to neurobiology. For these models the architectures are largely dictated by the application needs. Many such neural networks are represented by the so-called *connectionist models*.

1.1.1   Biological-Type Neural Networks

It is estimated that the human brain contains over 100 billion (10^{11}) neurons and 10^{14} synapses in the human nervous system. Studies of brain neuroanatomy indicate more than 1000 synapses on the input and output of each neuron. Note that, although the neuron's switch time (a few *milliseconds*) is about a millionfold times slower than current computer elements, they have a thousandfold greater connectivity than today's supercomputers.

The main objective of biological-type neural nets is to develop a synthetic element for verifying hypotheses concerning biological systems. The neural nets are not directly used for data-processing purposes. For example, research on biological-type vision neural nets has focused on functions such as motion field, binocular stereo, and edge detection. Due to fragmentary knowledge about biological systems for these functions, only very coarse mathematical models are applied.

In natural retina vision processing, edge information is extracted via lateral inhibition between retinal neurons. In the cortex, there is a lateral excitation process that computes the lightness of a patch of the image bounded by edges. Depth perception, on the other hand, is formed by comparing images from the two eyes in primates. Finding the correct overall assignment (from the several depth assignments existing in each cortical neighborhood) takes numerous trials before the cortical net finds a "solution". Interestingly, this process is analogous to the relaxation process in many numerical algorithms run on current digital computers. Many such biological processing examples have provided useful clues for the development of artificial neural networks. For example, the retina and cochlea chips in [193] have a strong biological similarity. The architecture of the cerebral cortex can be reasonably modeled by 3 to 6 layers of neurons, each neuron connecting to about 10 others.

Neurons and the interconnection synapses constitute the key elements for neural information processing. Most neurons possess tree-like structures called dendrites which receive incoming signals from other neurons across junctions called synapses [55]. Some neurons communicate with only a few nearby ones, whereas others make contact with thousands. A simplified sketch of a natural neural network is illustrated in Figure 1.1. There are three parts in a **neuron**: (1) a neuron cell body, (2) branching extensions called *dendrites* for receiving input, and (3) an *axon* that carries the neuron's output to the dendrites of other neurons. The **synapse** represents the junction between an axon and a dendrite.

How two or more neurons interact remains largely mysterious and complexities of different neurons vary greatly. Generally speaking, a neuron sends its output to other neurons via its axon. An axon carries information through a series of action potentials, or waves of current, that depend on the neuron's voltage potential. More precisely, the membrane generates the action potential and propagates down the axon and its branches, where axonal insulators restore and amplify the signal as it propagates, until it arrives at a synaptic junction. This process is often modeled as a propagation rule represented by a *net value* $u(\cdot)$, cf. Figure 1.2(a).

A neuron collects signals at its synapses by summing all the excitatory and inhibitory influences acting upon it. If the excitatory influences are dominant, then the neuron fires and sends this message to other neurons via the outgoing synapses. In this sense, the *neuron function* can be (and indeed often is) modeled as a simple threshold function $f(\cdot)$. As shown in Figure 1.2(a), the

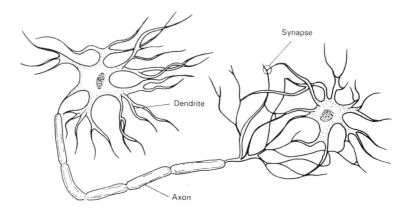

Figure 1.1: A simplified sketch of biological neurons. (Reprinted with permission from [58], © AIP-AFCEA International Press.)

neuron fires if the combined signal strength exceeds a certain threshold.

1.1.2 Application-Driven Neural Networks

In general, neurons and axons are mathematically modeled by activation functions and net functions (or basis functions) respectively, cf. Figure 1.2(b). Lacking more advanced knowledge on nervous systems, it is impossible to specifically define the neuron functionalities and connection structures merely from a biological perspective. Consequently, the selection of these functions often depends on the applications the neural models are for. In other words, application-driven neural models are only loosely tied to the biological realities. Instead, they are strongly associated with high-level and intelligent processing in recognition and classification. They have the potential to offer a truly revolutionary technology for modern information processing. The strength of application-driven neural networks hinges upon three main characteristics:

1. *Adaptiveness and self-organization:* it offers robust and adaptive processing capabilities by adopting adaptive learning and self-organization rules.

2. *Nonlinear network processing:* it enhances the network's approximation, classification and noise-immunity capabilities.

3. *Parallel processing:* it usually employs a large number of processing cells enhanced by extensive interconnectivity.

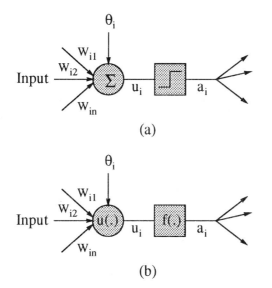

Figure 1.2: (a) A simplified neural model with linear net function and a threshold neuron function. (b) A general neural model. The net value is represented by a net function $u(\cdot)$ and the neuron value by an activation function $f(\cdot)$.

These characteristics have played an important role in neural network's applicabilities to signal and image processing and analysis. An application-driven neural model can be very precisely defined. *A neural network architecture comprises massively parallel adaptive processing elements with hierarchically structured interconnection networks.* Under these circumstances, application-specific parallel processing machines (e.g., hypercube or pipelined array processors) arise naturally as candidate architectures. Indeed, parallel and adaptive architectures have become indispensable in many signal- and image-processing applications. Under the application-driven perspective, the ultimate goal is to develop a new-generation (massively parallel) information-processing system.

Chapter Organization

The overall objective of the chapter is to present a unified perspective of applications, algorithms, and architectures of neural models. In Section 1.2, a plausible top-down integration perspective of neural information processing is provided. The influential aspects of application, algorithm, and architecture of neural information processing are reviewed. Moreover, the total system

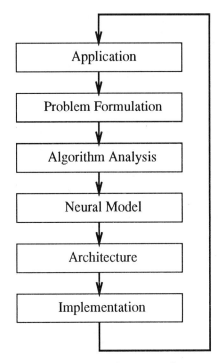

Figure 1.3: A top-down integrated perspective on neural processing.

concept for neural information processing is explored. Section 1.3 introduces the fundamental characteristics of neural models. Basic neural modeling considerations as well as the retrieving and learning phases are introduced. This is then followed by a survey on several basic design issues, including supervised and unsupervised learning, neuron and basis functions, network structures, training strategies, static vs. temporal patterns, and decision vs. approximation/optimization based formulations.

1.2   Applications, Algorithms, and Architectures

In order to have an integrated understanding on neural networks, we adopt a *top-down* perspective, that is, from application, algorithm, to architecture. See Figure 1.3. *Our approach is application-motivated, theoretically-based, and implementation-oriented: (a) The main applications are for signal/image processing and pattern recognition. (b) The algorithmic treatment represents a combination of mathematical theory and heuristic justification for neural models. (c) The ultimate objective is the implementation of digital neuro-*

computers, embracing technologies of VLSI, adaptive, digital, and parallel processing.

1. **Applications and Problem Formulations:** It is critical to identify specific applications where neural networks offer unique advantages. Prominent examples are OCR, image classifiers, data compression, target recognition, sonar systems, target identification from radar pulse trains, radar surveillance, speech coding, and seismic processing. See, for example, [124, 159].

2. **Algorithms, Theory, and Models:** Current algorithmic research of the connectionist models has embraced a very broad scope of neural processing models. *There is an urgent need to establish the fundamentals of neural network theory.* The ongoing basic research areas include data representation, invariance property, computation efficiency, network structure, stability/convergence, and generalization.

3. **Architectures and Implementations:** The objective is to develop high-speed flexible hardware for neural nets. High-priority research topics include advanced simulators, massive parallelism, robustness of neural nets, neural processing units, and neural net chip architectures.

1.2.1   Application Paradigms of Neural Models

From an application-driven perspective, one can explore neural networks' strengths in nonlinear, adaptive, and parallel processing. Neural networks have found many successful applications in computer vision, signal/image processing, speech/character recognition, expert systems, medical image analysis, remote sensing, robotic processing, industrial inspection, and scientific exploration. The application domains of neural nets can be roughly divided into the following categories: association/clustering/classification, pattern completion, regression/generalization, and optimization. Their mathematical formulations are summarized in Table 1.1.

Association, Clustering and Classification

In this paradigm, input static patterns or temporal signals are to be classified or recognized as shown in Figure 1.4. Ideally, a classifier should be trained such that when a slightly distorted version of a stimulus is presented it can

Network Type	Application Paradigms	Training-Phase Formulation	Retrieving-Phase Formulation
Supervised training	Classification	Given x_i, target symbol (s_i), find W, s.t. $y = s_i$.	Given x_i, W, determine symbol s_i.
	Approximation	Given x_i, target value (t_i), find W, s.t. $\sum_i [t_i - \Phi(x_i, W)]^2$ is minimum.	Given x_i, W, find the value of $y = \Phi(x_i, W)$.
	Regularization	Given x_i, target value (t_i), find W and Φ, s.t. $\sum_i [t_i - \Phi(x_i, W)]^2 + \lambda P(\Phi(x, W))$ is minimum.	Given x_i, W, find the value of $y = \Phi(x_i, W)$.
Unsupervised training	Classification	VQ or clustering, or competitive learning techniques.	Given x_i, determine the group to which it belongs.
Fixed-weight	Association	Weight predetermined (Hebbian rule, sometimes)	Given W, x', find x, the "local" minimum of $E(x, W)$.
	Optimization	Weight predetermined via the energy function	Given W, find x, the "global" minimum of $E(x, W)$.

Table 1.1: The training and retrieving formulations for various application paradigms.

still be correctly recognized. Equivalently, the network should possess a certain noise immunity feature, that is, it should be able to recover a "clean" signal from noisy environments or channels. This is critical to holographic, associative, retrieval applications.

- **Association:** Of special interest are the two **association** formulations: auto-association and hetero-association, shown in Figure 1.4(a). The *auto-association* problem is to retrieve the complete pattern, given partial information of the desired pattern. The *hetero-association* (Figure 1.4) is to retrieve a corresponding pattern in set B, given a pattern in set A. The weights in associative networks are often predetermined based on a Hebbian-type (correlation-type) formulation. Usually, the auto-correlation of the set of the stored patterns determines the weights in auto-association networks. On the other hand, the cross-correlation of multiple pairs of the patterns is used to determine the weights of a hetero-association network.

- **Unsupervised Clustering:** For this application paradigm, the synaptic weights of the network are trained by an unsupervised learning rule, that is, the network adapts the weights and verifies the result based exclusively on the input patterns. For example, the VQ-type clustering schemes and the competitive learning networks are all meant for clustering applications.

- **Supervised Classification:** The supervised classification adopts some forms of approximation or interpolation criteria . In many classification applications, for example, OCR or speech recognition, the training data consist of pairs of input/output patterns. In this case, it is more advantageous to adopt supervised networks such as the well-known back-propagation network. It is more suitable for the applications problems, which involve a large number of classes with more complex separating borders.

Pattern Completions

In many classification applications, an implied task is *information completion*, that is, recovery of the original pattern given only partial information. There are two kinds of *pattern completion problems*: temporal and static. Most conventional multilayer nets, Boltzmann machines, and Hopfield nets are for static pattern completion, whereas Markov models and time-delay dynamic networks are for temporal pattern completion and recognition. A temporal pattern often encounters uncertain time-variability and time-redundancy problems, such as time shifts or warping effects. The proper use of contextual information is key to a successful recognition.

Regression and Generalization

Linear or nonlinear *regression* provides a smooth and robust curve fitting to training patterns, as shown in Figure 1.5(a). It can be extended to an interpolation problem. The system is trained by a large set of training samples based on a supervised learning procedure. A network is considered successfully trained if it can closely approximate the teacher values for the trained data space and can provide smooth interpolations for the untrained data space. *The objective of generalization is to yield a correct output response to an input stimulus to which it has not been trained before.* The system must induce the salient feature of the input stimuli and detect the regularity. Such regularity discovery ability is critical to many applications. It enables the system to function competently throughout the entire space, even though it has been trained only by a limited body of exemplary patterns. For an example, see Figure 1.5(b).

The regression problem has been mathematically and numerically well-defined and well studied. As to the generalization problem, formal treatments based on identification theory are analyzed in [8, 9, 178, 199]. Another complementary perspective is via a notion of network capacity and Vapnik-Chervonenkis Dimension [23, 264, 286]. The generalization results are often biased by the specific neural model chosen [178]. In fact, each neural model tends to impose its own prejudice in how to generalize from a finite set of training patterns. One intriguing example that illustrates the difficulty with generalization is the "parity-check" problem. In an experiment based on the back-propagation model, all but one patterns are used as the training data in the back-propagation network and the only deprived pattern is used as the test set. It can be demonstrated that the BP model consistently generalizes into a wrong result. Thus it may be concluded that the least-squares preference (or prejudice) of the back-propagation network is incompatible with the generalization inherent in the parity-check formulation.

Optimization

Neural nets offer an appealing tool for optimization applications, which usually involve finding a global minimum of an energy function. See Figure 1.6 and Table 1.1. Once the energy function is defined, then the determination of the synaptic weights is relatively straightforward. In some applications, the energy function is directly available. In some others, the energy function must be derived from the given cost criterion and special constraints. A major difficulty associated with the optimization problem is the high possibility of a solution converging to a local optimum instead of the global optimum. To battle the problem, several statistical techniques are proposed, for example, stochastic simulated annealing (SSA) and mean-field annealing(cf. Chapter 9).

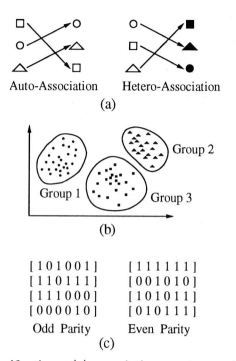

Auto-Association   Hetero-Association

(a)

Group 2

Group 1   Group 3

(b)

[1 0 1 0 0 1]   [1 1 1 1 1 1]
[1 1 0 1 1 1]   [0 0 1 0 1 0]
[1 1 1 0 0 0]   [1 0 1 0 1 1]
[0 0 0 0 1 0]   [0 1 0 1 1 1]
Odd Parity   Even Parity

(c)

Figure 1.4: Classification: (a) association: auto-association and hetero-association, (b) unsupervised classification, and (c) supervised classification.

1.2.2 Algorithmic Study on Neural Networks

Some neural models are based primarily on heuristic reasoning, stressing the similarity between the proposed models and natural biological systems. However, for application-driven neural networks, the emphases are fundamentally different. First, in order to have a systematic approach to the design of neural models it is important to clearly identify the design criteria and factors. In order to achieve a thorough algorithmic study, formal and theoretical treatments of the neural models will be indispensable.

Taxonomy of Neural Network Design

The design of application-driven neural networks hinges upon the choice of energy function. Many training mechanisms are governed by minimization of the energy function. Various application paradigms based on such a formulation are displayed in Table 1.1. In addition, each of the following design factors could be equally critical in characterizing the neural models (cf. Table

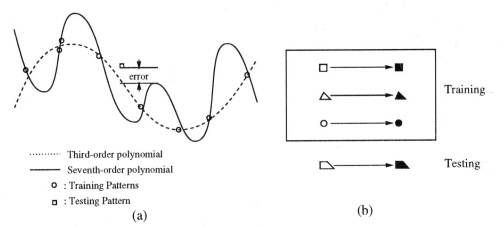

·········· Third-order polynomial
———— Seventh-order polynomial
o : Training Patterns
□ : Testing Pattern

(a)   (b)

Figure 1.5: (a) A regression example: it involves the approximation or regularization formulation. (b) A generalization example: the purpose is to extract the underlying rule from the training samples.

1.2):

- Supervised and unsupervised models;

- Basis functions and activation functions;

- Neural network structures;

- Mutual and individual training strategies;

- Static and temporal pattern recognitions;

- Decision and approximation/optimization formulations.

More details on these subjects will be provided momentarily in Section 1.3.

Formal Theory for Neural Models

Theoretical analyses provide an indispensable means to affirm the capability of the neural models. They provide a reliable basis for measuring the performance of a model, which cannot be substituted by simulations. Theoretical and mathematical analyses exist to support a variety of neural models. The following are just a few examples which will be covered in this book.

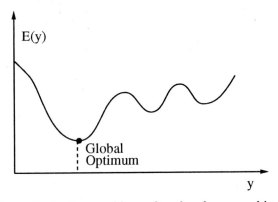

Figure 1.6: An optimization problem often involves searching for the global minimum of an energy function.

1. Capacity and convergence properties of the Hopfield associative memory (Chapter 2).

2. Self-organizing feature maps and adaptive resonance theory (Chapter 3).

3. Convergence of linear perceptron networks and decision-based learning principle (Chapter 4).

4. Back-propagation learning rules (Chapter 5).

5. Approximation vs. generalization from both identification and capacity perspectives (Chapter 5).

6. Temporal dynamic models and unified learning rules for temporal networks (Chapter 6).

7. Training algorithm for hidden Markov model and its close relationship with the back-propagation rule (Chapter 7).

8. Neural networks for extracting principal components and the associated subspace methods (Chapter 8).

9. Optimization based on statistical annealing techniques and Boltzmann Machine (Chapter 9).

10. Mapping neural models onto parallel processors and implementation of digital neurocomputers (Chapter 10).

Pattern Type	Static		Temporal	
Training Scheme	Individual	Mutual	Individual	Mutual
• Model $\begin{pmatrix} \text{Energy or} \\ \text{Discriminant} \\ \text{Functions} \end{pmatrix}$	• OCON (LSE) • OCON $\begin{pmatrix} \text{Likelihood} \\ \text{Function} \end{pmatrix}$	• BP (LSE) • DBNN $\begin{pmatrix} \text{LBF} \\ \text{RBF} \end{pmatrix}$	• HMM $\begin{pmatrix} \text{Likelihood} \\ \text{Function} \end{pmatrix}$ • PBIT $\begin{pmatrix} \text{Prediction} \\ \text{Error} \end{pmatrix}$	• TDNN • DBNN $\begin{pmatrix} \text{Prediction,} \\ \text{Likelihood,} \\ \text{or DTW.} \end{pmatrix}$

Table 1.2:   A possible taxonomy of supervised neural models, characterized by the network structure, energy function, temporal property, training strategy, and neuron/basis function. As to the acronym: OCON (one-class-one-net), BP(back-propagation), HMM(hidden Markov model), TDNN(time-delay neural network), DBNN(decision-based neural network), PBIT(prediction-based independent training), and DTW(dynamic time warping).

1.2.3   Architectures of Neural Networks

Most neural algorithms are computationally intensive and iterative in nature. Most applications also demand very high throughput, especially in a real-time processing environment. For this, massively parallel processing represents a very natural and desirable solution. Some parallel-processing neural networks already exist in analog, digital, and mixed circuits. Implementation examples are digital parallel architectures [10, 36, 115, 275], analog (VLSI) electronics [11, 86, 106, 261], optical technologies [65, 66, 167, 294], and some commercially available neural processing coprocessors [93].

The choice from these different device technologies depends on both the intended application type (associative retrieval, classification, approximation, or optimization) and the application domain (general-purpose or special-purpose). In fact, many design factors have to be involved, for example, speed, learning and weight-updating capabilities, system size, linear/nonlinear functionality and control circuits, I/O data links and interfaces, memory size, word length, clock rate, and power consumption. The technology and architecture selected should maximize the trade-offs among many performance indicators such as effective array configuration, programmability for different networks, flexibility of problem partitioning, fault tolerance to improve system reliability, word length effect in fixed/floating-point arithmetic, and efficient memory utilization.

Whether to use digital or analog circuits hinges upon several key factors, for example, the learning mechanism and adaptivity of the network structure and synaptic weights; the speed of learning and/or retrieval; the precision required and/or achievable (range of values of synaptic weights and neural states); storage and transfer of digital/analog signals; and the system design issues such as programmability, reconfigurability, expandability, and fault tolerance of the design. In general, analog circuits are somewhat more attractive for biological-type neural networks; however, they suffer from inadequate accuracy and programmability. Therefore, it becomes very questionable whether analog circuits can remain suitable for the connectionist-type neural networks, where the computational models require high accuracy and programmability. Digital technology has enjoyed a tremendous growth in both CPU (central processing unit) speed and RAM (random-access memory) space since 1980. The CPUs assume 20%-100% improvement per year, whereas DRAM (dynamic random-access memory) performance has a steady 7 % improvement per year. Furthermore, their prices have rapidly dropped over the years. For example, the price of DRAM memory chips — independent of capacity — has dropped to as low as $2 per chip. (See [220].)

Digital neural networks are useful only when massively parallel hardware (special-purpose or programmable) is made available economically. This requires the important concept of building-block-based design. The building-block approach allows us *to systematically derive massively parallel processors that yield high utilization performance.* This can be accomplished by taking advantage of the now mature CAD (computer-aided design) technology [194] and array processor mapping methodology [151, 152]. Two main aspects of array architecture design involve (1) the interconnection structure of the array system influenced by the *connectivity structure* of the neural network, and (2) the functional complexity of the processing element (PE) in order to fully support the *neural processing units.*

The interconnection architecture is more dependent on the connectivity structure than the neuron or basis functions. The neural net can be either a single-layer (module) feedback network or a multilayer feedforward network. In a single-layer feedback neural net, the neural processing units are interconnected through a synaptic-weights network, which can be either a fully interconnected network or a locally interconnected network.

As to functional design, it could sometimes be very handy to have both the learning and retrieving operations share the same storage and/or processing hardware. This not only speeds up real-time learning, but also avoids the difficulty of reloading synaptic weights for retrieval. Proper digital arithmetic techniques (such as a lookup table or cordic techniques) must be identified to efficiently compute the nonlinear activation function. Finally, neural algorithms can be expressed in terms of very basic matrix operations. They contain inner-product, outer-product, and matrix multiplication. These regular and recursive algorithmic property facilitates a high-efficiency mapping (up to 100% utilization rate) to array processor architectures.

An ideal digital neurocomputer provides an adaptive and flexible platform for neural network algorithms. It is often comprised of a large number of processing elements enhanced with extensive and/or structured interconnectivity. For hardware implementation, the neural models must first be mapped onto processing circuits and the proper supporting software must be provided. Based on the applications intended, the neurocomputers can be divided into two categories: (1) the dedicated neural processor, for which the structure of a neural model is directly mapped onto hardware for optimal efficacy; (2) the general-purpose neurocomputer, for which the indirect approach is more suitable because the inherent neural algorithmic properties can then be harnessed to reduce the hardware cost. Ultimately and ideally, an automated design procedure can lead us to VLSI array architectures such as *systolic* or *wavefront* arrays [149, 152]. These architectures maximize the strength of VLSI in terms of massively parallel and pipelined computing and yet circumvent its main limitation of communication.

The general-purpose neurocomputers are programmable, whereas dedicated neural circuits have very limited programmability. Although general-purpose neurocomputers are applicable to a broad range of neural networks, dedicated neural processors offer efficient hardware for very specific models. Chapter 10 surveys the possible architectural choices for general-purpose neurocomputers. Key design examples of dedicated neural processors and digital parallel neurocomputers are provided in the chapter.

1.2.4 Total Information Processing Systems

In order to holistically analyze a total system for neural information processing, it is important to clearly identify the role of each of its subsystems. As an example, one such total system example is depicted in Figure 1.7. As another example, the experimental airline reservation system developed at AT&T Bell Lab includes speech recognition, expert system, and speech synthesis. Neural information processing (i.e., hidden Markov models) and parallel processing (for the computationally intensive neural computation) technologies constitute the main portion of the novel development.

	OCR	TEXTURE CLASSIFICATION	SPEECH RECOGNITION
Instantiation process	Handwritten characters	Texture samples	Time-warped words
Feature extraction	Structural coding	Cooccurrence/ reduced spectrum	FFT, LPC, Walsh coding
Neural network	HMM network	DBNN	Multilayer perceptron

Table 1.3: The processes of several different application examples.

A total recognition system involves the mappings between several different spaces.

- *Instantiation Space:* During the instantiation process, a symbol is instantiated into a physical object. The instantiation space contains all actual occurrences of objects. Typically, each symbol (e.g., a character "a", "b", or "c" in the character-recognition application) can have different instantiations (see Figure 1.9). So a *data-expansion* process is incurred to yield a more robust set of training data in the instantiation space.

- *Feature Space:* In the feature space, the object is described in terms of a set of primitives (features). The mapping from instantiation space to feature space is called *feature extraction.* Moreover, this mapping represents a *data-compression* stage. In fact, the power of neural networks hinges upon the representation. This is one of the most essential and/or difficult stages in neural application study.

- *Symbol Space:* Finally, the symbol space contains the symbols representing classes of objects. The mapping from feature space to symbol space is called *classification.*

Listed in Table 1.3 are the specific spaces involved in OCR (optical character recognition), texture classification, and speech recognition. The size of training data also differs greatly from one application to another. Middle-size examples are around 5-10 Kbytes for OCR and NetTalk. Examples of larger size are around 50-100 Kbytes for sonar and phoneme applications.

The actual processing stages for the *training phase* and the *retrieving phase* are somewhat different. In the retrieving phase, a neural processing system consists of two subsystems: a feature extractor and a (classification)

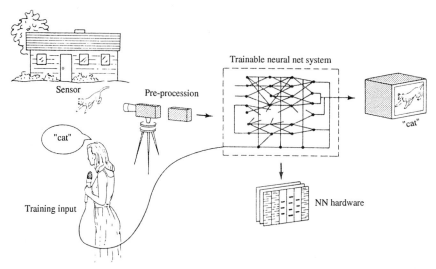

Figure 1.7: An example of a neural information-processing system. (Reprinted from [58] with permission from ©AIP-AFCEA International Press.)

neural network; Figure 1.8(a). In the training phase, however, an additional instantiation process is required prior to the feature-extraction and neural-network subsystems; Figure 1.8(b). Note that the instantiation process is absent in the retrieval phase, because instantiations of test patterns are usually directly available in the data acquisition. In the following, we use a simplified toy OCR example to illustrate the notion of total system design.

Example 1.1 (A Toy OCR Example)

For simplicity, we first study a "toy" example of an OCR system. Feature extraction involves a mapping from instantiation space to feature representation space. Figure 1.9(a) provides a simple illustration of a trivial representation. Every instantiation (input) is a bit map divided evenly into upper and lower blocks. The pattern can be represented by two features: the density measures of the upper and lower blocks respectively. In other words, in this feature-extraction process, each pattern is mapped to a point in two-dimensional feature space in Figure 1.9(b). The neural classifier processes the feature-space input to produce a desired symbol. As exemplified by Figure 1.9(c), the neural net maps two input nodes onto three symbol outputs. The classification can be regarded as a mapping from a "vertical pattern array" onto a "horizontal neuron array". The number of output nodes depends on the number of distinct clusters of input patterns.

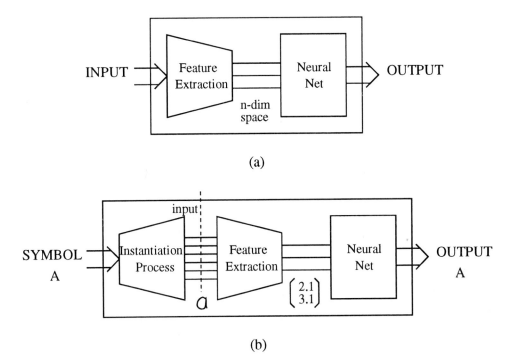

(a)

(b)

Figure 1.8: (a) A neural processing/retrieving system consists of two subsystems: feature extraction and a neural net. (b) When training a neural processing system, an additional instantiation process is required.

Now let us turn the attention to a more practical OCR system. For a printed character recognition problem, there are 12 fonts and 6 sizes as well as italic and boldface versions of the characters in both lowercase and uppercase. In terms of **instantiation space**, there are 432 possible instantiations of each character. In handwritten character recognition, the number of possible instantiations of any character is practically unlimited since all kinds of variations may be written by the same or different person.

As an example of the mapping to **feature space**, feature extraction can be carried out by creating the skeleton of a character, segmenting it and finally mapping each segment to the feature primitives. A primitive could be, for example, a line or an arc with a particular orientation. Each character is expressed as a sequence of lines and arcs, each having one of 12 possible orientations. For data compression, the mapping of instantiation space to feature space is usually restricted to the permissible feature region. The **symbol space** consists of 26 symbols, one for each letter of the English

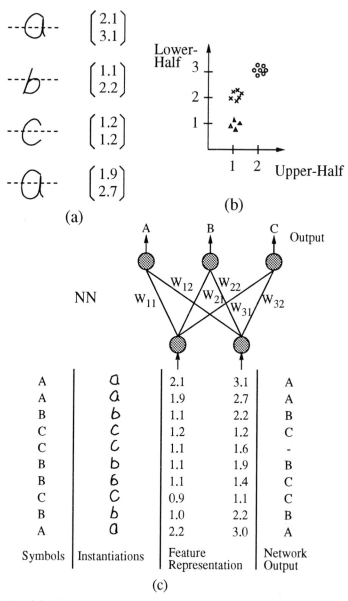

Figure 1.9: (a) A simple feature-extraction example in a toy OCR system. (b) A two-dimensional feature space. (c) The overall operations in the training phase of the simplified OCR system. In this classification example, a "vertical data array" of 10 input patterns is mapped onto a "horizontal cell array" of 3 output neurons.

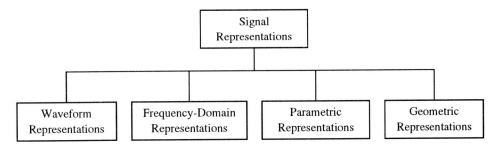

Figure 1.10: Signal representations can be classified into waveform representations, frequency-domain representations, parametric representations, and geometric representations.

alphabet. The training data, presented as pairs of feature sequence/class, are applied to train the neural classifier which will in turn be used to perform the task of classification (i.e., mapping from feature space to symbol space).

1.2.5   Representation and Feature Extraction

Feature extraction and representation are indispensable to a neural information processing system. The power of neural networks lies in the details of representation and coding of pattern vectors. It is essential that a representation can provide concise, invariant, and/or intelligible information of the input patterns. They dictate the ultimate performance of the system. Ultimately, the application intended will dictate the choice of representation. As an example, for speech processing, there is a very wide variation in data rates, from 75 bits per second for parametric text representation to 200,000 bits per second for simple waveform representation [67]. Some applications will require a high level representation that is less dependent on the environment. In image and vision analysis, it is necessary to have an explicit description of objects preceding any high-level analysis. Raw image data must be preprocessed to extract the vital characteristics that are less dependent on imaging geometry. In natural visual systems, it is known that image data are preprocessed before they are sent to the cortex [281]. Similarly, a neural vision system can also benefit greatly by using representations at a higher level than raw image.

It is not easy to select an optimal representation. A general rule is to use one with a good metric condition as well as a high compression ratio. Other factors such as overall cost, data rates, flexibility of representation, and quality of signal, should also be taken into account. The following are general criteria for measuring the quality of a feature representation.

1. *Data Compression:* to extract vital representations or features.

2. *Invariance:* to reduce the dependency of the features on imaging conditions.

3. *Fidelity:* to best preserve intelligibility of the features.

As shown in Figure 1.10, the representations can be classified into four categories:

1. **Waveform Representations:** A one-dimensional sampled signal can be expressed as a data sequence, $x[n]$, where n is an integer. As an example, cepstrum or LPC spectrum used in speech processing. A two-dimensional sampled signal is commonly referred to as a digital image, represented by an array of pixels. For example, a digital image can be the luminance function of an object, say, $x[m, n]$, where m and n are integers. In yet other applications, higher-dimension signals are encountered. Application examples include tomographical image reconstruction and video-signal processing. The main concern of the waveform representation is the preservation of information content in signal waves or image brightness during the processes of sampling and quantization [208, 257].

2. **Frequency-Domain Representations:** Most transforms use a set of fixed orthogonal functions as bases. For example, DFT, FFT, Cosine/Sine, and Hadamard transforms are very popular fixed-weight techniques. They often enjoy the very efficient fast algorithms which have been available for decades. For example, these transform coding techniques are often applied in image restoration and data compression [118]. On the other hand, for some other types of transforms, for example, Karhunen-Love, SVD, and principal component analysis(PCA), the transform bases are chosen adaptively. They are often based on optimizing certain statistical properties of the ensembles of the (training) patterns.

3. **Parametric Representations:** Model-based representations often effectively utilize the underlying statistical property. Assuming that the ensemble of the processes is stationary, thus the (estimated) mean and

covariance functions can provide the most critical information of a process. Such a representation is useful for the entire class or an ensemble of signal/image processes rather than for an individual process. Popular models for representing such stationary processes are moving-average (MA), autoregressive (AR), and autoregressive moving-average (ARMA) models.

4. **Geometric Representations:** For picture-pattern recognition, geometric techniques offer perhaps the most effective representations. **Edge detection** is vital in many image-analysis tasks, such as segmentation and identification of objects in scenes. Edges represent boundaries of objects and appear at pixels where abrupt change of grey level occurs. Edge-detection operations are often represented by a convolution of a $p \times p$ mask $H = h[m, n]$ and the image $U = u[m, n]$:

$$(U, H)_{m,n} = \sum_i \sum_j h[i, j] u[m - i, n - j]$$

Image segmentation is important for image analysis, which allows an image to be decomposed into smaller components. Each of the components can be separately processed for information extraction. The **contour** of an object offers a more reliable representation than the grey levels of image pixels. Examples for contour and shape representations include chain codes, fitting line segments, B-spline representation, autoregressive models, and Fourier descriptors.

In the **structural representation**, an object is represented by a set of structural primitives (or symbols). In this representation, the emphasis is placed on the relationship (e.g., sequence) between features. For example, contour or shape features can be represented in terms of a temporal sequence of structural primitives representing angles(A), line segments(L), circles(C), rectangles(R), etc. (More sophisticated primitives will be needed for more complex objects, for example, parallelograms, cylinders, skew symmetry, and circular arcs.) Such a representation is especially appealing for syntactic pattern recognition, which relies on grammars for the strings and rules for describing relations between symbols. Two classes of objects can be distinguished in terms of order, number, and spatial relations of the structural primitives. For example, a triangle is represented as LALALA and a rectangle as LALALALA. This should be viewed as a temporal sequence, which allows temporal variations. For example, any time-shift of a sequence has to be recognized as belonging to the same class. In this sense, the recognition machine also serves as a language parser [71, 181, 187, 279, 296].

1.3   Taxonomy of Neural Networks

Associated with the memory unit of a computer system, there are writing and reading phases. In the writing phase, a storing mechanism is used to specify the information to be remembered. The stored information is to be later retrieved in the reading phase. Analogous to the writing and reading phases, there are also two phases in neural information processing. They are the *learning phase* and the *retrieving phase*. In the training phase, a training data set is used to determine the weight parameters that define the neural model. This trained neural model then will be used later in the retrieving phase to process real test patterns and yield classification results. (The learning and retrieving phases are sometimes associated with long-term memory (LTM) and short-term memory (STM), respectively.)

- **Retrieving Phase:** Various nonlinear systems have been proposed for retrieving desired or stored patterns. The results can be either computed in one shot or updated iteratively based on the retrieving dynamics equations. The final neuron values represent the desired output to be retrieved.

- **Learning Phase:** A salient feature of neural networks is their learning ability. They learn by adaptively updating the synaptic weights that characterize the strength of the connections. (In very rare cases, the adaptation also involves altering the pattern of connections.) The weights are updated according to the information extracted from (new) training patterns. Usually, the optimal weights are obtained by optimizing (minimizing or maximizing) certain "energy" functions. For example, a popular criterion in supervised learning is to minimize the least-squares-error between the teacher value and the actual output value.

Real-world applications may face two very different kinds of real-time processing requirements. One requires real-time retrieving but off-line training speed. The other demands both retrieving and training in real-time. These two lead to very different processing speeds, which in turn affect the algorithm and hardware adopted.

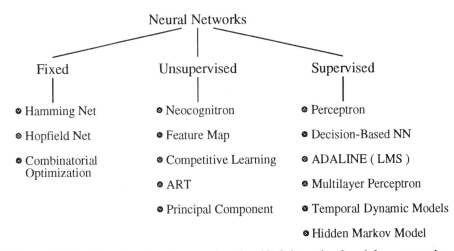

Figure 1.11: Neural networks can be classified into fixed-weights networks, unsupervised networks, and supervised networks.

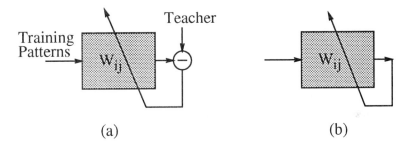

Figure 1.12: Schematic diagrams training synaptic weights: (a) supervised learning and (b) unsupervised learning.

A possible taxonomy of neural networks is displayed in Table 1.2. The following are critical factors for a systematic design of neural models: supervised and unsupervised models; basis functions and activation functions; structures of neural networks; mutual and individual training strategies; static and temporal pattern recognitions; and decision-based and optimization formulations. These are the subjects to be further elaborated in this section.

1.3.1 Supervised and Unsupervised Networks

As displayed in Figure 1.11, the neural networks are commonly categorized in terms of their corresponding training algorithms: fixed-weight networks, unsupervised networks, and supervised networks. There is no learning re-

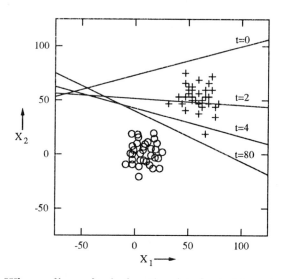

Figure 1.13: When a linear basis function is adopted in a training process, linear hyperplanes are adjusted to best classify one group from another group. Similar figures may be drawn for the radial-basis function and others.

quired for the fixed-weight networks, so a learning model is supervised or unsupervised.

Supervised Learning Rules

Supervised learning networks have been the mainstream of neural model development. *The training data consist of many pairs of input/output training patterns. Therefore, the learning will benefit from the assistance of the teacher*, cf. Figure 1.12(a). As an example of supervised training, Figure 1.13 shows that the decision (classification) boundaries are linear hyperplanes specified by the synaptic weights w_{ij}. The hyperplanes separate one class of patterns from another. Given a new training pattern, say, $(m+1)$th, the weights may be updated as follows:

$$w_{ij}^{(m+1)} = w_{ij}^{(m)} + \triangle w_{ij}^{(m)} \tag{1.1}$$

In this particular example, the amount of adjustment is proportional to the difference between the actual response and the teacher value and the hyperplanes are according adapted, cf. Figure 1.13. Note that the classification performance is gradually improved. As another example, Figure 1.14 shows a two-layer network for the exclusive-or (XOR) problem, where (the representation space of) the hidden layer is gradually trained to better separate the two classes.

Unsupervised Learning Rules

For an unsupervised learning rule, the training set consists of input training patterns only. Therefore, the network is trained without benefit of any teacher, as shown in Figure 1.12(b). The network learns to adapt based on the experiences collected through the previous training patterns. Typical examples are the Hebbian learning rule [92], and the competitive learning rule [88].

A simple version of Hebbian learning is that when unit i and unit j are simultaneously excited, the strength of the connection between them increases in proportion to the product of their activations. As an example of competitive learning, if a new pattern is determined to belong to a previously recognized cluster, then the inclusion of the new pattern into that cluster will affect the representation (e.g., the centroid) of the cluster. This will in turn change the weights characterizing the classification network. If the new pattern is determined to belong to none of the previously recognized clusters, then (the structure and the weights of) the neural network will be adjusted to accommodate the new class (cluster).

1.3.2 Basis Function and Activation Function

A basic neural model is illustrated in Figure 1.2(b). It can be characterized by the functional descriptions of the *connection network* and *neuron activation*. Each neural cell (processing unit) has a neuron value a_j. This value is propagated through a network of unidirectional connections to other cells in the network. Associated with each connection, there is a *synaptic weight* denoted by $\{ w_{ij} \}$, that dictates the effect of the jth cell on the ith cell. The inputs to the ith cell from other cells are accumulated, together with the external threshold θ_i, to yield the *net value* u_i. The mapping is mathematically described by a *basis function*. The net value u_i will then be further transformed by a nonlinear *activation function* f to yield a new activation value a_i. The final output $\mathbf{y}$ can usually be expressed as function of the input and the weights $\mathbf{y} = \phi(\mathbf{x}, \mathbf{W})$.

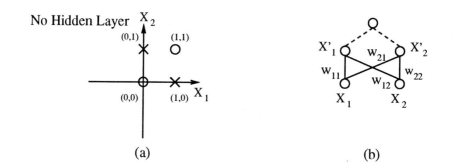

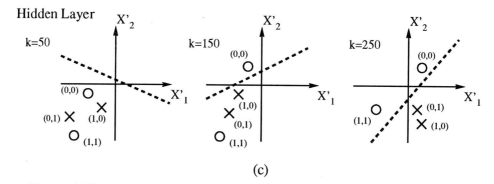

(c)

Figure 1.14: In this simulation of a two-layer BP network for the XOR problem, the hidden-unit representations change with the iterations. (a) The XOR problem. (b) A two-layer network. (c) The change of weights (representation) gradually adjusts the coordinates. Eventually, when iteration number $k > 250$, the representation becomes linearly separable by the upper layer.

Basis Function (Net Function)

For an analytical study, the connection networks are mathematically represented by a basis function $u(\mathbf{w}, \mathbf{x})$, where $\mathbf{w}$ stands for the weight matrix, and $\mathbf{x}$ for the input vector. The basis function has two common forms (cf. Figure 1.15):

1. Linear-basis function (LBF) is a hyperplane-type function. This is a first-order linear basis function. The net value is a linear combination of the inputs,

$$u_i(\mathbf{w}, \mathbf{x}) = \sum_{j=1}^{n} w_{ij} x_j$$

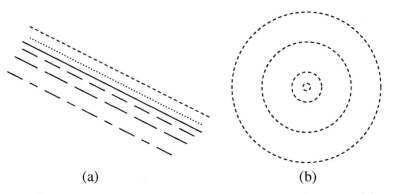

(a)   (b)

Figure 1.15: Equipotential lines for two types of basis functions: (a) linear-basis (hyperplane-type) function, and (b) radial-basis (hypersphere-type) function.

2. Radial-basis function (RBF) is a hypersphere-type function. This involves a second-order (nonlinear) basis function. The net value represents the distance to a reference pattern,

$$u_i(\mathbf{w}, \mathbf{x}) = \sqrt{\sum_{j=1}^{n}(x_j - w_{ij})^2}$$

The second-order function can also be extended to a (more general) elliptic-basis function.

Activation Function (Neuron Function)

The net value as expressed by the basis function, $u(\mathbf{w}, \mathbf{x})$, will be immediately transformed by a nonlinear activation function of the neuron. For example, the most common activation functions are *step*, *ramp*, *sigmoid*, and *Gaussian functions*, (cf. Figure 1.16). In particular,

- sigmoid function:

$$f(u_i) = \frac{1}{1 + e^{-u_i/\sigma}}$$

- Gaussian function:

$$f(u_i) = ce^{-u_i^2/\sigma^2}$$

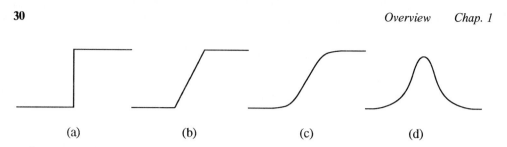

(a)   (b)   (c)   (d)

Figure 1.16: Four examples of activation functions: (a) step function, (b) ramp function, (c) sigmoid function, and (d) Gaussian function.

1.3.3   Structures of Neural Networks

The major structural factors are *connection structures*, *network size*, and *ACON versus OCON approaches*.

Interlayer and Intralayer Connection Structures

As depicted in Figure 1.17, a neural network comprises the *neuron* and *weight* building blocks. The behavior of the network depends largely on the interactions between these building blocks. There are three types of neuron layers: input, hidden, and output layers. Two layers of neurons communicate via a weight connection network. There are four types of weighted connections: feedforward, feedback, lateral, and time-delayed connections.

1. *Feedforward Connections:* For all the neural models, data from neurons of a lower layer are propagated forward to neurons of an upper layer via feedforward connection networks.

2. *Feedback Connections:* Feedback networks bring data from neurons of an upper layer back to neurons of a lower layer.

3. *Lateral Connections:* One typical example of a lateral network is the winner-takes-all circuit, which serves the important role of selecting the winner (cf. Chapter 2). In the feature map example, by allowing neurons to interact via the lateral network, a certain topological ordering relationship can be preserved (cf. Chapter 3). Another example is the *lateral orthogonalization network* which forces the network to extract orthogonal components (cf. Chapter 8).

4. *Time-Delayed Connections:* Delay elements may be incorporated into the connections to yield temporal dynamic models (cf. Chapter 6). They are more suitable for temporal pattern recognitions.

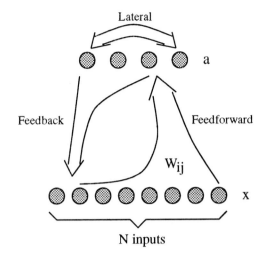

Figure 1.17: A basic network structure comprises of neurons and weight layers. Four types of weight connections are feedforward, lateral, feedback, and time-delayed (not shown here) connections.

The synaptic connections may be fully or locally interconnected, see Figures 1.18 (a) and (b). Also, a neural network can be either a single layer feedback model or a multilayer feed-forward model. It is possible to cascade several single layer feedback neural nets to form a larger net [191].

Sizes of Neural Networks

In a feed-forward multilayer neural net, there are one or more layers of *hidden neuron units* between the input and output neuron layers. The sizes of networks depends on the number of layers and the number of hidden-units per layer.

1. *Number of layers:* In a multilayer network, there are one or more layers of *hidden neuron units* between the input and output neuron layers. The number of layers is very often counted according to the number of weight layers (instead of neuron layers).

2. *Number of hidden-units:* The number of hidden-units is directly related to the capabilities of the network. For the best network performance (e.g., generalization), an optimal number of hidden-units must be properly determined.

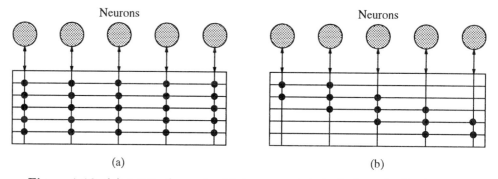

Figure 1.18: (a) A fully (cross-bar) interconnected single-layer feedback neural net. (b) A locally interconnected single-layer feedback neural net.

ACON Versus OCON Approaches

The issue at hand is how many networks should be used for multi-category classification. Typically, one output node is used to represent one class. As an example, in an alpha-numeric recognition problem, there are 36 (26 alphabets and 10 digits) classes, so there are a total of 36 output nodes. Given an input pattern in the retrieving phase, the winner (i.e., the class that wins the recognition) is usually the output node that has the maximum among all the output values.

Two plausible network structures are All-Class-in-One-Network(ACON) and One-Class-in-One-Network(OCON) (cf. Figure 1.19). In the ACON approach, all the classes are lumped into one giant-size super-network, cf. Figure 1.19(a). It is sometimes advantageous to decompose a huge network into many subnets, so that each subnet has a small size. For example, a 36-output net can be decomposed into 12 subnets, each responsible for 3 outputs. The most extreme decomposition is the so-called OCON structure, where one subnet is devoted to one class only. Although the number of subnets in the OCON is relatively large, each individual subnet has considerably smaller size than the ACON super-network. This may be explained by Figure 1.19(b), in which a full-size net is partitioned into many subnets by eliminating all the "cross-class" connections in the upper layer.

For convenience, all the subnets are assumed to have a uniform size, say k. The number of hidden units of the ACON super-network is denoted as K. (Obviously, $k << K$.) The ACON and OCON differ significantly in *size* and *speed*, that is the total numbers of synaptic weights and the training time. Let us denote the input and output vector dimensions as n and N. The number of the total synaptic weights for the ACON structure is $(N + n) \times K$. Likewise, the number for the OCON structure is $N \times (n + 1) \times k \approx N \times n \times k$. Two extreme situations are analyzed below. When N is relatively small (compared with n), ACON could have compatible or less weights than OCON. If N is very large, then OCON could have a major advantage in terms of network size. See Problem 1.5.

In addition, the OCON seems to prevail over ACON in training and recognition speed when the number of classes is large.

In the ACON approach, the single supernet has the burden of having to simultaneously satisfy all these classes, so the number of hidden units K is expected to be very big. Empirical results confirm that the convergence rate of ACON degrades drastically with respect to the network size because the training is influenced by conflicting signals from different teachers. By eliminating the inter-class connections, the OCON approach helps obviate such confusion. Each subnet in OCON is specialized for distinguishing its own class from the alien patterns. So the number of hidden units k needed should be relatively small. Experimental results based on some speech and OCR applications suggest that 3-5 hidden units are all it needs per subnet. The OCON may offer computational savings in the training phase and performance improvements in the retrieving phase. See Section 5.5.3.

1.3.4   Mutual and Individual Training Strategies

The training strategies may be divided according to the presence or absence of cross reference between different outputs. In a **mutual (individual)** training rule, cross-references among the outputs can (cannot) be used to assist the training. More precisely, in mutual training, the training of all the weights is influenced by *all* the output values. In individual training, the training of an individual subnet will not be influenced by the outputs of other subnets.

Mutual Training Strategy

In a mutual training rule, the training of all the weights is influenced by all the output values. Consequently, such a mutual training mechanism allows two neighboring categories to "negotiate" their mutual decision boundary. This leads to more acute boundaries. The drawback is that it may take substantially more iterations to reach a mutual agreement between all the nodes.

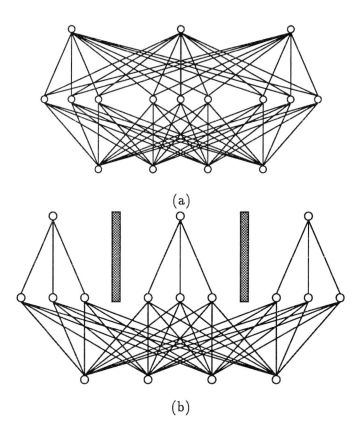

(a)

(b)

Figure 1.19: (a) The (supernet) structure for an ACON model. (b) An OCON structure viewed as a result of partitioning a single supernet into many small subnets.

1. *ACON Training*

The ACON structures invariably adopt mutual and discriminative training strategy. The reason is explained below. For the ACON structure, the network is inherently *mutually trained* since each of the output nodes will surely affect each other via the commonly shared hidden nodes. (The back-propagation errors originated from all the output nodes influence all hidden nodes.) For training the ACON structure, the single supernet must be trained by the *discriminative training* strategy, whose definition will be provided momentarily. This is because the commonly shared *hidden layer* has to accommodate all categories, so all training patterns (i.e., including positive and counter examples) are involved in the training.

2. *OCON Training*

As depicted in Table 1.2, there are many options available for training OCON structures. The OCON structure can be trained either by mutual or individual training.

Individual Training Strategy

In individual training, cross-references among the outputs cannot be allowed to influence the training. In other words, the training of an individual subnet is strictly trained by the outputs of itself. The advantage is its obvious simplicity. The drawback is the limitation on its ability to cope with complex decision boundaries. The individual training strategy may be further divided according to the *training data* involved.

1. *Discriminative Training:* The strategy uses *all* the training patterns (both the positive and negative examples) to train each subnet. In other words, all the patterns are involved in all the weight training. This strategy, though more extensively involving the training patterns, provides a clearer definition of the class boundaries and so far has prevailing advantage.

2. *Independent Training:* The alternative is the totally independent training in which each subnet is trained by its corresponding *positive-examples* only.

The independent training is conceptually simpler. It could actually be computationally simpler for temporal pattern recognition. However, it is deemed as inappropriate for static neural models. For the latter, a very special training optimization formulation would have to be designed.

Hierarchical Training Strategy

The tradeoffs between the mutual vs. individual training strategies are very obvious. For higher performance the mutual training should be used. For simpler and faster training, the individual training is very attractive. To maximize the training efficiency, a hierarchical two-stage training strategy should be considered. The initial phase involves individual training as shown in Figure 1.20(a). (Within this phase, there might be advantage in training

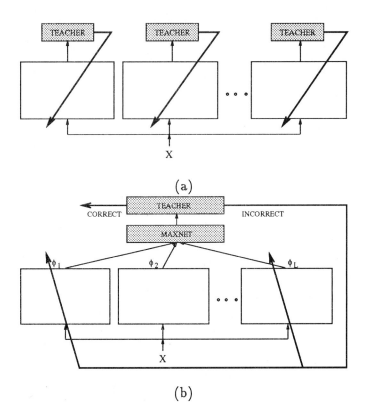

Figure 1.20: (a) The subnets are individually trained in the first stage. (b) In the next phase, the network are mutually trained and only the "critical" subnets will be updated trained (indicated by the arrows from the teacher).

highly complex models to adopt the independent training prior to the discriminative training.) After the individual training phase, it could be beneficial to further finetune the network by mutual training strategies, cf. Figure 1.20(b). A typical second-stage mutual training is via the decision-based approach, cf. Chapter 4. Several examples for static and temporal pattern recognition will be discussed in Chapters 4 and 6 respectively.

1.3.5   Static and Temporal Pattern Recognitions

Two types of patterns are recognized: (a) *static patterns* and (b) *temporal patterns*. Static patterns are not order-sensitive. An input pattern can be viewed as a random point in an N-dimensional vector space. For classification of static patterns, the coordinates can be permuted or relabeled without affecting the inherent statistics of the pattern distribution. In contrast, *temporal patterns have strong order sensitivity*. They should be viewed as temporal sequences. For example, a vector formed by the prices of 10 different stocks at the same session can be considered as a static pattern. On the other hand, a vector formed by the prices of the same stock over 10 consecutive sessions should be treated as a temporal sequence.

Static Pattern Completion and Recognition

In conjunction with pattern recognition, a related problem is pattern completion. Suppose that we are to classify the employees of a company into different categories of insurance policy. The decision factors are represented by the binary feature space based on the individual's status on whether he or she is "married, 30 or older, smoker, with children, home owner". Suppose that some information about an employee is missing. An incomplete pattern is for example "1 ? 0 1 1". The information to be completed is whether the employee is 30-or-older. The answer depends on the relevant statistics and data base. Now let us reverse the order of the queries, and the feature space is rearranged into "home owner, with children, smoker, 30 or older, married". Thus the incomplete record is reshuffled to become: "1 1 0 ? 1". Still, this should not affect the pattern completion result.

Temporal Pattern Completion and Recognition

Temporal pattern completion or recognition will depend on the specific order used. For example, a missing segment of a speech waveform may be reconstructed from the segments immediately before and after. The stock prices of several consecutive sessions may be used to predict the short-term future of that stock. As another example, suppose that an incomplete word "M A ? E" is to be completed. The missing character "?" may be "D", "K", "R", "L", or "Z", corresponding to MADE, MAKE, MARE, MALE, or MAZE. If the order of the characters are reshuffled into "A ? M E", then the missing character is most likely C (for "ACME"). This example shows that a temporal pattern (sequence) usually contains rich temporal contextual information, which should be properly exploited. The accompanied difficulty is the inherent temporal variability of the patterns pertaining to the same class. This problem can be dealt with by incorporating *memory units* into the temporal models. (Recall that for static pattern recognition, no memory units need to be introduced in the neural model.) In Chapters 6 and 7, two types of memory mechanisms will be introduced:

- **Deterministic temporal networks:** For example, the temporal dynamic networks are usually represented by difference equations (or differential equations for the continuous-time case), where the memory may be manifested by the *time-delay* units.

- **Stochastic temporal networks:** for example, in the (hidden) Markov models, the memory mechanism is embedded in the *state transition probability* which can be trained to best model the temporal behavior.

The independent training rule is very appealing to temporal pattern recognition, in which each temporal model deal with one category of signals only. This is true for several temporal models, for example, prediction-based nets and (hidden) Markov models(HMM).

1.3.6   Decision and Approximation/Optimization Formulations

The formulations of supervised neural networks can be divided into decision-based and optimization-based categories.

Decision-Based Formulation

In a decision based neural network(DBNN), the teacher only tells the correctness of the classification for each training pattern. The teacher is a set of symbols, $\mathcal{T} = \{t_i\}$, labeling the correct class for each input pattern. This is unlike the approximation formulation where the exact values of teachers would be required. *The objective of the training is to find a set of weights which yields a correct classification.* It is very important to identify a proper discriminant function in order to best distinguish each class in the presence of other classes. The selection of such discriminant functions varies significantly between the static and temporal recognitions.

Approximation/Optimization Formulation

The training process involves finding the weights which optimize the training energy function. The most popular function is the minimum-squares-error between the teacher and the actual response. Obviously, the exact teacher's values have to be available as a reference at the output. However, the exact

Neural Networks	Measure Function E	Weights Derivation	Comments
Parallel Hopfield associative network	$E = -\frac{1}{2}\sum_{i=1}^{N}\sum_{j=1}^{N}$ $w_{ij}a_i a_j - \sum_{i=1}^{N}\theta_i a_i$	$w_{ij} = \sum_{m=1}^{M}$ $(2a_i^{(m)}-1)(2a_j^{(m)}-1)$	$\theta_i = -\frac{1}{2}\sum_{j=1}^{N}w_{ij}$
Bidirectional associative memory	$E = -\sum_{i=1}^{N}\sum_{j=1}^{K}$ $w_{ij}(2a_i-1)(2b_j-1)$	$w_{ij} = \sum_{m=1}^{M}$ $(2a_i^{(m)}-1)(2b_j^{(m)}-1)$	$\theta_i = -\frac{1}{2}\sum_{j=1}^{K}w_{ij}$ $\theta_j' = -\frac{1}{2}\sum_{i=1}^{N}w_{ij}$
Competitive learning network	$E = \frac{1}{2}\sum_{j=0}^{J-1}$ $(x_j - w_{ij})^2$	$w_{ij}^{(m+1)} = w_{ij}^{(m)} +$ $\eta(x_j - w_{ij}^{(m)})$	Feature map
Boltzmann machine	$E = \sum_{\forall a_v}$ $Pr^+(a_v)\ln\frac{Pr^+(a_v)}{Pr^-(a_v)}$	$w_{ij}^{(m+1)} = w_{ij}^{(m)} +$ $\eta(p_{ij}^+ - p_{ij}^-)$	$p_{ij}^{\pm} = \sum_{\forall a}$ $Pr^{\pm}(a)a_i a_j$
Linear perceptron network	$E = \frac{1}{2}\sum_{m=1}^{M}$ $(t^{(m)} - y^{(m)})^2$	$w_j^{(m+1)} = w_j^{(m)} + \eta\times$ $(t^{(m)} - y^{(m)})z_j^{(m)}$	Decision-based learning rule
Single-layer ADALINE	$E = \frac{1}{2}\sum_{m=1}^{M}$ $(b^{(m)} - u^{(m)})^2$	$w_j^{(m+1)} = w_j^{(m)} + \eta\times$ $(b^{(m)} - u^{(m)})z_j^{(m)}$	Delta learning rule
Back-propagation network	$E = \frac{1}{2}\sum_{m=1}^{M}\sum_{i=1}^{N}$ $(t_i^{(m)} - a_i^{(m)}(L))^2$	$w_{ij}^{(m+1)}(l) = w_{ij}^{(m)} +$ $\eta\delta_i^{(m)}(l)f'(u_i^{(m)}(l))\times$ $a_j^{(m)}(l-1)$	$\delta_i^{(m)}(l) =$ BP error
Principal component analysis	$E = wR_x w^T / ww^T$	$w(t+1) = w(t) +$ $\beta(a(t)x(t) - a(t)^2 w(t))$	Normalized Hebbian rule
Hidden Markov model	$E = Pr(O\|\lambda)$ $= \sum_{j=1}^{N}\alpha_T^{(m)}(j)$	$a_{ij}^{(m+1)}(t) = \eta\xi_t^{(m+1)}(i,j)$ $= \eta a_{ij}^{(m)}(t)\beta_t^{(m)}(i)\times$ $b_i^{(m)}(o_t)\alpha_{t-1}^{(m)}(j)$	Baum-Welch re-estimation

Table 1.4: A unified framework for various neural models.

values will not be required if the likelihood function is used as the training criterion. In summary, the key is to identify a proper training criterion to be optimized, which depends on the application(s) intended and on whether static or temporal patterns are involved.

1.4 Concluding Remarks

The development of digital neural networks requires cross-disciplinary research, covering neural science, biology, psychology, computer science, computer engineering, signal/image processing, mathematics, physics, optics, and VLSI electronics technology. Therefore, the field of digital neural networks opens up a new frontier for a truly cross-disciplinary information processing research field. The ultimate goal is to attain a unified study on applications, algorithms, and architectures for neural networks.

The applications dictate the proper choices of representation, neural model, and hardware implementation. These choice will in turn determine the effectiveness of the neural processing systems. For signal/image processing and pattern recognition, it will be mutually beneficial to explore the rich theoretical relationship between the neural network approaches and the conventional system identification and nonlinear signal-processing techniques. See, for example, [126, 177, 212].

As to the implementation of digital neurocomputers, it is useful to develop a unified framework that provides a common basis for various neural models. We note that neural models involve primarily repetitive and regular operations, paving the way for massively parallel processing. Therefore, neural processing research can provide a viable digital technology for future real-time information processing. Table 1.4 lists a unified formulation of various neural models [165]. The table suggest a strong coherence between the seemingly very different models. From a hardware architecture perspective, the unified presentation will be instrumental in the design of neurocomputers.

Finally, and most importantly, from a theoretical perspective, the field of neural networks has attracted researchers from very different backgrounds, theoretical as well as applicational. It provides a unified common language for many very diverse disciplines. It is therefore most critical that a fundamental and coherent *neural network system theory* is established. If so, it would serve as a foundation for future research advances and long-term application impacts. Hopefully, this book represents a positive step towards this goal.

1.5   Problems

Exercise 1.1 Neural models depend on the nonlinear activation functions,

   (a) Show that a step function is a special case of a sigmoid function.

   (b) Is a ramp function a special case of the sigmoid function?

   (c) Use a combination of two sigmoid functions to roughly approximate a Gaussian function.

Exercise 1.2 A recognition system consists of a sequence of mappings between different spaces: *instantiation space*, *feature space*, and *symbol space*. Elaborate by example the definition of each space for the following applications:

   (a) speech processing,

   (b) image classification,

   (c) shape classification,

   (d) NetTalk for a "text-to-speech" processing system.

Exercise 1.3 For each of the following cases, identify a suitable application example. The neural networks are arranged in the following orders:

(a) fixed-weights networks, unsupervised networks, and supervised networks
(b) fixed-weights networks and unsupervised networks
(c) fixed-weights networks and supervised networks
(d) unsupervised networks and supervised networks

Create an example that belongs to the "none-of-the-above" category.

Exercise 1.4 For classification, identify situations when the RBF model is likely to outperform the LBF model, and vice versa.

Exercise 1.5 The ACON and OCON differ significantly in the total numbers of synaptic weights. For convenience, all the subnets of OCON are assumed to have a uniform size, say k. The number of hidden units of the ACON super-network is denoted as K. We denote the input dimension and output dimensions n and N. Verify the following analyses.

(a) When the number of outputs N is relatively small with respect to n, the ratio is

$$\frac{\text{number of ACON weights}}{\text{number of OCON weights}} = \frac{(N+n) \times K}{N \times n \times k} \approx \frac{l}{N}$$

where

$$l = \frac{K}{k} < N$$

so ACON should have less weights. The two numbers of weights are compatible if $K \approx N \times k$.

(b) When N is very large (compared with n), the ratio now becomes

$$\frac{\text{number of ACON weights}}{\text{number of OCON weights}} \approx \frac{l}{n}$$

When N is very large, it is quite plausible that

$$n < l$$

so OCON should have advantage in terms of number of weights used.

Exercise 1.6 For the following patterns or applications, identify their pattern type: *static* or *temporal*.

(a) parity-check problem
(b) speech recognition, where a class represents a phoneme
(c) numeric OCR applications
(d) alphabetic OCR, with a dictionary as a data base.

Exercise 1.7 Compute the number of multiplications and additions involved when a 3×4 matrix is postmultiplied by a 4×12 matrix.

Exercise 1.8 In hardware implementation,
  (a) When are analog circuits preferred over digital circuits?
  (b) When are digital circuits preferred over analog circuits?
  (c) When are hybrid circuits preferred over either analog or digital circuits?

Exercise 1.9 An eigenfunction of a system is an input function that, when applied to the system, yields an output that is identical to itself except for some scaling. Show that $\{e^{j\omega n}\}$ is the eigenfunction of a discrete linear time invariant (LTI) system.

Exercise 1.10 A (sampled) trace function is expressed by a complex function

$$u(n) = x(n) + jy(n), \qquad n = 0, \ldots, N-1$$

whose DFT representation is

$$a(k) = \sum_{n=0}^{N-1} u(n) exp\left(\frac{-j2\pi kn}{N}\right), \quad 0 \le k \le N-1$$

The complex coefficients $a(k)$ are called the Fourier descriptors(FDs) [223]. Two shapes are considered similar if their (normalized) FDs have a small distance. The FDs are invariant with respect to many geometric transformations. For example, the FDs can be used to match similar shapes even if they have different size and orientation. Show that
  (a) Normalized FDs are invariant to scaling.
  (b) The magnitudes of the FDs $\mid a(k) \mid$ for all k's except $k = 1$ have invariant properties with respect to starting point, rotation, and reflection.
  (c) The magnitudes of FDs are invariant to shift.

Exercise 1.11 Give your opinion on two fundamental motivating issues of the modern neural network research [243]:
  (a) How and in what form is information sensed and stored by a biological system?
  (b) How does information influence recognition and behavior?

PART II: UNSUPERVISED MODELS

Chapter 2

Fixed-Weight Associative Memory Networks

2.1 Introduction

Memory is critical for any information-processing system that remembers or deduces information. The memory of a neural network lies in the synaptic weights, which can be either prestored or adaptively trained by a learning mechanism. The neural networks can be classified, in terms of how the synaptic weights are obtained, into three categories: they are *fixed-weight*, *unsupervised* and *supervised models*.

Associative memory networks are designed for best recovering the original noise-free pattern from an incomplete or distorted signal. Pioneering works on associative memory networks have been independently developed by Anderson, Kohonen, and Nakano [15, 135, 206]. The development of the *association networks* evolved from the primitive Hebbian rule, to learning matrices, and then to the matrix models of associative memory networks [14, 266, 307]. More recently, a popular neural model for associative retrieval was proposed by Hopfield and colleagues [104, 105, 106, 269].

Chapter Organization

This chapter studies several key fixed-weight association networks, including typical examples such as linear associative memory and Hopfield association network. Their main characteristics is that the synaptic weights are pre-computed and prestored. In Section 2.2, the *feedforward* associative memory networks are briefly reviewed. Section 2.3 then presents *feedback* associative memory networks, namely the Hopfield models. The convergence properties of the models are discussed. Moreover, theoretical analyses on the capacities of Hopfield and Hamming networks are provided.

2.2   Feedforward Associative Memory Networks

As depicted in Figure 1.17 in Chapter 1, a basic association network has one layer of *input neurons* and one layer of *output neurons*. An input pattern x is represented as a point in the N-dimensional real or binary vector space, denoted as R^n or I^n, respectively. Two types of fixed-weight associative memory will be considered; one is of the feedforward type (e.g., linear and nonlinear associative memory) and the other is of the feedback type (e.g., the Hopfield network) where feedback connections are adopted to facilitate recurrent operations. The main difference between the two types is that a feedforward network is designed to retrieve patterns in one shot. In contrast, a feedback network cannot yield the correct pattern in a single forward pass. It is accomplished only after many iterations via the same network.

2.2.1   Linear Associative Memory

An associative memory network is mathematically a mapping from an input space to an output space as shown in Figure 2.1. Associative memory networks can be applied to either auto-association or hetero-association applications. In the auto-association application, the dimension of the input space is equal to that of the output space. On the other hand, in the hetero-association application, the dimensions of the input space and the output space are in general different. The input and output values can be real or binary.

A linear associative memory (LAM) is a single-layer feedforward network. The LAM is derived from a set of input/output pattern pairs $\{b^{(m)}, a^{(m)}\}$.

Here the input is $\mathbf{b}^{(m)} = [b_1^{(m)}, b_2^{(m)}, \ldots, b_K^{(m)}]^T$, and the output is $\mathbf{a}^{(m)} = [a_1^{(m)}, a_2^{(m)}, \ldots, a_N^{(m)}]^T$, for $m = 1, 2, \ldots, M$, where $[\cdot]^T$ denotes the transpose of a vector or a matrix. In the feedforward network, the input (stimulating) cells $\mathbf{b}^{(m)}$ and the output (response) cells $\mathbf{a}^{(m)}$ are located at the input layer and output layer, respectively. The objective of LAM is to recover the output pattern based on the full or partial information of the input pattern.

Continuous-Valued Input Patterns

The synaptic weight matrix $\mathbf{W}$ in linear associative memory is derived from taking the correlation of the (original) pattern pairs:

$$\mathbf{W} = \sum_m \mathbf{a}^{(m)} \, \mathbf{b}^{(m)^T}$$

where $\mathbf{a}$ and $\mathbf{b}$ are continuous-valued real-vectors, $\mathbf{a} \in R^N$ and $\mathbf{b} \in R^K$ (i.e., real-vectors). The entries of matrix are denoted [1]

$$w_{ij} = \sum_m a_i^{(m)} \, b_j^{(m)}$$

Ideal Pattern Retrieval Suppose that the input vectors are orthogonal to each other and that all the input vectors are normalized (i.e., $\mathbf{b}^{(k)^T}\mathbf{b}^{(k)} = 1$ and $\mathbf{b}^{(m)^T}\mathbf{b}^{(k)} = 0$, if $k \neq m$). When a noise-free vector $\mathbf{b}^{(k)}$ is input to the machine, then the original pattern $\mathbf{a}^{(k)}$ may be retrieved. This may be explained by a simple algebra,

$$\mathbf{W}\mathbf{b}^{(k)} = \sum_m \mathbf{a}^{(m)}\mathbf{b}^{(m)^T}\mathbf{b}^{(k)} = \mathbf{a}^{(k)}$$

Distortion by Input Noise There are no nonlinear processing units needed under the idealistic situation just specified. However, nonlinear units are critical to most practical applications. If an approximate or noisy version of $\mathbf{b}$ is used as test input, then vector $\mathbf{a}$ or a slightly perturbed vector will be recovered. Suppose that (1) the test input is $\mathbf{t} = \tilde{\mathbf{b}}^{(k)} = \mathbf{b}^{(k)} + \delta$, where δ represents a small perturbation vector; and (2) that for $k \neq m$, $\mathbf{b}^{(m)^T}\mathbf{b}^{(k)}$ is

---

[1] From a training perspective, the matrix is equivalently derived from a Hebbian rule: $\Delta w_{ij}^{(m)} = \eta \, a_i^{(m)} \, b_j^{(m)}$, where η is a small positive learning rate.

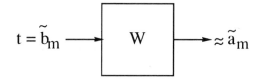

Figure 2.1: A linear associative memory (LAM) model, where $\mathbf{W}$ represents the feedforward synaptic weights.

also a small perturbation due to the nonorthogonality. Then the output will be distorted by the following perturbations:

$$
\begin{aligned}
\mathbf{W}\tilde{\mathbf{b}}^{(k)} &= \sum_m \mathbf{a}^{(m)}\{\mathbf{b}^{(m)^T}\mathbf{b}^{(k)} + \mathbf{b}^{(m)^T}\delta\} \\
&\equiv \mathbf{a}^{(k)} + \sum_m \mathbf{a}^{(m)}\{\text{perturbation}(m)\}
\end{aligned}
$$

Removal of such perturbations will require special *nonlinear processing* techniques discussed below.

Binary-Valued Input Patterns

If the inputs are (1/0) binary-valued, we adopt the following weight matrix $\mathbf{W}$, an $N \times K$ matrix with elements:

$$
w_{ij} = \sum_{m=1}^{M} (2a_i^{(m)} - 1)(2b_j^{(m)} - 1) \tag{2.1}
$$

where $\mathbf{a} \in I^N$ and $\mathbf{b} \in I^K$ (i.e., binary vectors). This formula has properly taken into account the (0.5) bias embedded in the (1/0) binary representation. Such adjustment allows an orthogonality condition to be more properly imposed (cf. Problem 2.1). To produce a binary-valued (1/0) output, the elements of the vector $\mathbf{Wt}$ are first adjusted by their respective thresholds:

$$
\theta_i = -\frac{1}{2}\sum_{j=1}^{K} w_{ij}
$$

and they will be processed by some nonlinear units (in the output nodes). If the adjusted value is positive then the output will be 1; otherwise, it will be 0.

Example 2.1 (An Auto-Association Example)

Two original pattern vectors to be stored (and retrieved), shown in Figures 2.2(a) and 2.2(b), are represented by the binary vectors

$$\mathbf{b}^{(1)} = \mathbf{a}^{(1)} = [111101111]^T \quad and \quad \mathbf{b}^{(2)} = \mathbf{a}^{(2)} = [101010101]^T$$

The weight matrix $\mathbf{W}$ *can be computed as*

$$\mathbf{W} = \begin{bmatrix} 2 & 0 & 2 & 0 & 0 & 0 & 2 & 0 & 2 \\ 0 & 2 & 0 & 2 & -2 & 2 & 0 & 2 & 0 \\ 2 & 0 & 2 & 0 & 0 & 0 & 2 & 0 & 2 \\ 0 & 2 & 0 & 2 & -2 & 2 & 0 & 2 & 0 \\ 0 & -2 & 0 & -2 & 2 & -2 & 0 & -2 & 0 \\ 0 & 2 & 0 & 2 & -2 & 2 & 0 & 2 & 0 \\ 2 & 0 & 2 & 0 & 0 & 0 & 2 & 0 & 2 \\ 0 & 2 & 0 & 2 & -2 & 2 & 0 & 2 & 0 \\ 2 & 0 & 2 & 0 & 0 & 0 & 2 & 0 & 2 \end{bmatrix}$$

and the thresholds as $[-4 \ -3 \ -4 \ -3 \ +3 \ -3 \ -4 \ -3 \ -4]^T$. *If the test pattern is given as in Figure 2.2(c),*

$$\mathbf{t} = [\ 1 \ 0 \ 1 \ 1 \ 0 \ 0 \ 1 \ 0 \ 1\ ]^T$$

then

$$\mathbf{Wt} = [\ 8 \ 2 \ 8 \ 2 \ -2 \ 2 \ 8 \ 2 \ 8\ ]^T$$

After adjusting the values by the thresholds and nonlinear processing, the final binary vector is

$$[\ 1 \ 0 \ 1 \ 0 \ 1 \ 0 \ 1 \ 0 \ 1\ ]^T$$

This is the correct solution, cf. Figure 2.2(b), based on the minimum Hamming distance criterion. (The Hamming distance is the number of inconsistent bits.) If the test pattern is (cf. Figure 2.2(d))

$$\mathbf{t} = [\ 0 \ 1 \ 0 \ 1 \ 0 \ 1 \ 1 \ 1 \ 1\ ]^T$$

then

$$\mathbf{Wt} = [\ 4 \ 8 \ 4 \ 8 \ -8 \ 8 \ 4 \ 8 \ 4\ ]^T$$

After the threshold nonlinear processing, the final binary vector is

$$[\ 0 \ 1 \ 0 \ 1 \ 0 \ 1 \ 0 \ 1 \ 0\ ]^T$$

which is neither of the two original patterns, so it is not a good retrieval.

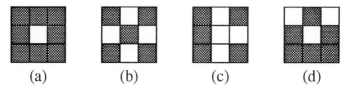

(a)   (b)   (c)   (d)

Figure 2.2: Bit map patterns for the auto-association example. The patterns to be "remembered" are (a) and (b). The test pattern is a noisy version of (a) shown as pattern (c). The retrieved pattern is (b). Pattern (d) is another test pattern whose retrieved pattern is neither (a) nor (b).

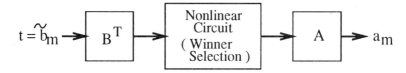

Figure 2.3: A nonlinear associative memory consists of three parts: (1) score matching (e.g., by measure of the inner-product or Hamming distance), (2) nonlinear processing units for winner selection (e.g, threshold or MAXNET processing), (3) displaying the selected pattern.

2.2.2   Nonlinear Associative Memory for Holographic Retrieval

The employment of a nonlinear processing unit, as shown in Figure 2.3, will prove essential in order to eliminate unwanted perturbation. Given a test pattern $\mathbf{t}$, we define a (matching) *score vector* $\mathbf{s}$ in terms of the inner-product between $\mathbf{b}^{(m)}$ and the test pattern $\mathbf{t}$ denoted by $< \mathbf{b}^{(m)}, \mathbf{t} >$. More precisely,

$$s = [< \mathbf{b}^{(1)}, \mathbf{t} >, < \mathbf{b}^{(2)}, \mathbf{t} >, \cdots, < \mathbf{b}^{(M)}, \mathbf{t} >]$$

where the inner-product (bracketed) operation $< \mathbf{b}^{(m)}, \mathbf{t} >$ for real-valued inputs is defined as

$$< \mathbf{b}^{(m)}, \mathbf{t} > \; \equiv \; \mathbf{b}^{(m)^T} \mathbf{t} \; \equiv \; \sum_{i=1}^{K} b_i^{(m)} t_i \tag{2.2}$$

The score vector $\mathbf{s}$ is proceeded by nonlinear processing, leading to a (binary) *decision vector* $\mathbf{v}$,

$$v = \mathcal{N}\{s\}$$

which is expected to have only one non-zero element. If the non-zero element is correctly positioned, then a holographical retrieval can be obtained. The

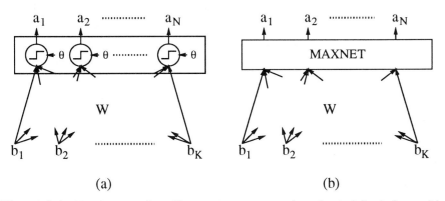

Figure 2.4: Two types of nonlinear operators can be adopted for holographic retrieval. (a) A threshold circuit. (b) A MAXNET, which can be digitally implemented by a special sorting circuit. For an analog design, see Figure 2.15.

pattern to be retrieved is the output value

$$\mathbf{A}\mathbf{v}$$

where $\mathbf{A}$ is the matrix formed from the column vectors $\mathbf{a}^{(k)}$.

The purpose of the nonlinear operator $\mathcal{N}\{\cdot\}$ is to elect one (and only one) winning node and simultaneously suppress all other nodes. The purpose is to suppress the noise, thus leading to *holographic retrieval*. The nonlinear operations can be manifested as either a thresholding device or a MAXNET circuit.

1. **Threshold Units** A basic threshold circuit is depicted in Figure 2.4(a). It is necessary to first estimate an optimal threshold θ, $0 < \theta < 1$. Suppose that we have a test pattern $\mathbf{t} = \tilde{\mathbf{b}}^{(k)}$ and that the noise level is low and the pattern vectors are approximately orthogonal. Then $< \mathbf{b}^{(m)}, \mathbf{b}^{(k)} >$ (for $m \neq k$) and $< \mathbf{b}^{(m)}, \delta >$ (cf. Eq. 2.1) should be sufficiently small so that the perturbational components are lower than the threshold. More exactly,

$$1 + \text{perturbation}(k) > \theta > \text{perturbation}(m) \quad \forall m \neq k$$

then the k-th pattern $\mathbf{a}^{(k)}$ can be holographically retrieved. If the threshold is set to be too low, then some inappropriate components may be falsely selected. On the other hand, if the threshold is set too high, then, in a noisy environment, it is possible that even the correct node will fail the threshold. The threshold θ is set commonly to 0.5.

2. **MAXNET** A MAXNET can be used to pick the winner as the one which has the maximum node value. In terms of digital implementation, a typical sorting or tree structure could be adopted. In analog implementation, however, it requires a dynamic circuit implementation (cf. Problem 2.16). The MAXNET provides another effective tool for holographic retrieval. It selects the correct winner (and weed out the perturbation components) when

$$1 + \text{perturbation}(k) > \text{perturbation}(m) \quad \forall m \neq k$$

An important advantage of the MAXNET is that it avoids altogether the need to estimate the threshold θ.

2.2.3   Hamming Networks

When the inputs are binary-valued, then the use of Hamming networks becomes very appealing. The Hamming net selects a winner from the stored patterns, $\{\mathbf{b}^{(m)}, m = 1, \cdots, M\}$, which has the least Hamming distance from the input vector. For bipolar (1/-1) vectors, the same definition of inner-product introduced in Eq. 2.2 can be adopted. However, for binary-valued (1/0) inputs, the inner-product must be redefined to be:

$$< \mathbf{b}^{(m)}, \mathbf{t} > \equiv \sum_{i=1}^{K} (2b_i^{(m)} - 1)(2t_i - 1) \tag{2.3}$$

Therefore, we have

$$
\begin{aligned}
< \mathbf{b}^{(m)}, \mathbf{t} > &= \sum_{i=1}^{K} (2b_i^{(m)} - 1)(2t_i - 1) \\
&= \text{the total number of match bits} \\
&\quad -\text{the total number of mismatch bits} \\
&= K - 2 \, (\text{Hamming distance between } \mathbf{b}^{(m)} \text{ and } \mathbf{t})
\end{aligned}
$$

where the Hamming distance is the number of inconsistent bits between the two vectors. This proves that, in this case, either the inner-product measure or the Hamming-distance measure will yield the same effect. (A MAXNET can be adopted in the Hamming Net to select a winner.) An application example for numeric digit recognition will be studied in Example 2.4.

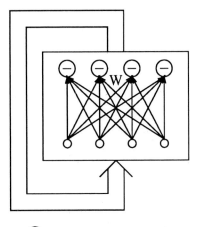

⊖ : Nonlinear Processing Unit

Figure 2.5: A feedback neural model, where **W** represents feedback synaptic weights.

2.3 Feedback Associative Memory Networks

Figure 2.5 shows a general configuration for a feedback neural model. Unlike the feed-forward models discussed in the last section, a *feedback network* needs many iterations before retrieving a final pattern. The most popular feedback auto-association network is the Hopfield model [104, 105, 106, 269], which has the following characteristics:

1. Synaptic weights (predetermined by the Hebbian rule or an energy function) are prestored.

2. Nonlinear thresholding operations are used in each stage to produce binary-valued states.

3. State feedbacks are used so that the states can be iteratively updated.

4. Iterations will converge to a solution that minimizes an energy function pertaining to the network.

In the following, a sequential (asynchronous) Hopfield model and a parallel (synchronous) Hopfield model will be introduced.

2.3.1   Sequential (Asynchronous) Hopfield Model

Derivation of Synaptic Weights   Given M binary-valued $(0/1)$ patterns (i.e., $\{a_i^{(m)}\}$ have binary values 0 or 1), the weights of the Hopfield network are derived as

$$w_{ij} = \begin{cases} \sum_{m=1}^{M}(2a_i^{(m)} - 1)(2a_j^{(m)} - 1) & i \neq j \\ 0 & i = j \end{cases} \qquad (2.4)$$

The thresholds of the network are given as

$$\theta_i = -\frac{1}{2}\sum_{j=1}^{N} w_{ij} \qquad (2.5)$$

Energy Functions and Convergence   The following notion of *energy function* (or *Liapunov function*) is useful [105, 106]:

$$E = -\frac{1}{2}\sum_i \sum_j w_{ij}a_i a_j - \sum_i \theta_i a_i \qquad (2.6)$$

Under the ideal circumstance that the stored vectors are perfectly orthogonal, then every original pattern represents a local (or global) minimum of the *energy function*, cf. Problem 2.5. [2] This motivates the design of a network that can iteratively search for a local minimum state. A gradient-type technique leads to the *sequential Hopfield model*. The difference of the energy functions before and after a state update is

$$\begin{aligned}
\Delta_k E &= E(k+1) - E(k) \\
&= -\frac{1}{2}\sum_i \sum_j w_{ij}a_i(k+1)a_j(k+1) - \sum_i \theta_i a_i(k+1) \\
&\quad + \frac{1}{2}\sum_i \sum_j w_{ij}a_i(k)a_j(k) + \sum_i \theta_i a_i(k) \\
&= -\sum_i [a_i(k+1) - a_i(k)]\left[\sum_j w_{ij}a_j(k) + \theta_i\right]
\end{aligned}$$

---

[2]Note that, under the general and practical situations, the stored patterns are only "almost" orthogonal, so this local minimum property does not hold true, cf. Problem 2.6. In addition, there exist many spurious attractors, cf. Problem 2.7.

$$-\frac{1}{2}\sum_i [a_i(k+1) - a_i(k)]\{\sum_j w_{ij}[a_j(k+1) - a_j(k)]\}$$

$$= -\sum_i u_i(k+1)\,\Delta a_i(k+1) - \frac{1}{2}\Delta \mathbf{a}^T(k+1)\mathbf{W}\,\Delta \mathbf{a}(k+1)$$

$$(2.7)$$

where

$$u_i(k+1) \equiv \sum_j w_{ij}a_j(k) + \theta_i$$

In case of a sequential (asynchronous) update, there is only one bit updated at one time. Without loss of generality, let us assume it to be $\Delta a_i(k+1)$ on the ith bit,

$$\Delta_k E = -u_i(k+1)\Delta a_i(k+1) - \frac{1}{2}w_{ii}$$

Because $w_{ii} = 0$,

$$\Delta_k E = -u_i(k+1)\Delta a_i(k+1) \qquad (2.8)$$

Let us introduce a discrete version of the gradient as

$$\frac{\Delta_k E}{\Delta a_i(k+1)} = -u_i(k+1)$$

In order to guarantee the decrease of the energy function, $\Delta a_i(k+1)$ should be updated in the negative gradient-descent direction, that is,

$$\Delta a_i(k+1) \propto u_i(k+1)$$

This leads to the following sequential Hopfield model.

Algorithm 2.1 (Sequential Hopfield Model)

Suppose that the input of the feedback network is **a**, *which is used as the initial state vector. That is, we set* $\mathbf{a} = \mathbf{a}(0) = [a_1(0),\ a_2(0),\ \ldots,\ a_N(0)]^T$ *and the iterations starts at* $k = 1$ *until convergence. During the kth iteration, the network performs bit update in a sequential order from* $i = 1$, $i = 2, \cdots$, *to* $i = N$:

(1) compute the net value

$$u_i(k+1) = \sum_j w_{ij} a_j(k) + \theta_i$$

(2) update the states

$$a_i(k+1) = \begin{cases} 1 & u_i(k+1) > 0 \\ 0 & u_i(k+1) < 0 \\ a_i(k) & u_i(k+1) = 0 \end{cases} \qquad (2.9)$$

Repeat the same process for the next iteration until convergence, which occurs when none of the elements changes state during any iteration.

■

The proof of convergence follows. To demonstrate the convergence, note that $\Delta a_i(k+1)$ is positive (negative) *if and only if* $-u_i(k+1)$ is negative (positive). Therefore, according to Eq. 2.8 if there is any energy change, it must be negative. Because E may not decrease indefinitely, the network iterations must terminate in a finite number of steps; thus, convergence is guaranteed. Furthermore, Eq. 2.8 also assures that there will be no oscillation of states. Note that it is necessary to use sequential (asynchronous) update of the neurons in order to guarantee convergence to a local minimum [105, 267].

Local Minima and Attractors in Sequential Hopfield Models   In the discrete-state case, a **local minimum** is defined as a point that has an energy level lower than or equal to any nearest neighbor. (The term local minimum is used to characterize the energy function state.) A state is an **attractor** of a network if it is an equilibrium state of the neural net, that is, once the network reaches that state it will stay there forever. (The term attractor is used to characterize the behavior of a neural model instead of an energy function.)

In the previous derivation, Eq. 2.8 indicates that state a_k is an *attractor* if and only if $\Delta_k E$ is nonnegative for any bit i. Furthermore, state a_k is a *local minimum* if and only if $\Delta_k E$ is nonnegative for any bit i. *Therefore, we conclude that, for the sequential Hopfield model, a local minimum state is an attractor and vice versa.*

More elaborately, the state must change if such a change would result in a decrease of the energy level. So the attractor state must be a *local minimum* of the energy function given in Eq. 2.6. Conversely, the state will change only if the change can result in a net decrease of energy. It implies that *every local minimum of the energy function must be an attractor in the sequential Hopfield model.*

Example 2.2 (Sequential or Asynchronous Update)

Consider the following two training pattern vectors $\mathbf{a}^{(1)}$ *and* $\mathbf{a}^{(2)}$:

$$\mathbf{a}^{(1)} = [\,1\,1\,1\,0\,]^T$$
$$\mathbf{a}^{(2)} = [\,1\,1\,0\,0\,]^T$$

We can form the weight matrix $\mathbf{W}$ *based on Hopfield's formulation; see Eq. 2.4:*

$$\mathbf{W} = \Phi(\,[2\mathbf{a}^{(1)} - 1]\,[2\mathbf{a}^{(1)} - 1]^T + ([2\mathbf{a}^{(2)} - 1]\,[2\mathbf{a}^{(2)} - 1]^T\,)$$

$$= \Phi\left(\begin{bmatrix} 2 & 2 & 0 & -2 \\ 2 & 2 & 0 & -2 \\ 0 & 0 & 2 & 0 \\ -2 & -2 & 0 & 2 \end{bmatrix}\right)$$

$$= \begin{bmatrix} 0 & 2 & 0 & -2 \\ 2 & 0 & 0 & -2 \\ 0 & 0 & 0 & 0 \\ -2 & -2 & 0 & 0 \end{bmatrix}$$

where the operator Φ *nullifies the diagonal elements of the matrix. It follows that*

$$\theta_1 = 0 \quad \theta_2 = 0 \quad \theta_3 = 0 \quad \theta_4 = 2$$

Now suppose that we have an input vector $\mathbf{b} = [0\,1\,0\,0]^T$. *If the asynchronous update is used with simple cyclic update ordering, we can get the following bit-update results:*

First Iteration
$$\text{initial vector} = [0\,1\,0\,0]^T$$
$$\text{1st bit update} = [1\,1\,0\,0]^T$$

$$\begin{aligned}
\textit{2nd bit update} &= [1\ 1\ 0\ 0]^T \\
\textit{3rd bit update} &= [1\ 1\ 0\ 0]^T \\
\textit{4th bit update} &= [1\ 1\ 0\ 0]^T
\end{aligned}$$

Second Iteration

$$\begin{aligned}
\textit{1st bit update} &= [1\ 1\ 0\ 0]^T \\
\textit{2nd bit update} &= [1\ 1\ 0\ 0]^T \\
\textit{3rd bit update} &= [1\ 1\ 0\ 0]^T \\
\textit{4th bit update} &= [1\ 1\ 0\ 0]^T
\end{aligned}$$

It converges!

In this example, there is only one real update on the first bit in the first iteration. (Note that $u_1(1) = \sum_j w_{1j} a_j(0) = 2 > 0$.)

Example 2.3 (Convergent State Depends on the Order of Update)

The retrieval phase of the sequential Hopfield network is dependent on the bit ordering adopted. Different ordering retrieves a different output. Such dependency can be best illustrated by an example. Let us study the sequential Hopfield model for retrieval of the following two patterns: $[0\ 0\ 1\ 1]^T$ and $[1\ 0\ 1\ 0]^T$. According to Eqns. 2.4 and 2.5, the weight matrix and θ vector should be

$$\mathbf{w} = \begin{bmatrix} 0 & 0 & 0 & -2 \\ 0 & 0 & -2 & 0 \\ 0 & -2 & 0 & 0 \\ -2 & 0 & 0 & 0 \end{bmatrix}$$

$$\theta = [1\ 1\ 1\ 1]^T$$

The final outputs can be obtained by following the energy-descending directions in a hypercube shown in Figure 2.6. (See Problem 2.7.)

There are more than one possible directions in which the energy level can descend. According to Figure 2.6, at point $[0\ 0\ 1\ 0]^T$, there are two paths that guide it to two different local minima. The selection of the paths is determined by the order of updating bits. The convergent solution depends on whether the update starts with the leftmost or rightmost bit. If the update starts with the leftmost bit, the input pattern $[0\ 0\ 1\ 0]^T$ will converge to $[1\ 0\ 1\ 0]^T$. But, if the update order is reversed (i.e., starts with the rightmost bit), the pattern will converge to a different solution, $[0\ 0\ 1\ 1]^T$. (See Figure 2.6.)

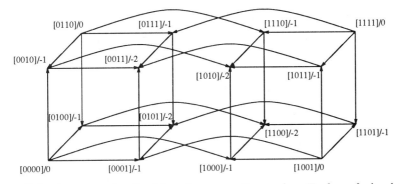

Figure 2.6: An example of a 16-node energy-flow cube. Each node is given a value equal to its energy level. The direction of flow is from the higher-energy node to the lower-level one (as shown with arrows). There is no flow between two nodes with the same energy level.

2.3.2   Parallel (Synchronous) Hopfield Model

The sequential Hopfield model suffers from a disadvantage in its disallowing parallel updating. In order to exploit the potential of parallel (i.e., synchronous) processing, the following model is proposed [161].

Derivation of Weights in the Parallel Hopfield Model   In the parallel model, the weights are defined as

$$w_{ij} = \sum_{m=1}^{M} (2a_i^{(m)} - 1)(2a_j^{(m)} - 1) \qquad (2.10)$$

Note that *the diagonal weights w_{ii} are no longer set to zero*. The thresholds of the network are given as

$$\theta_i = -\frac{1}{2} \sum_{j=1}^{N} w_{ij}$$

Algorithm 2.2 (Parallel Hopfield Model)

During the kth iteration:
   (1) Compute the net values in parallel for $i = 1, 2, \cdots, N$,

$$u_i(k+1) = \sum_j w_{ij} a_j(k) + \theta_i$$

(2) Update the states in parallel for $i = 1, 2, \cdots, N$,

$$a_i(k+1) = \begin{cases} 1 & u_i(k+1) > 0 \\ 0 & u_i(k+1) < 0 \\ a_i(k) & u_i(k+1) = 0 \end{cases}$$

Repeat the same process for the next iteration until convergence, which occurs when none of the elements changes state during any iteration.

            ■

Convergence: Gradual Decrease of Energy   The proof of convergence for this parallel Hopfield model is presented here. For the synchronous update, assume that at the kth parallel iteration, we have an energy function $E(k)$:

$$E(k) = -\frac{1}{2}\sum_i \sum_j w_{ij} a_i(k) a_j(k) - \sum_i \theta_i a_i(k)$$

According to Eq. 2.7, the energy-level change due to one iteration of parallel update is

$$\begin{aligned} \Delta_k E &= E(k+1) - E(k) \\ &= -\sum_i u_i(k+1)\,\Delta a_i(k+1) - \frac{1}{2}\Delta \mathbf{a}^T(k+1)\mathbf{W}\Delta \mathbf{a}(k+1) \\ &= \Delta_k E_1 + \Delta_k E_2 \end{aligned} \tag{2.11}$$

Because the $\mathbf{W}$ matrix is formed by the outer product without diagonal nullification (see Eq. 2.10), it is a nonnegative definite matrix, that is, $\Delta_k E_2 \leq 0$. It should be clear now that $\Delta_k E_1 \leq 0$. More precisely, $\Delta_k E_1 < 0$ if a nontrivial update occurs. (This also assures that there is no possibility of oscillation of any convergent state.)

Local Minima and Attractors in the Parallel Hopfield Model   First, let us note that the energy levels of all states in the parallel Hopfield model are exactly equivalent to that in the sequential Hopfield model. (See Problem 2.8.) Despite the fact that the energy levels between the sequential and parallel models are exactly the same, significantly different retrieval results can be obtained. Let us elaborate further on this point.

     A vector is called an attractor if it is an equilibrium state of the neural net. It can be easily verified that Eq. 2.9 and Eq. 2.8 together imply that *in the sequential model, an attractor must be a local/global minimum, and vice versa.* However, for the parallel Hopfield model, the situation is very different. *Whereas a local/global minimum must be an attractor, an attractor is not necessarily a local/global minimum.* (See Problem 2.9.)

As a result, there are many more spurious attractors in the parallel model than the sequential version. This is bad news. The good news, however, is that the parallel model does not get trapped to local minima as easily as the sequential model. In other words, even if a state is one bit away from a local minimum (or from any attractor), it is possible that it will not be trapped by that attractor, unlike the sequential model.

In the simulation results shown in Figure 2.8, the parallel model appears to outperform the sequential model in terms of percentages of correct retrieval. Moreover, if the capacity in the model is low, the weight matrix used in the parallel Hopfield model has a low rank property that can be exploited to reduce the computation. An inner-product technique to perform the matrix-vector multiplication has also been proposed [167]. This technique can achieve considerable hardware saving. (See Problem 2.26.) In contrast, the sequential model does not offer the same potential advantage.

2.3.3   Capacities of Hopfield and Hamming Networks

The capacity of a network is the number of distinct pattern vectors (say, M) that can be stored in, say, an N-neuron network. The capacity M can be shown to be at most $N/2 \log N$ as estimated via an information theoretical approach [192]. Our scheme of deriving the capacity is the following. Given p original pattern vectors, we first determine whether they qualify to be good attractors of the network. (Set the initial state of the network to be one of the original pattern vectors, if it is of sufficiently low probability that any bit may change then that pattern is considered a good attractor.) If all the p vectors are good attractors then the network is said to have a capacity p. Otherwise, the capacity is considered to be lower than p.

It is easier to work with the bipolar representation:

$$x_i^{(m)} = 2a_i^{(m)} - 1$$

where $a_i^{(m)}$ is the binary representation of the original patterns. Now we have

$$u_i = \sum_j w_{ij} x_j^{(n)}$$

$$u_i = \sum_j \sum_m x_i^{(m)} x_j^{(m)} x_j^{(n)} / N$$

$$= x_i^{(n)} + \sum_j \sum_{m \neq n} x_i^{(m)} x_j^{(m)} x_j^{(n)} / N$$

It follows that

$$x_i^{(n)} u_i = 1 - C_i^{(n)}$$

where

$$C_i^{(n)} = -x_i^{(n)} \frac{1}{N} \sum_j^{N} \sum_{m \neq n}^{p} x_i^{(m)} x_j^{(m)} x_j^{(n)}$$

The change of the bit $x_i^{(n)}$ will occur when and only when

$$x_i^{(n)} u_i < 0$$

(Show this!) Therefore, the bit error rate is

$$\text{bit-error-rate} = Prob(C_i^{(n)} > 1)$$

where $C_i^{(n)}$ has a distribution with mean 0 and variance $\sigma^2 = p/N$. When Np is very large, the distribution becomes

$$\text{bit-error-rate} = \frac{1}{\sqrt{2\pi}\sigma} \int_1^\infty e^{-x^2/2\sigma^2} \, dx \approx e^{-\frac{1}{2\sigma^2}}$$

To guarantee the total error probability to be less than ϵ, it is sufficient to make the error probability for each pattern to be less than ϵ/p, that is,

$$\text{bit-error-rate} \approx e^{-\frac{N}{2p}} < \frac{\epsilon}{Np}$$

Taking the logarithm on both sides,

$$-N/2p < -\log N - \log p + \log \epsilon$$

Assuming N very large, we have the approximation $N/2p > \log N$. This implies that the capacity of the network is

$$p < \frac{N}{2 \log N}$$

As suggested by Table 2.1, the capacity of the Hopfield net is theoretically much lower than that of the Hamming net. This is further confirmed by the following simulation example. Further progress on the study of capacity can be found in [50, 139, 145].

	Number of Weights	Computation Complexity	Storing Capacity
Hopfield	N^2	N^2	$\frac{N}{2\log N}$
Hamming Net	MN	MN	$2^{cN}, c \leq 1$

Table 2.1: Hardware and computation comparisons of hopfield models and the Hamming net. (The capacity result of the Hamming net is due to Venkatesh [287].)

Example 2.4 (Performance Comparison in Digit Recognition)

In this example, a simulational study on the performance comparison between Hopfield models and Hamming networks is conducted. It uses as many as 10 digit characters displayed in Figure 2.7, each digit in a 5 × 3 bit map representation. For an objective comparison, all experiments corresponding to classifications of 2, 3, ..., up to all the 10 digits, have been separately carried out. In the case of two characters, the digits "0" and "1" are recognized. For three characters, digits "0", "1", and "2" are recognized, and so on.

To generate the test patterns, each of the original characters is corrupted by noisy pixels. The experiments are conducted with 9 different (increasing) degrees of difficulty by increasing the number of noisy bits from 0,1,2, up to 8 bits. For each degree of difficulty, 20 test patterns are randomly generated. Therefore, if all 10 digits are to be recognized, there are a total of 9 × 20 × 10 test patterns randomly generated. The retrieved character is deemed correct if it matches the original character. In Figure 2.8, accuracy percentages are plotted for all experiments, each with different numbers of characters.

The simulation results are summarized in Figure 2.8. For the sequential Hopfield net, the parallel Hopfield net, and the Hamming net, the overall accuracy percentages are 22%, 26%, and 69%, respectively. The accuracies improve to 31%, 39%, and 95%, when the noise bits are less than or equal to 3. Due to their low network capacity, the performances of both the sequential and parallel Hopfield models fall considerably below the Hamming net.

Other Concerns on Feedback Associative Networks   In addition to the capacity limitation, there are several other serious concerns on the Hopfield networks.

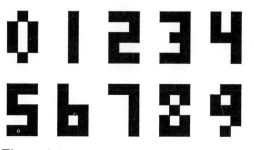

Figure 2.7: Numerical character examples.

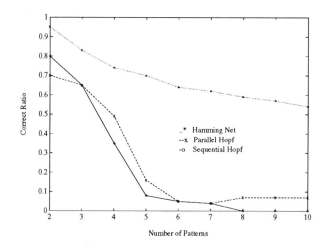

Figure 2.8: Simulation comparisons between Hopfield models and Hamming networks.

1. *Spurious Attractors.* A vector is called a spurious attractor if it is an attractor but not one of the originally stored patterns. For the Hopfield net, there exist a large number of spurious attractors (cf. Problem 2.5).

2. *Hardware Inefficiency.* The hardware efficiency of the Hopfield model is defined as the number of information bits per connection state. It is inferior as compared with the Hamming net (cf. Table 2.1). The efficiency is shown to be less than $0.5N^{-1}$. (See Problem 2.22.)

2.3.4　Bidirectional Associative Memory

The Hopfield model is only useful for auto-association with the purpose of reproducing a (noise-free) version of the pattern presented. It can be extended

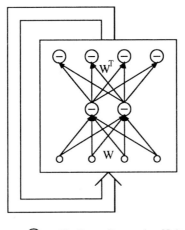

$\ominus$: Nonlinear Processing Unit

Figure 2.9: Bidirectional Associative Memory (BAM).

to handle hetero-association (i.e., pattern association). A prominent example is Bidirectional Associative Memory (BAM) proposed by Kosko [141, 142]. BAM includes the (parallel) Hopfield model as a special case.

In a hetero-association application, we are given M sets of I/O pattern pairs $\{\mathbf{b}^{(m)}, \mathbf{a}^{(m)}\}$, where $\mathbf{b}^{(m)} = [b_1^{(m)}, b_2^{(m)}, \ldots, b_K^{(m)}]^T$, and $\mathbf{a}^{(m)} = [a_1^{(m)}, a_2^{(m)}, \ldots, a_N^{(m)}]^T$, for $m = 1, 2, \ldots, M$. As illustrated in Figure 2.9, BAM can be constructed by two layers of parallel Hopfield models: the weight matrix $\mathbf{W}$ is used in the first layer and the weight matrix $\mathbf{W}^T$ is used in the second layer. For the first layer, weight matrix $\mathbf{W}$ is an N x K matrix with elements:

$$w_{ij} = \sum_{m=1}^{M} (2a_i^{(m)} - 1)(2b_j^{(m)} - 1) \qquad (2.12)$$

The thresholds for the first layer are

$$\theta_i = -\frac{1}{2} \sum_{j=1}^{K} w_{ij}$$

For the second layer, the weight matrix is changed to $\mathbf{W}^T$ and the thresholds are different from the first layer:

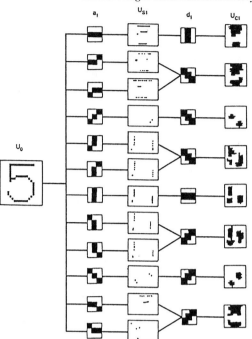

Figure 2.10: A BAM-processing example. (Source: [142].)

$$\theta'_j = -\frac{1}{2}\sum_{i=1}^{N} w_{ij}$$

The convergence proof of BAM basically follows the proof for the parallel Hopfield model. However, a new energy function $E(k)$ is adopted:

$$E(k) = -\sum_{i}\sum_{j} w_{ij}(2a_i(k) - 1)(2b_j(k) - 1)$$

The processing of BAM is best illustrated by the example in Figure 2.10.

2.3.5 Discrete-Time Continuous-State Hopfield Model

There are two versions of continuous-state Hopfield networks: the continuous-time continuous-state model and the discrete-time continuous-state model. The former is represented by a system of differential equations while the latter by difference equations. Motivated by the recent advent of switch-capacitor-device technology and the potential application to optimization problems, the study of the discrete-time continuous-state Hopfield model has recently received a lot of attention.

Retrieving Phase In order to imitate the continuous input-output relationship of real neurons and to simulate the integrative time delay due to the capacitance of real neurons the following *sigmoid* activation function $f(x)$ is proposed [105]:

$$f(x) = \frac{1}{1 + e^{-x/\sigma}} \tag{2.13}$$

and the following dynamic system for the retrieving phase is proposed [105, 267]:

$$u_i(k+1) = \sum_j w_{ij} a_j(k) + \theta_i \tag{2.14}$$

$$a_i(k+1) = \frac{1}{1 + e^{-u_i'(k+1)/\sigma}} \tag{2.15}$$

where $u_i'(k+1) = \kappa_1 u_i(k) + \kappa_2 u_i(k+1)$, and κ_1 and κ_2 are proper constants proposed in [267].

Convergence The convergence of sequential (asynchronous) and parallel (synchronous) updates has also been studied for the continuous-state case. The convergence with parallel update can be assured only when the (time-step) coefficient (κ_2) is small enough (and thus (κ_1) is very close to unity). Following Eq. 2.11, we note that the key to convergence is to assure that $\triangle_k E_2$ is always negative. In the earlier proof, we relied on the fact that matrix **W** is always non-negative-definite in the association applications. However, in most optimization applications, matrix **W** is not necessarily non-negative-definite. A simple analysis will show that such difficulty can be circumvented by insisting that the ratio $\triangle a_i(k+1)/a_i(k+1)$ be very small.

The following continuous-state model is proposed.

$$u_i(k+1) = \sum_j w_{ij} a_j(k) + \theta_i$$

$$a_i(k+1) = a_i(k) \left\{ 1 + \beta \ \text{sgn}[u_i(k+1)] \right\} \tag{2.16}$$

where β represents a small positive step size.

2.3.6   Stochastic Models and the Boltzmann Machine

With reference to Table 1.1, an optimization problem differs from associative memory in that its objective is to search the global optima — instead of the local optima. By incorporating statistical techniques into the Hopfield-type network, the model can be extended to handle optimization problems. Similarly, it can also be extended to the Boltzmann machine. To study stochastic neural networks, we assume that the states of the network follow a Boltzmann-Gibb distribution. The statistical equilibrium condition leads to the *Boltzmann learning rule* for state update. More details on these subjects are provided in Chapter 9.

2.4   Concluding Remarks

This chapter presents several associative memory models: the linear associative memories, Hamming nets, and the feedback Hopfield models. Both the sequential and parallel Hopfield models and the convergence properties are studied. It is our conclusion that, in digital implementation, the Hopfield models are inferior to the classical Hamming networks. Note however that substantial differences do exist between digital and analog implementations. While the sequential (asynchronous) processing of the Hopfield model is a serious disadvantage in digital implementation, it appears to be very natural in analog implementation. Such analog implementation of the feedback circuits can potentially yield "instant" convergence. When such a circuit technology is realized, it will offer a very promising possibility for the Hopfield-type feedback models.

2.5 Problems[3]

Exercise 2.1 Bipolar Pattern Representation
If the input patterns are bipolar-valued (-1/1), then we can use the following:

$$w_{ij} = \sum_{m=1}^{M} a_i^{(m)} b_j^{(m)}$$

then the test pattern shown in Figure 2.2(c) will lead to a correct retrieval. However, if the input patterns are binary-valued (0/1), then the weights shown in the formula can no longer lead to a correct retrieval for the same test pattern. This confirms that the formula in Eq. 2.1 is more suitable for the binary-value case.

Exercise 2.2 (Linear Associative Memory)
Design a LAM for the following 2×2 bit-map patterns:
   $\mathbf{a}^{(1)}$: $[1011]^T$ (representing an upper-case character L).
   $\mathbf{a}^{(2)}$: $[0101]^T$ (representing a lower-case character l).
Show that the LAM can retrieve an optimal solution in terms of the Hamming distance criterion for the following test patterns:
   $\mathbf{t}^{(1)}$: $[1101]^T$ (representing a rotated upper-case character L).
   $\mathbf{t}^{(2)}$: $[0011]^T$ (representing a rotated lower-case character l).

Exercise 2.3 Design a (sequential) Hopfield model to retrieve two pattern vectors, $\mathbf{a}^{(1)} = [1011]^T$ and $\mathbf{a}^{(2)} = [0101]^T$, as used in Exercise 2.2. Compute the weight matrix and threshold values. Compute the energy levels of different states. What are the retrieved patterns for the test vectors $\mathbf{t}^{(1)} = [1101]^T$ and $\mathbf{t}^{(2)} = [0011]^T$?

Exercise 2.4 Two binary-pattern vectors are given as shown in Figures 2.2(a) and 2.2(b). For the test pattern shown in Figure 2.2(c), find the pattern that can be retrieved by the Hamming network.

Exercise 2.5 (Minimum-Energy States for Orthogonal Patterns)
Suppose that all the training input patterns are orthogonal, that is,

$$\sum_{i=1}^{N} (2a_i^{(m)} - 1)(2a_i^{(k)} - 1) = 0 \quad \forall \, k \neq m$$

then all the states corresponding to these patterns have (the same) globally minimal energy levels. For the parallel Hopfield model,

---

[3]The basic problems in this chapter are Problems 2.1 to 2.15. The remaining are of intermediate difficulty.

(a) If all the pattern vectors are orthogonal, show that every original pattern is an attractor and a global minimum.

(b) Show that every "negative" of the original patterns is also an attractor and a global minimum.

(c) In general, there exist other global minima.

(d) Show that parts (a) to (c) also hold true for the sequential Hopfield model.

Exercise 2.6 *This problem shows that a wrong retrieval is possible, even though the input pattern to the Hopfield network is the original.* Show that for the Hopfield network in Problem 2.7, vector $t_3 = a^{(1)} = [01101000]$ is neither a local minimum nor an attractor.

Exercise 2.7 Hopfield Net Is Not Equivalent to a Hamming Net
Design a (sequential) Hopfield model to retrieve three pattern vectors:
$a^{(1)} = [01101000]^T$, $a^{(2)} = [10010101]^T$, and $a^{(3)} = [11110100]^T$.

(a) Show that $t_1 = [01010100]^T$ converges to $a^{(2)}$.

(b) It is not an optimal solution in terms of the Hamming distance criterion.

(c) The vector $t_2 = [00001011]$ is a spurious attractor.

Exercise 2.8 *This problem shows the equivalence between the energy-flow cube and the sequential Hopfield model.*

An energy-flow cube is a 2^N-node hypercube, each node labeled with a value equal to its energy level. The directions of the energy flows depend on the relative energy level between two adjacent nodes: It flows from the higher-level node to the lower-level one. (There is no flow between two nodes with the same energy level.) As an example, an energy-flow cube for the Hopfield model in Example 2.3 is depicted in Figure 2.6. Show that (cf. Eq. 2.9) *the updating process in the Hopfield network follows exactly the directions of the energy flows.*

Exercise 2.9 Show that the energy levels of all the states in the parallel Hopfield model are equivalent to those in the sequential Hopfield model.

Exercise 2.10 For the parallel Hopfield models, show that (a) a local/global minimum must be an attractor, and (b) an attractor is not necessarily a local/global minimum.

Exercise 2.11 Suppose that there are only TWO orthogonal pattern vectors. Show that there are no global minima other than the original patterns or those complementary to those patterns. (This is true for both sequential and parallel Hopfield models.)

Exercise 2.12 Let O denote the set of original patterns (plus their complementary patterns) to be memorized by an associative Hopfield, L the set of local minima, G the set of global minima, and A the set of attractors.

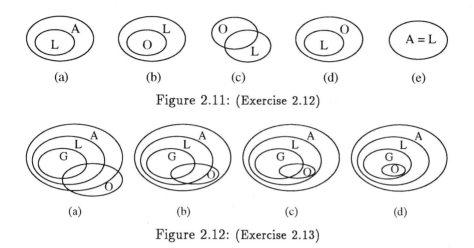

Figure 2.11: (Exercise 2.12)

Figure 2.12: (Exercise 2.13)

(a) For the sequential Hopfield model, which (one or more) of the set relationships in Figure 2.11 is generically valid? Justify your answer. (Note Figure 2.11 represents a "proper" subset relationship. The same is true for the other figures in the following problems.)

(b) Repeat the same for the parallel Hopfield model.

Exercise 2.13 Continuing Problem 2.12, for the parallel Hopfield model, which (one or more) of the set relationships in Figure 2.12 is generically valid? Justify your answer.

Exercise 2.14 Continuing Problem 2.12, for the parallel Hopfield model, let A1 denote the set of attractors when the diagonal terms of the synaptic weight matrix are set to 0, A2 the set of attractors when the diagonals are set to be $w_{ii}/2$, and A3 the set of attractors when the diagonals are set to w_{ii}. (Assume that $w_{ii} > 0$.)

Which (one or more) of the set relationships in Figure 2.13 is generically valid? Justify your answer.

Exercise 2.15 Continuing Problem 2.12, suppose all the original patterns have the orthogonality property.

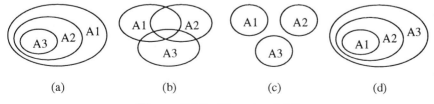

Figure 2.13: (Exercise 2.14)

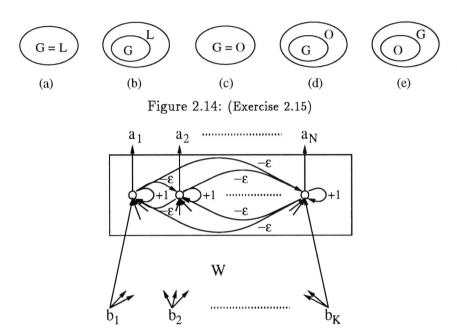

Figure 2.14: (Exercise 2.15)

Figure 2.15: Dynamic circuit diagram of an implementation example of analog MAXNET.

(a) For the sequential Hopfield model, which (one or more) of the set relationships in Figure 2.14 is generically valid? Justify your answer.

(b) Repeat the same for the parallel Hopfield model.

Exercise 2.16 MAXNET

In the MAXNET in Figure 2.15, assume that $\epsilon > 0$, and that in the beginning, we operate in the linear region. Study the evolution of the differences between the largest element and the rest of the elements.

(a) If the initial values of all units are positive and the slope of the linear part of the nonlinearity is 1, show that the dynamic system will gradually force all elements to zero, except for the single unit that initially has the largest value.

(b) If the slope is larger than 1, show that the final vector can have more than one non-zero element. Discuss the case where the slope is less than 1.

(c) Show that the MAXNET becomes an unstable linear system if the nonlinear thresholding is absent. (Hint: The trace of a matrix is equal to the sum of its eigenvalues.)

Exercise 2.17 Show by example that if the weights are set according to Eq. 2.4, the convergence property based on a parallel (synchronous) update cannot be guaranteed.

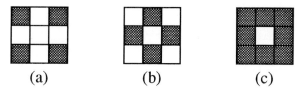

Figure 2.16: Bit map patterns for Problem 2.21.

Exercise 2.18 (Energy-Flow Cube for a Sequential Hopfield Network)
(a) Based on Exercise 2.3, draw a figure of a 4-cube with each vertex representing a possible state. Compute the energy level associated with each of the 16 states.
(b) Verify that the sequential Hopfield network guides any initial vector to a local minimum.

Exercise 2.19 (State-Flow Cube for a Parallel Hopfield Network)
Based on Example 2.3, derive the corresponding parallel Hopfield network and draw a 16-node energy-function hypercube.
(a) Determine all the state-flow arcs in the hypercube for the parallel Hopfield network. Compare it with the energy-flow cube of the sequential model.
(b) Determine the number of attractors.

Exercise 2.20
(a) Given original patterns, $\mathbf{a}^{(1)} = [01101000]^T$, $\mathbf{a}^{(2)} = [10110101]^T$, and $\mathbf{a}^{(3)} = [11010110]^T$, if we use the parallel updating mechanism on a Hopfield model with a nullified-diagonal weight matrix, show that oscillation can occur between two states, $[11011000]$ and $[01100110]$.
(b) Prove that such oscillation will not occur for any parallel model defined by Eq. 2.10.
Hint: By Eq. 2.7, ΔE will be strictly negative if there is a change of state.

Exercise 2.21 Given two binary pattern vectors as shown in Figures 2.16(a) and 2.16(b), what pattern will be retrieved at the output nodes if the test pattern shown in Figure 2.16(c) is input to the parallel Hopfield model?

Exercise 2.22 (Hardware Efficiency of a Hopfield Model)
(a) Show that storage of M memories with N bits of information each requires N^2 connections each with $2M+1$ possible values. (b) Show that the hardware efficiency, defined as the number of information bits per connection state, is less than $0.5N^{-1}$.

Exercise 2.23 Prove the convergence of BAM. (Hint: Follow basically the proof for the parallel Hopfield model.)

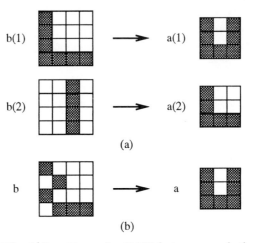

(a)

(b)

Figure 2.17: (a) The I/O patterns for BAM hetero-association processing; (b) a test pattern.

Exercise 2.24 Given the I/O patterns in Figure 2.17, design a hetero-association BAM model. The two pairs of I/O pattern vectors are

$$\mathbf{b}^{(1)} = [1000100010001111]^T$$
$$\mathbf{a}^{(1)} = [101101111]^T$$

and

$$\mathbf{b}^{(2)} = [0010001000100010]^T$$
$$\mathbf{a}^{(2)} = [100100111]^T.$$

Given a test pattern

$$\mathbf{t}^{(1)} = [1000100010000111]^T$$

what is the retrieved output?

Exercise 2.25 Show that the parallel Hopfield model can be regarded as a special case auto-association of BAM, that is, $\mathbf{W} = \mathbf{W}^T$.

Exercise 2.26 Show that if the capacity in the model is low, the weight matrix used in the parallel Hopfield model has a low rank property. Show how to exploit the property to reduce the computation and to achieve hardware savings.

Chapter 3

Competitive Learning Networks

3.1 Introduction

The fixed-weight models discussed in Chapter 2 have limited application since they cannot adapt to changing environments. This chapter discusses a variety of competitive learning networks, whose synaptic weights adapt according to unsupervised learning rules. These models can learn in the absence of teacher's guidance. In other words, the training is based exclusively on the the input (training) patterns. The class of *competitive learning networks* includes, for example, self-organization networks, adaptive resonance, and neocognitron [73, 88, 137]. Self-organization and adaptive resonance approaches incorporate lateral inhibitions into the cooperative-competitive neural models. This can be linked to the separate development of the (multilayer) neocognitron. A basic competitive learning network has one layer of *input neurons* and one layer of *output neurons*. An input pattern x is a sample point in the n-dimensional real or binary vector space. Binary-valued (1 or 0) *local representations* are most often used for the output nodes. That is, there are as many output neurons as the number of classes and each output node represents a pattern category. (The exact number may be known or unknown in advance.)

As illustrated in Figure 3.1, a competitive learning network comprises the feedforward excitatory network(s) and lateral inhibitory network(s). The feedforward network usually implements an *excitatory* Hebbian learning rule. (The Hebbian learning rule is that when an input cell persistently partici-

73

pates in firing an output cell, the input cell's influence on firing that output cell is increased.) The lateral competitive network is *inhibitory* in nature. The network serves the important role of selecting the winner, often via a competitive learning process, highlighting the "winner-take-all" schema. In a winner-take-all circuit, the output unit receiving the largest input is assigned a full value (e.g., 1), whereas all other units are suppressed to a 0 value. The winner-take-all circuit is usually implemented by a (digital or analog) **MAXNET** network. (For an analog implementation example, see Figure 2.15.) Another example of a lateral network is Kohonen's self-organizing feature map [136, 137]. By allowing the output nodes to interact via the lateral network, the neural model can be trained to preserve certain topological ordering.

Unsupervised classification procedures are often based on some kind of clustering strategy, which forms groups of similar patterns. The clustering technique is very useful for pattern classification problems. Furthermore, it plays a pivotal role in many competitive learning networks. For a clustering procedure, it is necessary to define a similarity measure to be used for evaluating how close the patterns are. Some popular measures are listed below, among them the most common is the Euclidean distance.

1. Inner Product: $< x_i, x_j > \equiv x_i^T x_j \equiv \|x_i\|\|x_j\|cos(x_i, x_j)$

2. Euclidean Distance: $d(x_i, x_j) \equiv \sum_k [x_i(k) - x_j(k)]^2$

3. Weighted Euclidean Distance.

Chapter Organization

This chapter focuses on a variety of competitive learning networks for clustering and classification applications. In Section 3.2, basic competitive learning networks are introduced. Section 3.3 explores competitive learning networks with adjustable output nodes, including the VQ and ART models. Section 3.4 presents models with neighborhood sensitivity, particularly the self-organizing feature map and its close variant with history sensitivity. Finally, Section 3.5 presents the neocognitron using a hierarchical representation structure.

3.2   Basic Competitive Learning Networks

Using no supervision from any teacher, unsupervised networks adapt the weights and verify the results based only on the input patterns. One popular scheme for such adaptation is the competitive learning rule, which allows the units to compete for the exclusive right to respond to (i.e., to be trained by) a particular training input pattern. It can be viewed as a sophisticated clustering technique, whose objective is to divide a set of input patterns into a number of clusters such that the patterns of the same cluster exhibit a certain degree or type of similarity [97]. Various kinds of competitive learning networks have been developed by von der Malsburg; Grossberg; Fukushima; Fukushima and Miyaki; and Kohonen. The training rules are often the Hebbian rule for the feed-forward network and the winner-take-all (WTA) rule for the lateral network. (See Figure 3.2.) They have the following distinctive features:

1. Competitive learning networks extend the simple Hebbian rule to the very sophisticated *competition-based* rule. The training procedure is influenced by both the Hebbian rule and the winner-take-all rule.

2. In order to implement competitive learning, the lateral networks are usually *inhibitory*, cf. Figure 3.1. A *winner-take-all* (WTA) circuit is used to select a winner, based on a distance metric over the pattern vector space. Most important, a unit learns if and only if it wins the competition among all the other units.

3.2.1 Minimal Learning Model

A basic competitive learning model consists of feedforward and lateral networks with fixed output nodes. The input and output nodes are assumed to have binary values (1 or 0). When and only when both the ith input and the jth output are high $(= 1)$, $C_{ij} = 1$; otherwise, $C_{ij} = 0$. The strength of the synaptic weight connecting input i with output j is designated by w_{ij}. Given the k-th stimulus, referring to Figure 3.2, rule(1), a possible learning rule is

$$\Delta w_{ij} = \begin{cases} g[\frac{x_i(k)}{n_k} - w_{ij}] & \text{if and only if } C_{ij} = 1 \\ 0 & \text{otherwise} \end{cases} \qquad (3.1)$$

where g is a small positive constant, n_k is the number of active input units for stimulus pattern k, $x_i(k) = 1$ if input unit i is high for the kth stimulus pattern and $x_i(k) = 0$ otherwise.

Only the links from a high input to a high output are updated by the training pattern. If an output node does not respond to a pattern, there will be no learning on all the weights connected to that output. Likewise, if an

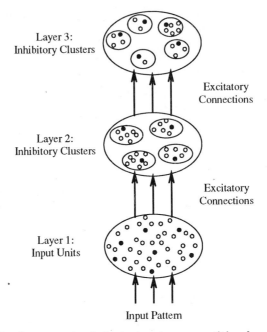

Figure 3.1:   Basic concept of clustering in competitive learning. (Adapted from [246].)

input node does not contribute to the firing of the output, there will be no learning on all the weights originated from the input node.

3.2.2   Training Rules Based on Normalized Weights

In order to ensure a fair competition environment, the sum of all the weights linked to all the output nodes should be normalized. For example, let w_{ij} be the weights connected to an output node (say, j), then $\sum_i w_{ij} = 1$. The aforementioned learning rule cannot meet this constant. This problem can be solved by the Malsburg learning rule [10], originally proposed for modeling the self-organization mechanism of the visual cortex. According to Anderson [16], there are excitatory and inhibitory cells that interact strongly in the Malsburg's model. The connection strengths are a function of distance between cells, which exhibits significant locality nature. The excitatory cells usually have a shorter range of connections than inhibitory cells. The inhibitory cells inhibit only the next-to-immediate-neighbor cells. This is analogous to a prominent organization in the mammalian visual system, where a ring of inhibition surrounds a central core of excitation.

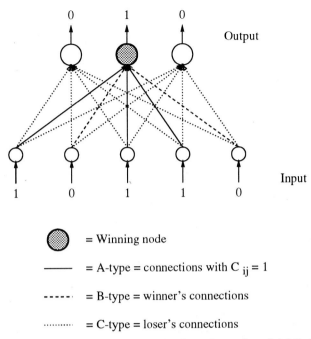

Figure 3.2: Examples of basic competitive learning rules: (1) Minimal learning rule: only connections of type A are trained. (2) Malsburg learning rule: only connections of type A and type B are trained. (3) Leaky learning rule: all connections (types A, B, and C) are trained.

In Malsburg learning rule [293], a neuron unit shifts weight from its inactive to active input connections, cf. Figure 3.2, rule(2). "If a unit wins the competition, then each of its input lines gives up some proportion g of its weight and that weight is then distributed equally among the active input lines."[246] This leads to the following learning rule [247]:

$$\Delta w_{ij} = \begin{cases} g[\frac{x_i(k)}{n_k} - w_{ij}] & \text{if unit } j \text{ wins on stimulus } k \\ 0 & \text{if unit } j \text{ loses on stimulus } k \end{cases} \qquad (3.2)$$

One important feature of the Malsburg learning rule is that renormalization is incorporated into the updating rule such that the sum of synaptic weights to any output remains 1. (See Problem 3.2.)

3.2.3   Training Rules for Leaky Learning

In order to prevent the possibility of totally unlearned neurons, a *leaky learning model* is introduced [247]. "Since a unit never learns unless it wins, it is possible that one of the units will never win, and therefore never learn." One way to alleviate the problem of non-learning is by having all the weights in the network involved in the training with different degrees of strength. This is proposed in the following leaky learning rule (cf. Figure 3.2, rule(3)):

$$\Delta w_{ij} = \begin{cases} g_l[\frac{x_i(k)}{n_k} - w_{ij}] & \text{if } j \text{ loses on stimulus } k \\ g_w[\frac{x_i(k)}{n_k} - w_{ij}] & \text{if } j \text{ wins on stimulus } k \end{cases} \qquad (3.3)$$

In the leaky learning model, parameter g_l is made an order of magnitude smaller than g_w. Therefore, slower learning occurs at the losing units than that at the winning units. According to [247]: "This change has the property that it slowly moves the losing units into the region where the actual stimuli lie, at which point they begin to capture some units and the ordinary dynamics of competitive learning takes over."

3.3   Adaptive Clustering Techniques: VQ and ART

In practical unsupervised learning, the number of classes may be unknown a priori. Therefore, the number of output nodes cannot be accurately determined in advance. To overcome this difficulty, it is useful to introduce a mechanism allowing adaptive expansion of the output layer until an adequate size is reached. To this end, two well-known techniques may be adopted: the Vector Quantizer(VQ) and the adaptive resonance theory(ART).

3.3.1   Vector Quantizer(VQ)

A Vector Quantizer is a system for mapping a set of vectors into a finite cluster for digital storage or communication. It is one of the very first unsupervised clustering techniques. From the coding perspective, the goal of quantization is to obtain the best possible fidelity for the given compression rate. A vector quantizer maps a set of discrete vectors into a representation suitable for communication over a digital channel. In many applications, such as digital communication, better data compression has been achieved by using vector quantizer instead of scalar quantizer. The VQ procedure is summarized below:

1. Given a new pattern, identify the best old cluster to admit the pattern. (The criterion is usually the Euclidean distance.)

2. The centroid of the selected cluster is adjusted to accommodate its new member.

3. If none of the old clusters can admit the new pattern, a new cluster will be created for it.

4. Repeat the procedure for all the successive patterns.

3.3.2   Binary-Valued ART

More recently, a more sophisticated clustering technique for adaptively adjusting the number of clusters was introduced by Carpenter and Grossberg. This is called *adaptive resonance theory*(ART) [41, 88]. In addition to the forward networks between the input neurons and output neurons, a backward network is adopted for vigilance test. Two versions of ART are addressed in the subsequent discussion: ART1 for binary-valued patterns and ART2 for continuous-valued patterns. Figure 3.3 shows a configuration of ART, adapted from [213]. It can adaptively create a new neuron for an incoming input pattern if it is determined (by a vigilance test) to be sufficiently different from the existing clusters. Such a vigilance test is incorporated into the adaptive backward network.

Suppose that w_{ij} and t_{ij} are the forward and backward weights between neuron j and input i, respectively. Note that x_i's and t_{ij}'s are binary-valued while w_{ij}'s are real. Assume that the j^*th neuron has the maximum score for a new input vector $\mathbf{x}$. The algorithm of the ART1 (cf. Figure 3.3) is presented below:

(1) Given a new training pattern, a MAXNET is adopted to select the winner as the maximum of all the net values $\sum_{i=1}^{N} w_{ij}x_i$. The winner is denoted by j^*.

(2) *Vigilance Test:* A neuron passes the vigilance test if and only if

$$\frac{\sum_{i=1}^{N} t_{ij^*}x_i}{\sum_{i=1}^{N} x_i} > \rho \ \ (vigilance\ threshold)$$

   2.a If the winner fails the test, then mask the current winner and repeat step (1) to select another new winner.

2.b Repeat such process until a winner passes the vigilance test, then go to step (4).

2.c Otherwise, if none of the old neurons passes the vigilance test, go to step (3).

(3) Since none of the old neurons passes the vigilance test, a new neuron unit is created to accommodate the new pattern. Then go to step (1).

(4) If a winner (i.e., the j^*-th neuron) passes the vigilance test:

(a) Adjust the feedforward weights from inputs to neuron j^*:

$$w_{ij^*}^{(m+1)} = \frac{t_{ij^*}^{(m)} x_i}{0.5 + \sum_{i=1}^{N} t_{ij^*}^{(m)} x_i}$$

(b) Update the feedback weights from neuron j^* to inputs by the Boolean multiplication of $t_{ij^*}^{(m)}$ and x_i:

$$t_{ij^*}^{(m+1)} = t_{ij^*}^{(m)} x_i$$

According to the ART1 training rule, a higher vigilance implies a lower passing percentage and thus more clusters are likely to be created and it leads to a finer clustering. On the other hand, a lower vigilance results in less clusters and a coarser clustering.

3.3.3   Continuous-Valued ART

The ART2 algorithm is designed for continuous-valued (e.g., real value) patterns. Let $\mathbf{x}$ and $\mathbf{w}_j$ denote the input vector and the weight of neuron j respectively. The criterion of selecting the winner is based on a minimum distance measure (e.g., Euclidean or other distance).

(1) Given a new training pattern, a MINNET (Minimum Net) is adopted to select the winner, which yields the minimum distance $||\mathbf{x} - \mathbf{w}_j||$. The winner is denoted as j^*.

(2) *Vigilance Test:* A neuron j^* passes the vigilance test if and only if

$$||\mathbf{x} - \mathbf{w}_{j^*}|| < \rho$$

where the vigilance value ρ determines the radius of a cluster.

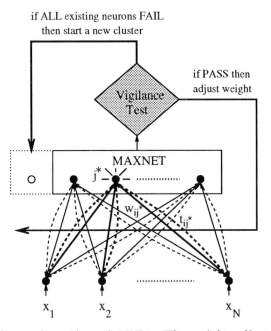

Figure 3.3: The configuration of ART1. The weight adjustments apply to both the feedforward weights $w_{ij^*}^{(m)}$ and the feedback weights $t_{ij^*}^{(m)}$ to and from winning neuron j^*. The configuration of ART2 is similar except that (1) the backward weights are the same as the forward weights, and (2) the MAXNET is replaced by MINNET, so the minimum-distance solution is chosen as the winner.

(3) If the winner fails the vigilance test, a new neuron unit k is created with weight $\mathbf{w}_k = \mathbf{x}$.

(4) If the winner passes the vigilance test, adjust the weight of the winner j^* by

$$
\mathbf{w}_{j^*}^{(new)} = \frac{\mathbf{x} + \mathbf{w}_{j^*}^{(old)}||cluster_{j^*}^{(old)}||}{||cluster_{j^*}^{(old)}|| + 1}
\tag{3.4}
$$

where $||cluster_i||$ denotes the number of members in $cluster_i$.

For example, suppose that 10 real-value patterns $\mathbf{x} = [x_1, x_2]$ are presented in the order displayed in Table 3.1(a). If the vigilance threshold is $\rho = 1.5$, then the ART2 will yield 3 clusters, as shown in Table 3.1(a). (Here the 1-norm $v(j) = |x_1 - w_{j1}| + |x_2 - w_{j2}|$ is adopted as the distance measure.) The key steps are explained below:

Step 1: The initial Cluster No. 1 with centroid $(1.0,0.1)$ is created.

Step 2: For the second pattern $(1.3,0.8)$, Cluster No. 1 is the winner, since there are no other competitors. The test value is 1.0 which is smaller than the vigilance test (i.e., passing). After the pattern is included into the cluster, the new centroid becomes $(1.15,0.45)$, cf. Eq. 3.4.

Step 3: For the third pattern $(1.4,1.8)$, Cluster No. 1 is the winner, but it fails the vigilance test. So a new cluster No. 2 with centroid $(1.4,1.8)$ is created.

Step 4: (Omitted.)

Step 5: For the fifth pattern $(0.0,1.4)$, Cluster No. 2 is the winner, but it fails the vigilance test. So a new cluster No. 3 with centroid $(0.0,1.4)$ is created.

Steps 6-10: (Omitted.)

The clustering result of ART2 is affected by vigilance threshold and the order of presentation. This is now explained by examples.

Effect of Different Order of Pattern Presentation   The ART is sensitive to the presenting order of the input patterns. This is confirmed by an experiment shown in Table 3.1(b). It shows that the ART2 yields a different clustering on the same input patterns when they are presented in the reverse order. Even though the vigilance threshold remains the same, it yields only two clusters. The new clustering result is shown in Figure 3.4.

Effect of Vigilance Thresholds   Figure 3.5 shows the results of ART2 for clustering 30 input patterns with different vigilance thresholds, $\rho = 0.6$ and $\rho = 0.4$ respectively. (Here, the Euclidean distance is adopted.) In general, the smaller the vigilance threshold the more clusters are generated.

Effect of Reclustering   In Figure 3.5(a), some input patterns from Clusters No. 1 or No. 2 are actually closer to the centroid of Cluster No. 3. This undesirable result is partially due to the presentation order of the patterns. An simple solution is the reclustering described below: (1) use the current centroids as the initial reference for clustering; (2) recluster one by one each of the training patterns; and (3) repeat the entire process until there is no change of clustering during one entire sweep. Figure 3.6(b) shows the new boundaries after the reclustering and there are no deserting patterns.

Order	Pattern	Winner	Test Value	Decision	Cluster 1 Centroid	Cluster 2 Centroid	Cluster 3 Centroid
1	(1.0,0.1)	-	-	new cluster	(1.0 0.1)		
2	(1.3,0.8)	1	1.0	pass vigilance test	(1.15,0.45)		
3	(1.4,1.8)	1	1.6	fail ⇒ new cluster		(1.4,1.8)	
4	(1.5,0.5)	1	0.4	pass vigilance test	(1.27,0.47)		
5	(0.0,1.4)	2	1.8	fail ⇒ new cluster			(0.0,1.4)
6	(0.6,1.2)	3	0.8	pass vigilance test			(0.3,1.3)
7	(1.5,1.9)	2	0.2	pass vigilance test		(1.45,1.85)	
8	(0.7,0.4)	1	0.63	pass vigilance test	(1.13,0.45)		
9	(1.9,1.4)	2	0.9	pass vigilance test		(1.6,1.7)	
10	(1.5,1.3)	2	0.5	pass vigilance test		(1.58,1.6)	

(a)

Order	Pattern	Winner	Test Value	Decision	Cluster 1 Centroid	Cluster 2 Centroid
1	(1.5,1.3)	-	-	new cluster	(1.5 1.3)	
2	(1.9,1.4)	1	0.5	pass vigilance test	(1.7,1.35)	
3	(0.7,0.4)	1	1.95	fail ⇒ new cluster		(0.7,0.4)
4	(1.5,1.9)	1	0.75	pass vigilance test	(1.63,1.53)	
5	(0.6,1.2)	2	0.9	pass vigilance test		(0.65,0.8)
6	(0.0,1.4)	2	1.25	pass vigilance test		(0.43,1.0)
7	(1.5,0.5)	1	1.17	pass vigilance test	(1.6,1.28)	
8	(1.4,1.8)	1	0.72	pass vigilance test	(1.56,1.38)	
9	(1.3,0.8)	1	0.84	pass vigilance test	(1.52,1.28)	
10	(1.0,0.1)	2	1.47	pass vigilance test		(0.58,0.78)

(b)

Table 3.1: The execution sequence of the ART2 with the vigilance threshold 1.5.

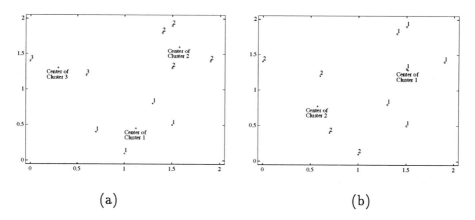

(a)   (b)

Figure 3.4: The results of ART according to different presenting order of input patterns. (a) With the original order. (b) With the input patterns presented in the reverse order.

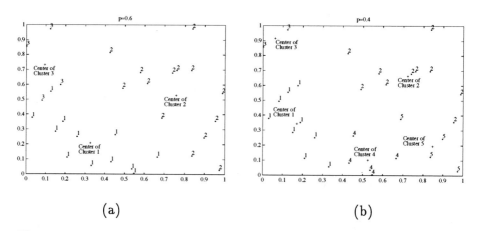

(a)   (b)

Figure 3.5: The results of ART according to different vigilance values. (a) $\rho = 0.6$. (b) $\rho = 0.4$.

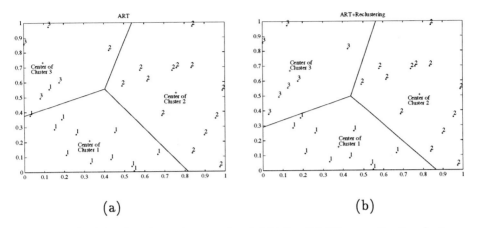

(a)   (b)

Figure 3.6: (a) The clustering result of ART2. (b) The result of reclustering. The solid lines represent the boundaries according to the (old and new) centroids.

3.4 Self-Organizing Feature Map: Sensitivity to Neighborhood and History

The basic idea is to incorporate into the competitive learning rule some degree of sensitivity with respect to the neighborhood or history. This provides a way to avoid totally unlearned neurons and it helps enhance certain topological property which should be preserved in the feature mapping.

3.4.1 Self-Organizing Feature Map

Suppose that an input pattern has N features and is represented by a vector x in an N-dimensional pattern space. The network maps the input patterns to an output space. The output space in this case is assumed to be one-dimensional or two-dimensional arrays of output nodes, which possess a certain topological orderness. The question is how to train a network so that the ordered relationship can be preserved. Kohonen proposed to allow the output nodes interact laterally, leading to the *self-organizing feature map* [136, 137]. This was originally inspired by a biological model. For example, as illustrated by Figure 3.7, a random sequence of two-dimensional patterns can be mapped to an array of output nodes, with a preserved topology.

A simple configuration of the self-organizing feature map is illustrated in Figure 3.8(a). The most prominent feature is the concept of excitatory learning within a neighborhood around the winning neuron. The size of the

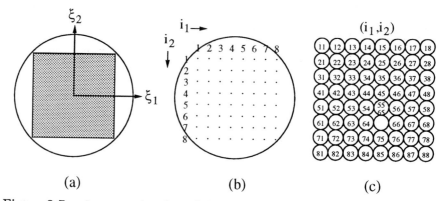

(a)   (b)   (c)

Figure 3.7:   An example adapted from Kohonen's work that shows that the topological relationship of the input feature space is preserved in the output.

neighborhood slowly decreases with each iteration, cf. Figure 3.8(b). A more detailed description of the **training phase** is provided below:

1. First, a winning neuron is selected as the one with the shortest Euclidean distance

$$||\mathbf{x} - \mathbf{w}_i||$$

   between its weight vector and the input vector, where $\mathbf{w}_i$ denotes the weight vector corresponding to the ith output neuron.

2. Let i^* denote the index of the winner and let I^* denote a set of indices corresponding to a defined neighborhood of winner i^*. Then the weights associated with the winner **and** its neighboring neurons are updated by

$$\Delta \mathbf{w}_j = \eta(\mathbf{x} - \mathbf{w}_j)$$

   for all the indices $j \in I^*$, and η is a small positive learning rate. The amount of updating may be weighted according to a preassigned "neighborhood function", $\Lambda(j, i^*)$.

$$\Delta \mathbf{w}_j = \eta \Lambda(j, i^*)(\mathbf{x} - \mathbf{w}_j) \tag{3.5}$$

   for all j. For example, a *neighborhood function* $\Lambda(j, i^*)$ may be chosen as

$$\Lambda(j, i^*) = \exp(-|\mathbf{r}_j - \mathbf{r}_{i^*}|^2/2\sigma^2) \tag{3.6}$$

   where $\mathbf{r}_j$ represents the position of the neuron j in the output space. The convergence of the feature map depends on a proper choice of η.

One plausible choice is that $\eta = 1/t$. The size of neighborhood (or σ) should decrease gradually as depicted in Figure 3.8(b). [1]

3. The weight update should be immediately succeeded by the normalization of $\mathbf{w}_i$.

In the **retrieving phase**, all the output neurons calculate the Euclidean distance between the weights and the input vector and the winning neuron is the one with the shortest distance.

Figures 3.9 and 3.10 illustrate two examples mapping two-dimensional input space to 2-D and 1-D output feature spaces respectively. Many interesting experiments and applications have been performed. One example demonstrated in Figure 3.11 is a network for frequency map. This involves a feature map from 5-dimensional input to 1-dimensional output. After the network converges, the units exhibit characteristics of a tuned receiver – each unit has its own value for the frequency at which it is most sensitive. There are many practical applications, see [241] for a data compression application example by ordered feature maps.

3.4.2   Competitive Learning with History Sensitivity

Incorporating some history/frequency sensitivity into the competitive learning rule provides another way to alleviate the problem of totally unlearned neurons or prejudiced training. There are two approaches:

1. Modulate the selection of a winner by the frequency sensitivity.

2. Modulate the learning rate by the frequency sensitivity.

The *selection of a winner* can be modulated by the frequency sensitivity of the output nodes. In a model proposed by [30], a history-dependent sensitivity threshold is introduced so that the level of relevant activation is proportional to the amount by which the node exceeds this threshold. Moreover, the threshold is constantly adjusted. It decreases value whenever a unit loses and increases whenever it wins. In this manner, when an output node is not winning enough inputs, it becomes increasingly sensitive. On the other hand, if it is winning too many inputs, it decreases its sensitivity. Such a sensitivity

---

[1] A formal mathematical analysis for the proper learning rate η, the size of the neighborhood, and the convergence of the model, is still missing. For an informal discussion, see Problem 3.10.

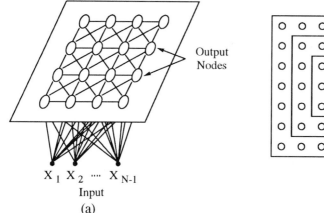

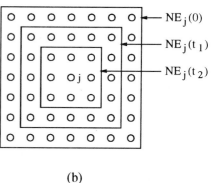

(b)

Input

(a)

Figure 3.8: (a) A network for a self-organizing feature map. By updating all the weights connecting to a neighborhood of the target neurons, it enables the neighboring neurons to become more responsive to the same input pattern. Consequently, the correlation between neighboring nodes can be enhanced. (b) Once such a correlation is established, the size of a neighborhood can be decreased gradually, based on the desire of having a stronger identity of individual nodes.

modulation makes all the output nodes eventually respond and engage in learning.

The *rate of training* can also be modulated by frequency sensitivity. As an example, we present the following competitive learning rule proposed in [6]:

1. Select a winner i^* as the neuron with, for example, the smallest Euclidean distance

$$d_i = \sum_{j=0}^{J-1} [x_j(t) - w_{ij}(t)]^2$$

2. Update the weights associated with the winner

$$\mathbf{w}_{i^*}(t+1) = \mathbf{w}_{i^*}(t) + \epsilon(t)[\mathbf{x}(t) - \mathbf{w}_{i^*}(t)]$$

This technique is called frequency-sensitive competitive learning in [6], where parameter $\epsilon(t)$ is a function of how frequent the i^*-th node is selected as the winner. For example, two possible such functions are [6]: $\epsilon(t) = [t - u_{i^*}(t)]/t$ or $\epsilon(t) = Ae^{-[u_{i^*}(t)/t]}$, where $u_{i^*}(t)$ denotes the number of winning times by the i^*th node up to time t.

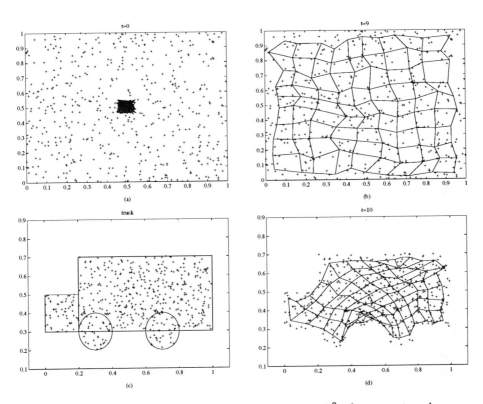

Figure 3.9: Given a two-dimensional input space, R^2, the output nodes are to be arranged in a two-dimensional mesh. (a) Random input patterns and the initial weights for the output. Input patterns are generated randomly with uniform probability distribution over the square $\{0 \leq x_1 < 1, 0 \leq x_2 < 1\}$. The initial weights were random patterns clustered near (0.5,0.5). (b) This illustrates how the weights were pulled apart and reorganized into a mesh. Here 500 two-dimensional input patterns are mapped to a 10×10 mesh. (c) The input feature space could even have a convex or non-convex shape. This is a truck-like input space example. (d) The mapping of 500 input patterns from the truck-like space to a 10×10 mesh.

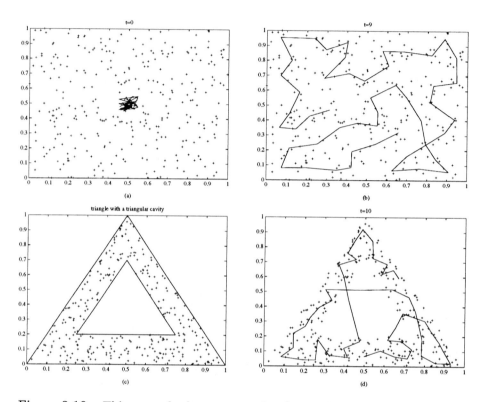

Figure 3.10:   This example shows a mapping from 2-dimensional input space
to a 1-dimensional output array. The algorithm used is very similar to the algorithm previously described, cf. Eq. 3.5, except that the original two-dimensional
output index r_i (cf. Eq. 3.6) should now be replaced by a one-dimensional index. (a) Random input patterns and the initial weights for the output. (b)
The result of mapping from 300 two-dimensional input patterns to a 50-point
one-dimensional curve. (c) A hollow triangular-shaped input space. (d) The
result of the mapping from 300 input patterns in it to a one-dimensional curve.
These two examples indicate that the topological orders of the input space can
only be approximately preserved by the feature map.

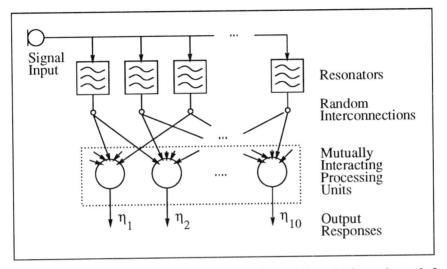

Figure 3.11: A feature mapping example adapted from Kohonen's work for frequency map. In this experiment, the final frequencies are arranged in correct order: [0.99, 0.98, 0.98, 0.97, 0.90, 0.81, 0.73, 0.69, 0.62, 0.59].

3.5 Neocognitron: Hierarchically Structured Model

Most existing neural networks could not effectively deal with patterns that were shifted in position or distorted. To combat the problem, Fukushima and Miyake proposed the so-called *neocognitron* model, which is applicable specially to space image recognition regardless of position or distortion [73, 74, 75]. The basic ideas for the neocognitron are described as follows:

1. Hierarchical Representation Structure

   The neocognitron uses successive (say, M) stages that can recognize patterns. (See Figure 3.12.) It progresses stage by stage from the input layer to the output layer. The levels of representation in the layers exhibit a hierarchical structure. More precisely, the first layer (or the first few layers) extracts local features, such as a line at a particular orientation. More global features are extracted in later layers. The objective of such a hierarchical representation structure is that by going deeper through successive layers, the position of the symbol in the input pattern becomes less and less important.

2. Intra-Layer Structure

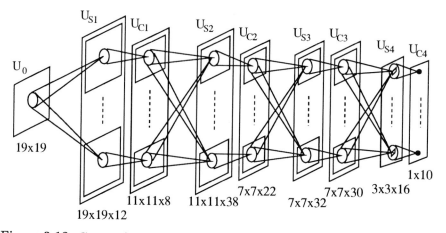

Figure 3.12: Connection diagram between layers in a neocognitron. (Adapted from [74].)

Each layer consists of one simple sublayer of u_s cells and one complex sublayer of u_c cells. Each layer of u_s cells or u_c cells is divided into subgroups according to the features to which they respond. The cells in each subgroup are arranged in a two-dimensional array. The u_s cells match an input pattern with the template of the receptive fields of the cells. The u_c cells receive excitatory signals from its corresponding u_s cells; cf. Figure 3.13.

(a) Feature-Extracting u_s Cells: Feature-extracting cells are denoted by u_s. Connections converging to these cells are variable and re-inforced by learning (or training). The process of learning and the mechanism of feature extraction by u_s cells are based on self-organizing networks discussed before. Briefly, only the one cell that gives the maximum response has its input connections rein-forced. (Consequently, the other cells are forced, or persuaded, to become more responsive to other different features.) After finishing the learning, u_s cells can extract features from the input pattern. Only when a relevant feature is presented at a certain position in the input layer will the corresponding u_s cell be activated.

(b) Position-Readjusting u_c Cells: The u_c sublayer immediately fol-lows the u_s sublayer. The u_c cells are used to compensate for positional errors. Connections from u_s cells to u_c cells are fixed and invariable. An example of a detailed structure between layers

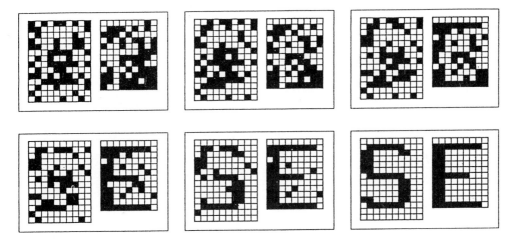

Figure 3.13: Schematic diagram showing an intra-layer structure in a neocognitron. (Reprinted with permission from [74], K. Fukushima, "A neural network for visual pattern recognition", IEEE Computer Magazine, March 1988, © 1988 IEEE.)

of u_s cells and u_c cells is shown in Figure 3.13. The number of u_c cells could be much less than u_s cells, because similar u_s cells will map to the same u_c cells.

Recall that, just like the u_s layer, each layer of u_c cells is divided into subgroups according to the features to which they respond. All the cells in a subgroup receive input connections of the same spatial distribution, but allowing a certain degree of position shift. In other words, each u_c cell receives signals from a group of u_s cells that extract the same feature but have slightly different positions. The u_c cell is activated if at least one of these u_s cells is active. Even if the position shift of the stimulus feature causes a nearby u_s cell to be activated instead of the original one, the same u_c cell will respond; thereby, the effect of a small shift can be nullified. Based on such a position-readjusting process, local features extracted in a lower stage can be smoothly and gradually integrated into more global features. This is illustrated in Figure 3.13.

3. Inter-Layer Structure

The inter-layer structure, that is, the mapping from a u_c sublayer to the u_s cells in the next layer, provides a further shift tolerance to com-

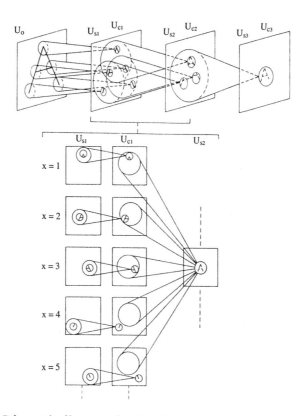

Figure 3.14: Schematic diagram showing inter-layer interaction in a neocognitron.

bat deformation of the training pattern. Figure 3.14 provides a simple illustration. In Figure 3.14(a), the u_s cell is to extract a global feature consisting of three local features of a training pattern "A". The cell can tolerate some positional error in each local feature as long as it falls within the circle, and the cell responds to the deformed patterns shown in Figure 3.14(b). Ideally, tolerating positional error stage by stage facilitates the recognition of distorted patterns. On the other hand, if the tolerance is set too large at each stage, the network may respond erroneously and recognize an unacceptable stimulus as an "A" pattern.

4. Final Layer

Finally, each u_c cell of the final (recognition) layer integrates all the information of the input pattern. Due to the competitive learning nature, only one cell in the final layer, corresponding to the category of

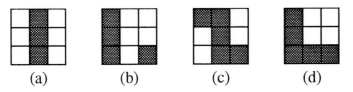

Figure 3.15: A set of patterns used for competitive learning and ART problems.

the input pattern, will be activated. Other cells respond to the patterns of other categories.

In summary, neocognitron is a self-organized, competitive learning, hierarchical multilayer network. It is useful for pattern classification without supervised learning, especially when there are possible shifts in position or distortion in shape. However, it is difficult to determine how well can the network cope with deformation of patterns, because there is no mathematical measure or proper model for such study. Moreover, although the neocognitron appears to be attractive in its high biological fidelity, it incurs a vast computational cost which is not easily affordable for most applications.

3.6 Concluding Remarks

The strength of the competitive learning networks lies in their effectiveness for clustering-type applications. Their common weakness, however, is the lack a formal treatment on the convergence and performance analyses. Further mathematical study of the models is needed. Several promising practical ideas, such as tracking of topological orderness, adaptive expansion of neurons, and utilization of hierarchical structures, can naturally be incorporated into the models. These possibilities deserve further exploration.

3.7 Problems

Exercise 3.1 Based on the patterns shown in Figure 3.15, suppose the winners are 1, 2, 1, and 2 for patterns (a),(b),(c), and (d), respectively. Derive the network weights by each of the following competitive learning rules:
(1) the minimal learning model,
(2) the learning rule with normalized weights, and
(3) the leaky learning rule.

Exercise 3.2 (a) Show that a renormalization rule is incorporated into the updating formula, Eq. 3.2, so that the total sum of synaptic weights connected to any output node remains a constant.

(b) Repeat the same for the leaky learning rule in Eq. 3.3.

Exercise 3.3 Design a new scheme that will allow the selection of a winner to be modulated by frequency sensitivity. Justify your scheme.

Exercise 3.4 Design a feature map network with the two-dimensional input patterns generated as

(a) uniformly distributed patterns in a disk centered at (0,0) with radius 1

(b) two-dimensionally Gaussian distributed patterns in a disk centered at (0,0) with deviation factor $\sigma = 0.5$, and

(c) uniformly distributed patterns in a triangle with the three vertices (1,0),(0,0), and (0,1).

The result should show that the neighborhood of features is well preserved.

Exercise 3.5 In an ART classifier, a lower vigilance usually implies a coarser classification. For the patterns depicted in Figure 3.15, find the values of a and b such that the ART classifier would create the following:

(a) 3 clusters if the vigilance is set to a.

(b) 2 clusters if the vigilance is set to b.

Does the number of output nodes change with the permutation of the training patterns for this example? Is this true in general?

Exercise 3.6 Explain why the steps 2.a, 2.b, and 2.c in ART1 is unnecessary for ART2.

Exercise 3.7 Suppose that we have 10 input patterns as shown in the following table:

Order	Pattern	Winner	Test Value	Decision	New Centroid
1	(0.4,0.6)				
2	(0.1,0.3)				
3	(0.2,0.4)				
4	(0.6,0.5)				
5	(0.9,0.8)				
6	(0.5,0.1)				
7	(0.6,0.4)				
8	(0.7,0.9)				
9	(0.7,0.2)				
10	(0.3,0.7)				

(a) Let vigilance threshold be $\rho = 0.6$. Follow the same algorithm (1-norm distance measure) shown by Table 3.1 and complete the above table.

(b) Repeat (a), but setting vigilance threshold $\rho = 0.4$.

(c) Reverse the presenting order of the same input patterns and then repeat (a).

Exercise 3.8 (Multiple-Winners Network) In a multiple-winners network, all the neurons that pass a given threshold are allowed to be trained. Discuss the merits and disadvantages of such learning networks.

Exercise 3.9 Durbin and Willshaw proposed an energy function, which might be useful for what we call the "traveling circus problem":

$$E\{\mathbf{w}\} = -\sigma^2 \sum_{\mu} \log[\sum_{j} \exp(-|\mathbf{x}^{\mu} - \mathbf{w}_j|^2/2\sigma^2)] + \frac{\kappa}{2} \sum_{j} |\mathbf{w}_{j+1} - \mathbf{w}_j|^2 \qquad (3.7)$$

where $\mathbf{x}^{\mu}$ and $\mathbf{w}_i$ represent the positions of city μ and stop i respectively. Besides, σ determines the effective radius of the city being visited. The constraint parameter κ assures that the consecutive cities are reasonably close to each other.

(a) Verify the following updating rule from Equation 3.7:

$$\Delta \mathbf{w}_i = \eta(\sum_{\mu} \Lambda^{\mu}(i)(\mathbf{x}^{\mu} - \mathbf{w}_i) + \kappa(\mathbf{w}_{i+1} - 2\mathbf{w}_i + \mathbf{w}_{i-1}))$$

where η is the learning rate and $\Lambda^{\mu}(i)$ is defined as

$$\Lambda^{\mu}(i) = \frac{\exp(-|\mathbf{x}^{\mu} - \mathbf{w}_i|^2/2\sigma^2)}{\sum_{j} \exp(-|\mathbf{x}^{\mu} - \mathbf{w}_j|^2/2\sigma^2)}$$

(b) Compare the Durbin and Willshaw algorithm with the Kohonen's algorithm (see Eq. 3.5). Comment on the possibility of adapting Kohonen's algorithm to the "traveling circus problem".

Exercise 3.10 (Convergence of Kohonen's Self-Organizing Feature Map) In this problem, we study the convergence property of Kohonen's feature map network by choosing $\alpha = 1/t$. Is there a theoretical basis for the convergence?

Consider a Kohonen self-organizing feature map with a single neuron. Assume that, at each time step k, the neural network gets as its input a noisy vector, $\vec{X}(k) = \vec{s} + \vec{N}(k)$, where $\vec{N}(k)$ is white, Gaussian, strictly stationary noise with a mean of 0 and a variance of σ^2. The weights of the feature map at each iteration are denoted $\vec{W}(k)$. The sequence of random vectors $\vec{W}(k)$ is said to converge to $\vec{s}$ with probability 1 if, for arbitrary $\epsilon > 0$,

$$\lim_{k \to \infty} P\{||W(k) - s(k)|| \geq \epsilon\} = 0$$

Show that, if $\eta = 1/k$ is taken to be the learning rate of the neuron, then the neuron's reference vector $\vec{W}(k)$ will converge to $\vec{s}$ with probability 1.

First Hint: Note that using the learning rate $\eta = 1/k$ is equivalent to taking the average of all input vectors. Try to solve the problem by using Chebyshev's inequality and the Law of Large Numbers. Chebyshev's inequality:

$$P\{|X - u| \geq \epsilon\} \leq \frac{\sigma^2}{\epsilon^2}$$

for arbitrary $\epsilon > 0$, where u and σ^2 denote the mean and variance of the random vector, respectively. (If still necessary, consult the more detailed hints that follow.)

Detailed Hints: We consider a single element $W(k)$ converging to a single value s with probability 1. Suppose that the initial weight vector is $W(1) = \Theta$. The updating formulas $W(k+1) = W(k) + \Delta W(k)$ and $\Delta W(k) = \frac{1}{k}[X(k) - W(k)]$ lead to the recurrence relation:

$$W(k+1) = \frac{k-1}{k} W(k) + \frac{1}{k} X(k) \quad \text{for } k = 1, 2, \ldots$$

can be established. Unrolling the recurrence relation,

$$W(k) = \frac{\sum_{i=1}^{k-1} X(i)}{k-1} \quad \text{for } k = 2, 3, \ldots$$

For the Chebyshev's inequality, we calculate the mean and variance of $W(k)$,

$$u_W(k) = E\{W(k)\} = \frac{\sum_{i=1}^{k-1} E\{X(i)\}}{k-1} = s$$

so

$$
\begin{aligned}
\sigma_W^2(k) &= E\{[W(k) - u_W(k)]^2\} \\
&= \frac{E\{\sum_{i=1}^{k-1}[X(i) - s] \sum_{j=1}^{k-1}[X(j) - s]\}}{(k-1)^2} = \frac{\sigma^2}{k-1}
\end{aligned}
$$

where we used $E\{[X(i) - s][X(j) - s]\} = 0$ if $i \neq j$. Apply Chebyshev's inequality, for arbitrary $\epsilon > 0$,

$$\lim_{k \to \infty} P\{|W(k) - s| \geq \epsilon\} \leq \lim_{k \to \infty} \frac{\sigma^2/(k-1)}{\epsilon^2} \approx 0$$

PART III: SUPERVISED MODELS

Chapter 4

Decision-Based Neural Networks

4.1 Introduction

Supervised-learning networks represent the main stream of the development in neural networks. Some examples of well-known pioneering networks include the perceptron network [243], ADALINE/MADALINE [305], and various multilayer networks [196, 216, 245, 301]. Two phases are involved in a supervised learning network: *retrieving phase* and *learning phase*. In the *retrieving phase*, the objective is to determine to which class a pattern belongs, based on the winner of the output values. The output values are functions of the input values and network weights, called *discriminant function*. In the *learning phase*, the weights are trained so that the (learned and/or unlearned) patterns are more likely to be correctly classified.

In supervised training, the training patterns must be provided in input/teacher pattern pairs, $[\mathcal{X}, \mathcal{T}] = \{ [x_1, t_1], [x_2, t_2], \ldots, [x_M, t_M] \}$, where M is the number of training pairs. The network is told by the teacher what decision is correct and make proper adjustments accordingly. This leads to the basic learning rule of a decision-based (or discrimination-based) neural network (DBNN). More precisely, in training a DBNN, the teacher does not have to know the exact output values of the neurons.

Let us first focus on the binary classification problem, where the pattern space is divided into two regions. Each class occupies its own region. In the clearly separable case, the two classes are separated by the *decision boundary*, defined as the hyper-surface on which the two discriminant functions have equal scores. For example, with reference to Figure 4.1(a), the facial patterns are to be classified into two groups, male (M) and female (F). Two sub-networks (or simply subnets) are adopted. The output of the first subnet $\mathbf{y_M}$ is a function of the input $\mathbf{x}$ and the weights $\mathbf{w_M}$:

$$\mathbf{y_M} = \phi_M(\mathbf{x}, \mathbf{w_M})$$

This is the **discriminant function** of the subnet. Similarly, the second subnet has a discriminant function:

$$\mathbf{y_F} = \phi_F(\mathbf{x}, \mathbf{w_F})$$

The classification is decided based on the values of the discriminant functions. More precisely, if

$$\phi_F(\mathbf{x}, \mathbf{w_F}) > \phi_M(\mathbf{x}, \mathbf{w_M})$$

then the pattern is classified to "F". Otherwise, it is classified to "M". The teacher in Figure 4.1(a) points out the correct class for each training pattern, M or F. In the DBNN, there is no need for training if a correct decision is made. If the decision is incorrect, then the weights ($\mathbf{w_M}$ and $\mathbf{w_F}$) will have to be updated. Once the network completes the learning phase, the network is ready for use in the *retrieving phase*. It recalls the pattern classification based on the trained discriminant functions.

For any binary classification problem, two classes can be separated by a single-output network, cf. Figure 4.1(b). Now the discriminant function of this network is chosen to be

$$\mathbf{y} = \phi(\mathbf{x}, \mathbf{w}) \equiv \phi_M(\mathbf{x}, \mathbf{w_M}) - \phi_F(\mathbf{x}, \mathbf{w_F})$$

At the network's output, a binary decision (d) is made based on the value of the discriminant function $\phi(\mathbf{x}, \mathbf{w})$. That is

$$d = \begin{cases} 1 & \phi(\mathbf{x}, \mathbf{w}) > 0 \\ 0 & \phi(\mathbf{x}, \mathbf{w}) < 0 \end{cases}$$

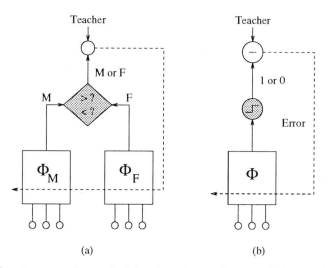

(a)   (b)

Figure 4.1: Suppose that a decision-based neural network (DBNN) is trained to determine whether a person is male (M) or female (F), from the given facial features. (a) In decision-based training, the teacher indicates where a correct classification is made. The updating strategy depends on the decision. (b) The binary classification model can be reduced into one network, with the *discriminant function* $\phi(\mathbf{x}, \mathbf{w}) = \phi_M(\mathbf{x}, \mathbf{w_M}) - \phi_F(\mathbf{x}, \mathbf{w_F})$.

In other words, the *decision boundary* is characterized by

$$\phi(\mathbf{x}, \mathbf{w}) = 0$$

Note that the distribution of training patterns dictate the decision regions, which in turn determine the choice of proper discriminant functions.

Linear Separability   Two classes of patterns are *linearly separable* if they can be separated by a linear hyperplane decision boundary. In other words, the decision boundary can be characterized by a **linear discriminant function**:

$$\phi(\mathbf{x}, \mathbf{w}) = \sum_{j}^{P} w_j x_j + \theta = 0$$

For two-dimensional inputs, for example, the decision boundary is

$$w_1 x_1 + w_2 x_2 + \theta = 0$$

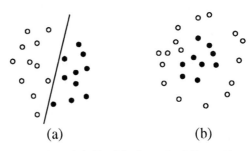

(a)   (b)

Figure 4.2: Two examples: (a) the black and white patterns are linearly separable, and (b) they are not linearly separable.

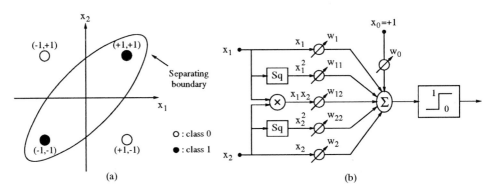

(a)   (b)

Figure 4.3: (a) The XOR-like problem is not linearly separable. They can be separated by a nonlinear decision boundary. (b) A possible network implementation for the elliptic discriminant function.

An example of a linear separating hyperplane is illustrated in Figure 4.2(a). A set of pattern vectors are called *linearly nonseparable* (or simply *nonlinearly separable*) if they are not linearly separable.

An important question is whether the two classes of patterns are *linear separable*. The patterns in Figure 4.2(b), for example, are linear nonseparable. The (XOR-like) problem in Figure 4.3(a), whose input/output mapping is

$$
\begin{aligned}
(+1, +1) &\longrightarrow 0 \\
(+1, -1) &\longrightarrow 1 \\
(-1, +1) &\longrightarrow 1 \\
(-1, -1) &\longrightarrow 0
\end{aligned}
\tag{4.1}
$$

provides an even simpler linearly nonseparable example. The XOR-like function, however, can be separated by an elliptic model function,

$$\phi(\mathbf{x}, \mathbf{w}) = x_1^2 + w_{12}x_1x_2 + w_{22}x_2^2 + w_0$$

with the weights $[w_{12}, w_{22}, w_0] = [1.4, 0.3, -1]$. The separating elliptic boundary is illustrated in Figure 4.3(a). In general, the elliptic discriminant function has the form:

$$\phi(\mathbf{x}, \mathbf{w}) = w_{11}x_1^2 + w_{12}x_1x_2 + w_{22}x_2^2 + w_1x_1 + w_2x_2 + w_0 = 0 \qquad (4.2)$$

Figure 4.3(b) depicts a possible network implementation for the elliptic discriminant function.

Nonseparable Clusters In the previous discussion, we assume that the patterns from different classes occupy clearly separable regions. In practice, it may not necessarily be the case. In fact, it is common that patterns from different classes do overlap in the border area, especially if they are generated from Gaussian-type probabilistic distribution functions. To handle such situations, some probabilistic criteria can be adopted. As shown below, this leads to either a linear or nonlinear decision boundary.

Suppose that the two classes (say, M and F) have the same a priori probability. It is natural to adopt $Prob(\mathbf{x}|M)$ and $Prob(\mathbf{x}|F)$ as their respective discriminant functions. Indeed, by the Bayesian decision rule, a pattern $\mathbf{x} \in F$ if and only if

$$Prob(\mathbf{x}|F) > Prob(\mathbf{x}|M)$$

If both the conditional probability functions are Gaussian with variance $= 1$ and centroids $\mathbf{c}_M$ and $\mathbf{c}_F$, respectively, then $Prob(\mathbf{x}|M) = \beta \exp\{-\|\mathbf{x} - \mathbf{c}_M\|^2\}$ and $Prob(\mathbf{x}|F) = \beta \exp\{-\|\mathbf{x} - \mathbf{c}_F\|^2\}$ where β is a normalization constant. Therefore, the decision will be F if and only if

$$\|\mathbf{x} - \mathbf{c}_M\|^2 > \|\mathbf{x} - \mathbf{c}_F\|^2$$

This leads to a **linear decision boundary**:

$$\mathbf{x}\mathbf{w} + \theta < 0$$

where $\mathbf{w} = \mathbf{c}_M - \mathbf{c}_F$ and $\theta = \|\mathbf{c}_M\|^2 - \|\mathbf{c}_F\|^2$. However, such idealistic assumption is invalid if the variances are different or the distributions are Gaussian-mixture. Under the more practical circumstance, it would be more effective to use a **nonlinear decision boundary**. This is discussed in Section 4.3.

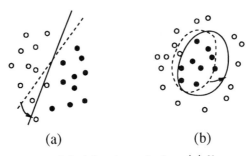

Figure 4.4: Adjustment of decision boundaries: (a) linear, and (b) nonlinear. The gradient-type adjustment of the weights cannot be explicitly reflected in the figure because it is not drawn on the w-plane.

Chapter Organization

This chapter explores various *decision-based neural networks* (DBNNs), ranging from the basic linear perceptron to the more sophisticated hierarchical networks. They all adopt the decision-based learning principle. Section 4.2 introduces the *linear perceptron* networks for the binary-category and multiple-category classifications. The linear perceptron is the first DBNN-type model introduced. However, linear decision boundaries are not practical for real-world applications. Nonlinear decision boundaries are generally more suitable. Therefore, a broader framework for the DBNNs is explored in Section 4.3. In particular, a hierarchically structured DBNN is proposed, which offers a great flexibility to accommodate complex decision boundaries. Finally, the DBNN-type mutual training can be applied to temporal pattern recognition in addition to static pattern recognition. This will be discussed in Chapter 6.

4.2   Linear Perceptron Networks

The objective of the learning phase is to determine the best discriminant functions, which in turn dictate the decision boundaries. Figure 4.4 depicts examples of adjusting linear and nonlinear decision boundaries in the pattern space. A pioneering decision-based neural model is the *perceptron* originally proposed by Rosenblatt [244]. The (linear) perceptron was designed to separate two classes by a linear decision boundary, cf. Figure 4.4(a). It has later evolved into a good number of more sophisticated variants.

4.2.1 Linear Perceptron for Binary Classification

The basic structure of a *linear perceptron* is shown in Figure 4.1(b), with a linear discriminant function

$$y = \phi(\mathbf{x}, \mathbf{w}) = \sum_{j}^{P} w_j x_j + \theta$$

We can regard for convenience the threshold value θ just as an additional weight parameter. Denote $\theta = w_{P+1}$, then

$$\mathbf{w} = [w_1 \; w_2 \ldots w_P \; \theta]^T$$

and

$$\mathbf{z} = [x_1 \; x_2 \ldots x_P \; 1]^T$$

that is, $\mathbf{z}$ is the augmented pattern $\mathbf{x}$. Now the linear discriminant function can be rewritten as

$$y = \phi(\mathbf{x}, \mathbf{w}) = \mathbf{w}^T \mathbf{z}$$

Recall that the decision value is binary, that is,

$$d = \begin{cases} 1 & y > 0 \\ 0 & y \leq 0 \end{cases}$$

A pattern is classified as Ω when $d = 1$; otherwise, it belongs to $\bar{\Omega}$. The teacher determines whether the pattern is correctly classified. *When (and only when) a misclassification occurs, the network will be adjusted.*

Algorithm 4.1 (Linear Perceptron Learning Rule) *Upon the presentation of the mth training pattern* $\mathbf{z}^{(m)}$, *the weight vector* $\mathbf{w}^{(m)}$ *is updated as*

$$\mathbf{w}^{(m+1)} = \mathbf{w}^{(m)} + \eta(t^{(m)} - d^{(m)})\mathbf{z}^{(m)} \tag{4.3}$$

where η is a positive learning rate.   ∎

More precisely, the above learning rule can be viewed from two perspectives:

- **Reinforced Learning:** If a pattern actually belongs to the class Ω but is not selected, then the weight vector should be reinforced by adding to it a proportion of that training pattern, $\mathbf{z}^{(m)}$. Note that $t^{(m)} - d^{(m)} = 1$, so the amount of updating is $\eta \mathbf{z}^{(m)}$.

- **Antireinforced Learning:** If a pattern does not belong to Ω but is unduly selected, then the weight vector should be antireinforced by subtracting from it a proportion of that training pattern, $z^{(m)}$. Noting now that $t^{(m)} - d^{(m)} = -1$, so the amount of updating is $-\eta z^{(m)}$.

The training will take as many sweeps as required, in each sweep all the M training patterns are presented. At the end of each sweep, the initial weights $w^{(0)}$ are set to $w^{(M)}$ before the next sweep is started. If there is no misclassification over one entire sweep, thus no learning incurs in the sweep and the training process should be terminated. (According to the learning rate used, it is possible to estimate the number of sweeps required, cf. Problem 4.13.)

Theorem 4.1 (Linear Perceptron Convergence Theorem) *If a set of training patterns is linearly separable, then the linear perceptron learning algorithm in Eq. 4.3 converges to a correct solution in a finite number of iterations.*

∎

To prove the theorem, let us assume w^* to be a correct solution, which separates all patterns $z^{(m)}$ correctly. After the mth iteration, we have

$$(w^{(m+1)} - w^*) = (w^{(m)} - w^*) + \eta(t^{(m)} - d^{(m)})z^{(m)}$$

If $z^{(m)}$ is correctly classified, there is no update. If $z^{(m)}$ is misclassified, then

$$\|w^{(m+1)} - w^*\|^2 = \|w^{(m)} - w^*\|^2 + \eta^2\|z^{(m)}\|^2 + 2\eta(t^{(m)} - d^{(m)})(w^{(m)} - w^*)^T z^{(m)}$$

It is easy to show that for every misclassified vector $z^{(m)}$,

$$(t^{(m)} - d^{(m)})w^{*T}z^{(m)} = |w^{*T}z^{(m)}| \geq 0 \tag{4.4}$$

and

$$(t^{(m)} - d^{(m)})w^{(m)^T}z^{(m)} = -|w^{(m)^T}z^{(m)}| \leq 0 \tag{4.5}$$

Thus, we have

$$\|w^{(m+1)} - w^*\|^2 = \|w^{(m)} - w^*\|^2 + \eta^2\|z^{(m)}\|^2 - 2\eta(|w^{*T}z^{(m)}| + |w^{(m)^T}z^{(m)}|) \tag{4.6}$$

Obviously, if the learning rate η is chosen to be sufficiently small, then the first-order term in this equation will dominate the second-order term. This will further guarantee the total squared error to decrease strictly. Because $\|w^{(m+1)} - w^*\|^2$ cannot become negative, so the iterations must terminate in a finite number of (say, ℓ) corrections. (Although the final weight vector $\hat{w}$ is a valid solution, it does not necessarily equal w^*.)

Constant Learning Rate   The convergence speed for a constant-rate perceptron varies greatly, depending on the choice of learning rates. If it is too small, it will be very slow. On the other hand, if it is too large, it can cause numerical problems. The convergence speed does depend on how large is the region of feasible solution in the w-space. Briefly speaking, let θ denote the angle spanned by the solution region, the number of updates for the perceptron learning is proportional to $1/\{\sin \theta/2\}^2$, cf. Problem 4.13.

Ideal Learning Rate   Ideally, assuming a feasible solution w^* is known, then the optimal step size can be derived by minimizing the square error in Eq. 4.6 over η_{opt}:

$$\eta_{opt} = \frac{|w^{*T}z^{(m)}| + |w^{(m)T}z^{(m)}|}{\|z^{(m)}\|^2} \tag{4.7}$$

The finite convergence is guaranteed because the total squared error always decreases with each update; cf. Problem 4.2. When a misclassification occurs, the perceptron learning rule becomes

$$\begin{aligned} w^{(m+1)} &= w^{(m)} + \frac{|w^{*T}z^{(m)}| + |w^{(m)T}z^{(m)}|}{\|z^{(m)}\|^2}(t^{(m)} - d^{(m)})z^{(m)} \\ &= w^{(m)} + \frac{(w^* - w^{(m)})^T z^{(m)}}{\|z^{(m)}\|^2} z^{(m)} \end{aligned}$$

The last equality is due to the use of Eqns. 4.4 and 4.5. This amounts to the following optimal step size

$$\eta_{opt} = \frac{|(w^* - w^{(m)})^T z^{(m)}|}{\|z^{(m)}\|^2} \tag{4.8}$$

which is in fact equivalent to Eq. 4.7. The step size in Eq. 4.8 can be illustrated with the help of a *geometric interpretation*. The optimal step size should be chosen so as to move the new weight as close as possible to w^*. A simple geometry in Figure 4.5(a) shows that such a step size corresponds to the projection of $(w^* - w^{(m)})$ onto $z^{(m)}$. The optimal learning rate, shown in the w-space, brings the new weight vector closest to w^*.

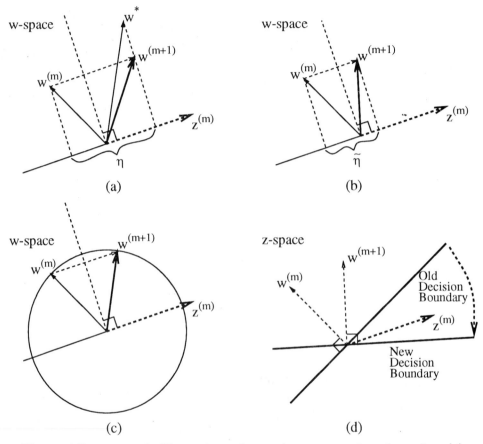

Figure 4.5: Geometric illustrations of several perceptron learning rules: (a) The optimal learning rate, shown in the w-space, brings the new weight vector closest to $\mathbf{w}^*$. (b) The weight update and the step size for the relaxation method. (c) The weight update for the normalized perceptron. Note that the updated weight vector remains normalized just like the old weight vector. (d) In the z-space, the decision border is shifted so that pattern $\mathbf{z}^{(m)}$ can be correctly classified.

Relaxation Method

Obviously, the rate in Eq. 4.7 is impractical, because $\mathbf{w}^*$ is unknown. The relaxation method offers a practical alternative. In this approach, the (unknown) term $|\mathbf{w}^{*T}\mathbf{z}^{(m)}|$ in Eq. 4.7 is substituted by a lower bound δ, $0 \leq \delta \leq \delta^*$, where

$$\delta^* \equiv \min_m |\mathbf{w}^{*T}\mathbf{z}^{(m)}|$$

Thus the revised learning rate is

$$\tilde{\eta} = \frac{\delta + |\mathbf{w}^{(m)T}\mathbf{z}^{(m)}|}{\|\mathbf{z}^{(m)}\|^2} \tag{4.9}$$

leading to the well-known *relaxation method*:

$$\mathbf{w}^{(m+1)} = \mathbf{w}^{(m)} + \frac{(t^{(m)} - d^{(m)})(\delta + |\mathbf{w}^{(m)T}\mathbf{z}^{(m)}|)}{\|\mathbf{z}^{(m)}\|^2}\mathbf{z}^{(m)} \tag{4.10}$$

It can be proved that the convergence can still be upheld. Figure 4.5 (b) shows (in the w-space) the learning step size for the relaxation method. It is advisable to set δ to be a small but positive value.

Normalized Perceptron Learning Rules

Now we address two practical numerical considerations:

1. The estimation of a constant learning rate η or the relaxation parameter δ (or δ^*) presents some difficulty.

2. It is numerically desirable to regulate the dynamic range of the weight vectors.

Both problems are properly addressed in the so-called normalized perceptron. In this section, we assume the initial weight vector is normalized. The task is to preserve the normalization property of $\mathbf{w}^{(m)}$ in each training iteration. In this scheme, the term $|\mathbf{w}^{*T}\mathbf{z}^{(m)}|$ in Eq. 4.7 is substituted by $|\mathbf{w}^{(m)T}\mathbf{z}^{(m)}|$, thus

$$\eta_{norm} = \frac{2|\mathbf{w}^{(m)T}\mathbf{z}^{(m)}|}{\|\mathbf{z}^{(m)}\|^2} \tag{4.11}$$

This is a *normalized perceptron learning rule*. It can be proved that such a choice of η_{norm} guarantees the total squared error in Eq. 4.6 to decrease strictly. (See Problem 4.3.) Therefore, the finite convergence is again guaranteed.

Figure 4.5 (c) shows the weight update for the normalized perceptron. Note that the updated weight vector remains normalized just like the old weight vector. Figure 4.5 (d) shows, in the z-space, how the decision border is shifted so that the pattern $\mathbf{z}^{(m)}$ can be correctly classified. (Note that the decision hyperplanes are orthogonal to the weight vectors.) The normalized perceptron offers a very attractive numerical algorithm, because it uses predictable (and ambitious) learning rates and yet preserves normalized vectors and guarantees convergence.

Simulation Comparison: Convergence Speed and Testing Accuracy

All perceptron learning variants yield a finite convergence, as verified by both theoretical and simulation analyses. The difference lies in their convergence speeds. For easily separable problems, the simulations indicate the best constant-rate or relaxation methods outperform the normalized perceptron learning. In contrast, as illustrated by Figure 4.6, the normalized perceptron holds slight advantage over the best constant-rate or relaxation methods for the difficult separable problem. In general, the normalized perceptron has a speed compatible with the best relaxation method. It is difficult to calibrate the convergence speed for a constant-rate perceptron learning, as its speed varies significantly. Even though the speeds are on the average compatible, the normalized perceptron obviates the preselection of a good constant learning rate η or relaxation parameter δ.

4.2.2 Linear Perceptron for Multiple Classification

The basic perceptron can be extended to the problem of classifying multiple (e.g., L) classes. For this purpose, the following important features are incorporated into the general DBNN:

- One subnet is designated for one class, that is, a One-Class-One-Net (OCON) structure, cf. Figure 4.7.

- The linear discriminant functions for the subnets are denoted as $\phi(\mathbf{x}, \mathbf{w}_i)$, for $i = 1, \cdots, L$. The discriminant function provides the score for each subnet (or each class).

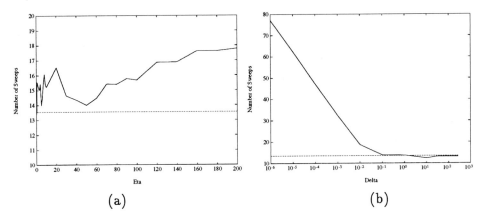

Figure 4.6: Comparison results on a relatively hard problem: (a) constant-rate (solid curve) vs. normalized perceptron (dashed curve) and (b) relaxation method (solid curve) vs. normalized perceptron (dashed curve).

- A MAXNET is used to select the subnet (or class) with the winning score, cf. Figure 4.7.

- The output is usually a symbol labeling the winner of the subnets, cf. Figure 4.8. The following *mutual training* scheme can be used. This output symbol will be compared with the teacher symbol. If the two symbols match, then the network will be left alone until a future training pattern is presented. If the symbols mismatch, then the weights will be updated by the reinforced and antireinforced learning rules, which will be explained momentarily (in Eq. 4.14).

When there are multiple clusters (classes), an idealistic situation would be that for each of the clusters, there exists a linear boundary separating it from all the other clusters. This is called *strongly linearly separable*. For example, the three clusters in a two-dimensional space shown in Figure 4.9(a) are strongly linearly separable. It is a simple task to classify strongly linearly separable clusters: One perceptron can be assigned to each of the three classes shown in Figure 4.9(a). The teacher value is set to high $(t = 1)$, if the net is designated for that class, or low $(t = 0$), otherwise. However, this condition is too stringent for practical applications. A more practical definition is described as follows.

Definition 4.1 (Linear Separability – Multiple Classification)
Suppose that $S = \{z^{(1)}, \ldots, z^{(M)}\}$ is a set of given training patterns, with

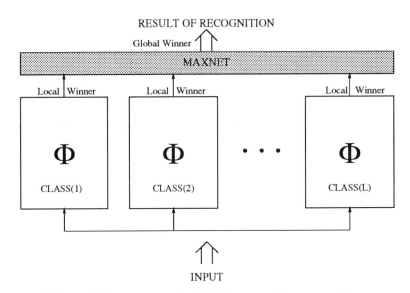

Figure 4.7: A schematic OCON network for recognition.

each element $z^{(i)} \in R^N$ *belonging to one of the L classes* $\{\ \Omega_i, i = 1, \cdots, L\ \}$.
The set is said to be linearly separable [1] *when (and only when) there exists
weight vectors* w_i, $i = 1, \ldots, L$, *such that for any pattern* $z \in \Omega_i$,

$$w_i^T z > w_j^T z \quad \text{for all } j \neq i \tag{4.12}$$

For example, the three clusters shown in Figure 4.9(b) are *linearly separable* but NOT *strongly linearly separable*. In this case, the borders between different classes are more subtly drawn, as compare with the strongly linearly separable case. Therefore, it calls for a more sophisticated algorithm to determine the decision boundaries.

Algorithm 4.2 (Linear Perceptron – Multiple Classification)
Suppose that $S = \{z^{(1)}, \ldots, z^{(M)}\}$ *is a set of given training patterns, with
each element* $z^{(m)} \in R^N$ *belonging to one of the L classes* $\{\Omega_i, i = 1, \cdots, L\}$;
and that the discriminant functions are $\phi(z, w_i) = w_i^T z$ *for* $i = 1, \ldots, L$.
Suppose that the mth training pattern $x^{(m)}$ *presented is known to belong to
class* Ω_i; *and that the winning class for the pattern is denoted by an integer
j, that is, for all* $l \neq j$,

$$w_j^T z > w_l^T z$$

---

[1] A set S is *strongly linear separable* when there exists a threshold ξ and network weights such that, for any pattern $z \in \Omega_i$, $w_i^T z > \xi > w_j^T z$ for all $j \neq i$.

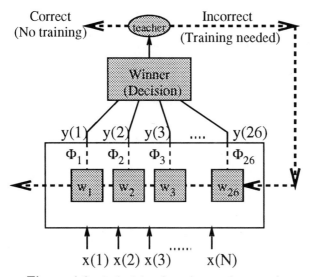

Figure 4.8: A decision-based neural network.

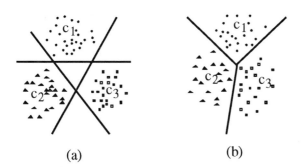

(a)   (b)

Figure 4.9: (a) Strongly linearly separable clusters. Only under this idealistic circumstance, each subnet may be *individually trained.* (b) In practice, the clusters are often linearly separable but not strongly linearly separable. In this case, the subnets must be *mutually trained* (by, e.g., DBNN) so that the boundaries between the clusters may be fine-tuned.

(1) *When $j = i$, then the pattern $z^{(m)}$ is already correctly classified, so no update will be needed.*

(2) *When $j \neq i$, that is, $z^{(m)}$ is still misclassified, then the following update will be performed:*

- **Reinforced Learning:** $w_i^{(m+1)} = w_i^{(m)} + \eta z^{(m)}$
- **Antireinforced Learning:** $w_j^{(m+1)} = w_j^{(m)} - \eta z^{(m)}$

The other weights remain unchanged: $w_l^{(m+1)} = w_l^{(m)}$ *for all $l \neq i$ and $l \neq j$.*

■

Theorem 4.2 (Linear Perceptron Convergence Theorem)
If the given multiple-class training set is linearly separable, then the linear perceptron learning algorithm converges to a correct solution after a finite number of iterations.

Proof: The proof can be found in [61], in which it is shown that the multiclass problem can be reduced to the two-class case. Suppose that $z \in \Omega_1$, so that Eq. 4.12 becomes

$$w_1^T z - w_j^T z > 0, \quad j=2,...,L$$

This set of inequalities can be expressed as

$$q^T p_{1j} > 0, \quad j=2,...,L, \tag{4.13}$$

where the (expanded) LN-dimensional weight vectors are denoted as follows:

$$q = [w_1^T, w_2^T, \ldots, w_L^T]^T$$

and

$$p_{12} = [z, -z, 0, \ldots, 0]^T$$
$$p_{13} = [z, 0, -z, \ldots, 0]^T$$
$$p_{1L} = [z, 0, 0, \ldots, -z]^T$$

The inequalities in Eq. 4.13 can be interpreted as the (expanded) weight vector q correctly classifies all $L - 1$ of the (expanded) LN-dimensional training patterns $p_{12}, p_{13}, \cdots, p_{1L}$. Note that, if $q^T p_{1j} > 0$ for all $j \neq 1$, then $w_i^T z - w_j^T z > 0$, and consequently z is correctly classified.

If $\mathbf{q}^T \mathbf{p}_{1j} < 0$ for any $j \neq 1$, that is, $\mathbf{w}_1^T \mathbf{z} - \mathbf{w}_j^T \mathbf{z} < 0$, then the teacher t and the response d are 1 and 0, respectively. (Show this!) Thus, the training becomes necessary. Here we apply the two-class perceptron learning rule to the much expanded space:

$$\mathbf{q}^{new} = \mathbf{q}^{old} + \eta(t - d)\mathbf{p}_{1j}$$

Only the first weight vector $\mathbf{w}_1$ and the jth weight vector $\mathbf{w}_j$ are updated in the training:

$$
\begin{aligned}
\mathbf{w}_1^{new} &= \mathbf{w}_1^{old} + \eta\mathbf{z} \\
\mathbf{w}_j^{new} &= \mathbf{w}_j^{old} - \eta\mathbf{z}
\end{aligned}
$$

This leads directly to the multiple-classification linear perceptron in Algorithm 4.2.

The importance of the construction procedure, originally due to Carl Kesler, lies in the fact that it converts a multiple classification problem into a binary classification problem; cf. Eq. 4.13. Then the convergence proof for the binary classification can be exploited to validate Algorithm 4.2 for the general case.

∎

4.3   Decision-Based Neural Networks

The *linear perceptron*, which is considered to be the pioneering DBNN, is applicable only when the classes of patterns are known to be separable by linear decision boundaries. In contrast, the *nonlinear perceptron* offers a much greater domain of practical applications. In training a complex network, the key lies in the following distributive decision-based credit-assignment principle:

- *When to update?* In the decision-based learning rule, weight updating is performed only when misclassification occurs.

- *Which subnets to update?* The learning rule is distributive and localized. It applies *reinforced learning* to the subnet corresponding to the correct class and *antireinforced learning* to the (unduly) winning subnet.

- *How to update?* Because the decision boundary depends on the discriminant function $\phi(\mathbf{x}, \mathbf{w})$, it is natural to adjust the boundary by adjusting the weight vector w either in the direction of the gradient of the discriminant function (i.e., reinforced learning) or opposite to that direction (i.e., antireinforced learning):

$$\Delta \mathbf{w} = \pm \eta \nabla \phi(\mathbf{x}, \mathbf{w}) \tag{4.14}$$

where η is a positive learning rate.

The gradient vector of the function ϕ with respect to $\mathbf{w}$ is denoted

$$\nabla \phi(\mathbf{x}, \mathbf{w}) = \frac{\partial \phi(\mathbf{x}, \mathbf{w})}{\partial \mathbf{w}} = [\frac{\partial \phi}{\partial \mathbf{w}_1}, \frac{\partial \phi}{\partial \mathbf{w}_2}, \cdots \frac{\partial \phi}{\partial \mathbf{w}_N}]^T.$$

The fundamental principle of *decision based neural networks* has been previously explored and established in [137, 244, 316, 317]. The following is based on a formulation proposed by Kung and Taur [166].

4.3.1 Decision-Based Learning Rule

Algorithm 4.3 (Decision-Based Learning Rule)
Suppose that $S = \{\mathbf{x}^{(1)}, \ldots, \mathbf{x}^{(M)}\}$ is a set of given training patterns, each corresponding to one of the L classes $\{\Omega_i, i = 1, \cdots, L\}$. Each class is modeled by a subnet with discriminant functions, say, $\phi(\mathbf{x}, \mathbf{w}_i)$ $i = 1, \ldots, L$. Suppose that the m-th training pattern $\mathbf{x}^{(m)}$ is known to belong to class Ω_i; and

$$\phi(\mathbf{x}^{(m)}, \mathbf{w}_j^{(m)}) > \phi(\mathbf{x}^{(m)}, \mathbf{w}_l^{(m)}), \quad \forall l \neq j \tag{4.15}$$

That is, the winning class for the pattern is the $j - th$ class (subnet).

(1) *When $j = i$, then the pattern $\mathbf{x}^{(m)}$ is already correctly classified and no update is needed.*

(2) *When $j \neq i$, that is, $\mathbf{x}^{(m)}$ is still misclassified, then the following update is performed:* [2]

$$\begin{aligned} \textit{Reinforced Learning:} \quad & \mathbf{w}_i^{(m+1)} = \mathbf{w}_i^{(m)} + \eta \nabla \phi(\mathbf{x}, \mathbf{w}_i) \\ \textit{Antireinforced Learning:} \quad & \mathbf{w}_j^{(m+1)} = \mathbf{w}_j^{(m)} - \eta \nabla \phi(\mathbf{x}, \mathbf{w}_j) \end{aligned} \tag{4.16}$$

∎

---

[2]The algorithm remains valid with the following modification: If there is more than one integer j', $j' \neq i$, such that $\phi(\mathbf{x}^{(m)}, \mathbf{w}_{j'}^{(m)}) > \phi(\mathbf{x}^{(m)}, \mathbf{w}_i^{(m)})$ then the antireinforced learning can be applied either to ALL such indices j' or to the highest winner j only.

Note that, for all $k \neq i$ and $k \neq j$, $\mathbf{w}_k^{(m+1)} = \mathbf{w}_k^{(m)}$ that is, those weights remain unchanged. Just like the *linear perceptron*, the M training patterns will be repeatedly used for as many sweeps as required for convergence.

In this learning rule, the reinforced learning moves $\mathbf{w}$ along the positive gradient direction, so the value of discriminant function will increase, enhancing the chance of the pattern's future selection. The antireinforced learning moves $\mathbf{w}$ along the negative gradient direction, so the value of discriminant function will decrease, suppressing the chance of its future selection.

Convergence   A remark about convergence is in order here. *Only for linear discriminant functions, the convergence of the DBNNs can be rigorously established.* Nevertheless, with a proper choice of discriminant function and network structure, the DBNNs can demonstrate very fast convergence and high performance in many practical applications; cf. Section 4.4.

Linear Basis Function   In the special linear case, the discriminant function adopted is based on the linear basis function (LBF)

$$\phi(\mathbf{x}, \mathbf{w}_l) = \mathbf{z}^T \mathbf{w}_l$$

Then the gradient in the updating formula, Eq. 4.14, is simply

$$\frac{\partial \phi}{\partial \mathbf{w}} = \mathbf{z}$$

which leads to the linear *perceptron* learning rule.

Radial Basis Function   One prominent example of the nonlinear decision-based learning rule is the *LVQ algorithm* proposed by Kohonen [137]. It uses a discriminant function based on the radial basis function (RBF). An RBF discriminant function is a function of the radius between the pattern and a centroid, $\| \mathbf{x} - \mathbf{w}_l \|$:

$$\phi(\mathbf{x}, \mathbf{w}_l) = -\frac{\| \mathbf{x} - \mathbf{w}_l \|^2}{2} \tag{4.17}$$

is used for each subnet l. So the centroid ($\mathbf{w}_l$) closest to the presented pattern is the winner. By applying the decision-based learning formula to Eq. 4.17 and noting that $\nabla \phi(\mathbf{x}, \mathbf{w}) = \mathbf{x} - \mathbf{w}$, the following learning rules can be derived:

$$\begin{aligned} \text{Reinforced Learning:} & \quad \mathbf{w}_i^{(m+1)} = \mathbf{w}_i^{(m)} + \eta(\mathbf{x} - \mathbf{w}_i^{(m)}) \\ \text{Antireinforced Learning:} & \quad \mathbf{w}_j^{(m+1)} = \mathbf{w}_j^{(m)} - \eta(\mathbf{x} - \mathbf{w}_j^{(m)}) \end{aligned} \tag{4.18}$$

DBNNs	Discriminant Function	Remarks
$HiPer(L_s)$	Linear basis function(LBF)	Variant of Perceptron
$HiPer(R_s)$	Radial basis function(RBF)	Variant of LVQ2
$HiPer(E_s)$	Elliptic basis function(EBF)	
$HiPer(L_h)$	Mixed sigmoid of LBF	Adopt BP Algorithm
$HiPer(R_h)$	Mixed Gaussian of RBF	

Table 4.1: Key variants of (HiPer) DBNNs for static pattern recognition. The models are characterized by the *basis function* and the *hierarchical structure* (i.e., hidden-node or subcluster). The alphabets in the parentheses, L, R, and E, stand for linear, radial, or elliptic basis functions, respectively. The subscript s and h denote a subcluster and a hidden-node structure respectively.

This is the basic formula for the LVQ (especially LVQ2) algorithm. The RBF decision-based learning is very effective for many practical applications, especially for nearest-neighbor-type clustering.

Elliptic Basis Function The basic RBF version of the DBNN discussed before is based on the assumption that the feature space is uniformly weighted in all the directions. In practice, however, different features may have varying degrees of importance depending on the way they are measured. This leads to the adoption of a (more versatile) elliptic discriminant function. The most general form of second-order basis functions is the (skewed) hyperelliptic basis function. In practice and for most applications, the EBF discriminant function is confined to the following (upright) version: The discriminant function (for each subnet l) can be generalized to an (upright) elliptic function:

$$\phi(\mathbf{x}, \mathbf{w}_l) = \sum_{k=1}^{N} \alpha_{lk}(x_k - w_{lk})^2 + \theta_l \tag{4.19}$$

where N is the dimension of the input patterns, and $\mathbf{w}_l$ is the vector comprising all the weight parameters $\{\alpha_{lk}, w_{lk}, \theta_l\}$. The learning formula can be derived from Eq. 4.16 in Algorithm 4.3.

4.3.2   Hierarchical DBNN Structure

If a subnet is modeled by a single-layer network, it will be in general inadequate to cope with complex decision boundaries. In order to provide

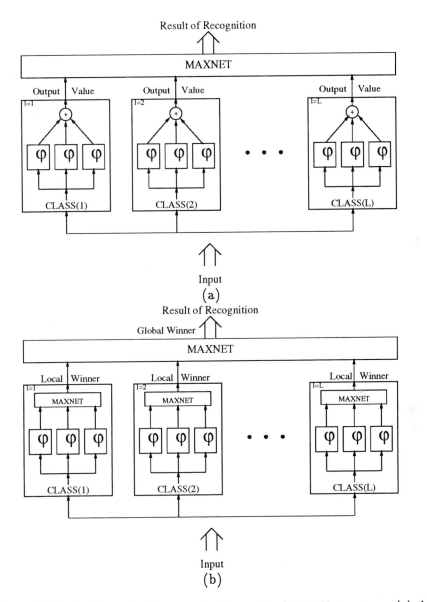

Figure 4.10: A schematic diagram of a hierarchical OCON structure: (a) the *hidden-node structure* and (b) the *subcluster structure*. In both structures, the higher level consists of multiple subnets (indexed by l), and the lower level consists of multiple subnodes in a subnet (indexed by k_l).

maximum flexibility to accommodate any nonlinear decision boundaries, a hierarchically structured DBNN is proposed. The DBNN is characterized by its *basis function* as well as its *hierarchical structure*. The DBNN combines the *perceptron-like learning rule* and the *hierarchical structure*, so it is named H̲ierarchical P̲erceptron (HiPer). For examples, some key variants of the (static) HiPer DBNN are listed in Table 4.1.

Basis Functions   In order to have a consistent indexing scheme for the hierarchical structure, we label the subnet level by the index l and label the subnode level (within a subnet) by the index k_l. More elaborately, the *discriminant function* for subnet l is denoted by $\phi(\mathbf{x}, \mathbf{w}_l)$. For the lower level, the *local discriminant function* for the subnode k_l is denoted by $\psi_l(\mathbf{x}, \mathbf{w}_{k_l})$, where the integer $k_l \in 1, \cdots, K_l$, and K_l denotes the number of subnodes in the lth subnet.

The most common basis functions, $\psi_l(\mathbf{x}, \mathbf{w}_{k_l})$, for the subnodes include linear basis functions (LBFs), radial basis functions (RBFs), and elliptic basis functions (EBFs).

- **Linear Basis Function (LBF).**   The local discriminant function $\psi_l(\mathbf{x}, \mathbf{w}_{k_l})$ represents a sigmoid function on the linear inner product of $\mathbf{x}$ and $\mathbf{w}_k$, that is,

$$\psi_l(\mathbf{x}, \mathbf{w}_{k_l}) = f(\mathbf{x}^T \tilde{\mathbf{w}}_{k_l} + \theta_l)$$

  (Here $f(\cdot)$ denotes the sigmoid function.)

- **Radial Basis Function (RBF).** Recently, the radial basis Gaussian function has gained a substantial popularity:

$$\psi_l(\mathbf{x}, \mathbf{w}_{k_l}) = e^{-\|\mathbf{x} - \tilde{\mathbf{w}}_{k_l}\|^2 / 2\sigma_{k_l}^2} \qquad (4.20)$$

- **Elliptic Basis Function (EBF).** The EBF $\psi_l(\mathbf{x}, \mathbf{w}_{k_l})$ has the same form given in Eq. 4.20 except the variance $\sigma's$ are different for different dimensions of the input pattern.

4.3.2.1   Hidden-Node DBNNs

One simple approach is the *hidden-node structure* depicted in Figure 4.10(a). In the hidden-node structure, the nonlinear discriminant function is modeled by a weighted sum of several hidden nodes. For example, a two-layer model can be used to represent each subnet; cf. Figure 4.10(a). In this case, a subnet consists of multiple hidden subnodes, each represented by a function $\psi_l(\mathbf{x}, \mathbf{w}_{k_l})$. The discriminant function of the subnet is a linear combination of the subnode values:

$$\phi(\mathbf{x}, \mathbf{w}_l) = \sum_{k_l=1}^{K_l} c_{k_l} \psi_l(\mathbf{x}, \mathbf{w}_{k_l}) \tag{4.21}$$

where $\{c_{k_l}\}$ denotes the coefficients in the upper layer, and $\mathbf{w}_l$ is the vector comprising all the weight parameters. The same decision-based learning rule is adopted (cf. Algorithm 4.3),

$$\Delta \mathbf{w}_l = \pm \eta \nabla \phi(\mathbf{x}, \mathbf{w}_l)$$

Such a discriminant function, with a proper basis function (LBF, RBF, or EBF), can closely approximate any function, cf. Section 5.4. This allows the structure a universal approximation power to accommodate almost any complex decision boundaries. Note that, under the decision-based formulation, introduction of extra nonlinear units at the subnet output has no effect on the winner selection.

4.3.2.2 Subcluster DBNNs

In order to further localize the training credit-assignments, a *subcluster structure* is proposed. Instead of using the weighted sum of the node values in the hidden-node structure, the new alternative uses a winner-take-all approach, cf. Figure 4.10(b). This is as if only the most representative of the upper weights has a nonzero weight 1 and all the others have zero weights.

For the subcluster hierarchical structure, we introduce notions of *local winner* and *global winner*. The *local winner* is the winner among the subnodes within the same subnet. The local winner of the lth subnet is indexed by s_l, that is,

$$s_l = \text{Arg} \max_{s_l} \psi_l(\mathbf{x}, \mathbf{w}_{s_l})$$

The *global winner* is the winner among all the subnets. The jth subnet will be labeled as the global winner if its local winner wins over all the other local winners, that is,

$$\psi_j(\mathbf{x}, \mathbf{w}_{s_j}) > \psi_l(\mathbf{x}, \mathbf{w}_{s_l}) \quad \forall l \neq j$$

A pattern is classified to the jth class if the jth subnet is the global winner.

The learning rule largely follows Algorithm 4.3, with the discriminant function of the subnets substituted by that of the local winners:

$$\phi(\mathbf{x}, \mathbf{w}_i) \Longleftrightarrow \psi_i(\mathbf{x}, \mathbf{w}_{s_i})$$

and

$$\phi(\mathbf{x}, \mathbf{w}_j) \Longleftrightarrow \psi_j(\mathbf{x}, \mathbf{w}_{s_j})$$

Algorithm 4.4 (Subcluster DBNNs)
Suppose that multiple subclusters are used to represent one class, with s_i, s_j, etc., representing the local winners. Suppose that the pattern $\mathbf{x}^{(m)}$ should belong to class Ω_i, but the jth subnet is selected as the global winner. When $j \neq i$, that is, $\mathbf{x}^{(m)}$ is misclassified, then do the following update:

$$
\begin{aligned}
\textit{Reinforced Learning:} \quad & \mathbf{w}_{s_i}^{(m+1)} = \mathbf{w}_{s_i}^{(m)} + \eta \nabla \psi(\mathbf{x}, \mathbf{w}_{s_i}) \\
\textit{Antireinforced Learning:} \quad & \mathbf{w}_{s_j}^{(m+1)} = \mathbf{w}_{s_j}^{(m)} - \eta \nabla \psi(\mathbf{x}, \mathbf{w}_{s_j})
\end{aligned}
\qquad (4.22)
$$

∎

In other words, the antireinforced learning is applied to the locally winning subcluster within the globally winning subnet; and the reinforced learning is applied to the local winner within the correct (and supposedly winning) class. Thus, this hierarchical structures can accommodate complex decision boundaries while only the selected subclusters in the subnets are involved in the updating.

In summary, the decision based learning rule represents a unified framework for an insightful understanding of several prominent decision-based networks, such as Perceptron[244] and LVQ[137], as well as the more flexible (HiPer-type) DBNNs as displayed in Table 4.1.

4.3.3   Static and Temporal DBNNs

In designing a decision based neural network(DBNN), the most challenging task is to identify a proper discriminant function in order to best distinguish each class from its competing classes. The selection of the discriminant function varies from one application to another. One of the most influential factors hinges upon whether static or temporal patterns are considered.

DBNN for Static Pattern Recognition

For static pattern recognition, many basis functions (e.g., LBF, RBF, and EBF) may be considered. The key variants of static DBNNs are listed in Table 4.1, where the hidden-node DBNNs are denoted $HiPer(L_h)$, $HiPer(R_h)$; and the subcluster DBNNs are $HiPer(L_s)$, $HiPer(R_s)$, and $HiPer(E_s)$. LBF or RBF DBNNs offer a much greater classification power compared with the conventional linear perceptron. The RBF DBNNs enjoy a stronger local clustering capability. Based on empirical results, they seem to have some slight performance advantage over the LBF DBNNs.

LVQ vs. Subcluster RBF DBNN The DBNNs with radial basis and elliptic basis functions, $HiPer(R_s)$ and $HiPer(E_s)$ have a strong resemblance to the well-known LVQ algorithm; cf. Eq. 4.18. The subcluster RBF DBNN ($HiPer(R_s)$) is closest to LVQ, especially LVQ2. They share many common attributes:

- They both adopt reinforced/antireinforced learning rule.

- They both adopt an radial basis subcluster scheme. Thus the amount of update is proportional to the distance between the pattern and the centroid; cf. Eq. 4.18. (Sometimes it is useful to further extend the radial basis DBNN to the elliptic basis version.)

There are some differences between the (RBF) DBNN and LVQ2 in the credit assignments. The DBNN learns only when there is a misclassification. Moreover, the updating subclusters are generally not the same for the two methods. The LVQ2 updates the local winner of the globally winning class and the local winner of the runner-up class. The DBNN updates the local winner of the globally winning class and the local winner of the correct (and supposedly winning) class. However, the correct class may not necessarily be selected as the runner-up class; therefore, the credit-assignment schemes of DBNN and LVQ2 are not the same.

Unsupervised VQ Method for Initial Weights Several approaches can be used to estimate the number of hidden nodes or subclusters. It can be either predetermined based on, for example, some prior knowledge on the training pattern distribution. It also can be determined based on the clustering technique adopted. One such example is the VQ algorithm [172]. To obtain a good initial estimation for the locations of the centroids, the VQ-type clustering (e.g., k-mean) algorithm can be adopted to determine the centroids for the subclusters within the class. Based on this initial condition, the decision-based learning rule can be applied to further fine-tune the decision boundaries. This scheme is used in the subsequent DBNN simulations.

Example 4.1 (Simulation on Two-Dimensional Artificial Data)
Four different sets of experiments on two-dimensional artificial data (cf. Figure 4.11), involving both the decision-based and approximation-based networks, were performed. The DBNNs were found to be trained rapidly, and consistantly classify the four sets. In contrast, the approximation-based nets had slower convergence and greater difficulty in forming correct boundaries. The performance of the approximation-based net depended critically on the initial conditions. The success rates were 100%, 0%, 20%, and 60% for the four experiments, respectively. In comparison, DBNNs derived the initial condition via the unsupervised clustering technique, leading eventually to 100% training accuracy for all the four experiments. The decision boundaries created by the two approaches are depicted in Figure 4.11.

DBNN for Temporal Pattern Recognition

Based on the simple winner-take-all principle, the (hidden-node or subcluster) DBNNs are naturally applicable to temporal pattern recognitions. In addition to the aforementioned basis function (LBF, RBF, etc.), there are other promising discriminant functions specially suitable for temporal models. The temporal functions worthy of consideration include, for example, DTW (dynamic time warping) distance, prediction error, and likelihood functions. In Section 4.4.3, the dynamic-time-warping(DTW) technique is incorporated into the DBNN. More detailed theoretical and application explorations on temporal models will be treated in Chapter 6.

4.3.4   Fuzzy Decision Neural Networks

When pattern categories are clearly separated, there is a range of feasible weight solutions. This fact can be exploited to attain the widest possible margin of separation (denoted as ϵ) between two neighboring regions. This further leads to a modified learning rule, nearly the same as Algorithm 4.3, with the exception that Eq. 4.15 is substituted by

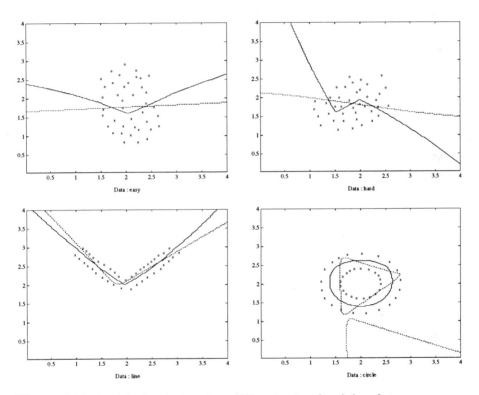

Figure 4.11: In this simulation, four different sets of training data are experimented. Each set has two classes (marked by "x" and "o") with 20 patterns in each class. The solid lines and dashed lines are the boundaries generated respectively from (EBF) DBNNs and (LBF) approximation-based conjugate-gradient technique. The numbers of hidden units used are 3, 5, 3, and 5 for the four data sets, respectively. The DBNNs successfully classify all the training sets. For the approximation-based net, the success rates are 10/10, 0/10, 2/10, and 6/10 respectively, based on 10 different initial conditions.

$$\phi(\mathbf{x}^{(m)}, \mathbf{w}_j^{(m)}) > \phi(\mathbf{x}^{(m)}, \mathbf{w}_l^{(m)}) + \epsilon \qquad (4.23)$$

Fortification by such a positive *vigilance* ϵ usually yields a better generalization. However, when classes are not clearly separable, a very different approach will be required to cope with patterns in the border area.

To illustrate this point, let us study distribution functions for the following two classes of artificial patterns:

$$p_1(x,y) = 0.9 \times N(x,3,s^2)N(y,2,s^2) + 0.1 \times N(x,3,5*s^2)N(y,2,5*s^2) \quad (4.24)$$

and

$$p_2(x,y) = 0.9 \times N(x,1,s^2)N(y,2,s^2) + 0.1 \times N(x,1,5*s^2)N(y,2,5*s^2) \quad (4.25)$$

where $N(t,\mu,s^2)$ is Gaussian with mean μ and variance s^2. The training patterns contain additive noise, represented by the second Gaussian terms in the distribution in Eq. 4.24 and Eq. 4.25. Due to the noise, the two classes overlap in the feature space, as shown in Figure 4.12. (Here, we set $s = 0.15$.) If a (hard) DBNN is used for the two classes, all the patterns are accounted for in the training process. An almost error-free training accuracy can be attained after iteratively adjusting the boundary. Depicted in Figure 4.12(a) is a very twisted decision boundary obtained by the DBNN. In order to achieve a better generalization, we need to incorporate some *tolerance* of misclassification.

One way of providing tolerance, for the nonseparable case, is simply to ignore the persistently undecided patterns. A more elegant and suitable approach can be derived based on a somewhat fuzzy decision, leading to the *Fuzzy Decision Neural Network* (FDNN) [128, 314]. More precisely, as depicted in Figure 4.13(a), there are different degrees of error associated with each decision, for example, marginally erroneous, erroneous, and extremely erroneous. The technique imposes a proper penalty function on all the "bad" decisions as well as the "marginally correct" ones. The final solution represents the best compromise in terms of the total penalty. In short, this allows "soft" or "fuzzy" decision, as opposed to the hard (yes or no) decision. To cope with "marginal" training patterns, and to provide a smooth "gradient" for learning, the penalty must be a function of the degree of error. This will be discussed below.

Following the notations used in DBNN, suppose that $S = \{\mathbf{x}^{(1)}, \ldots, \mathbf{x}^{(M)}\}$ is a set of given training patterns; and the discriminant function for the class

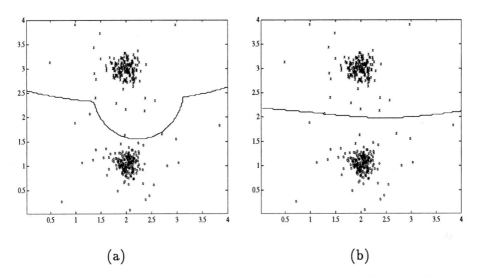

(a)   (b)

Figure 4.12:   Patterns from two nonseparable classes are labeled with x's and
o's. (a) The decision boundary obtained by DBNN(E_s), with two subclusters.
(b) The decision boundary by FDNN(E_s).

Ω_i is denoted $\phi(\mathbf{x}, \mathbf{w}_i)$, for $i = 1, \ldots, L$. For DBNN, the *winner* class is denoted as Ω_j where $j = arg\max_j \phi(\mathbf{x}^{(m)}, \mathbf{w}_j)$. However, for FDNN, an alternative denotation is adopted. Instead, Ω_j now denotes the leading *challenger*
among all the classes *excluding* the correct class Ω_i. That is,

$$j = arg\max_{j \neq i} \phi(\mathbf{x}^{(m)}, \mathbf{w}_j) \tag{4.26}$$

For a training pattern, a measure of misclassification can be introduced:

$$d = d^{(m)}(\mathbf{x}^{(m)}, \mathbf{w}) = -\phi_i(\mathbf{x}^{(m)}, \mathbf{w}_i) + \phi_j(\mathbf{x}^{(m)}, \mathbf{w}_j) \tag{4.27}$$

where $\mathbf{w}$ denotes all the involved weight vectors. In fact, a more general
measure was proposed in [123, 128, 129] as

$$d = -\phi_i(\mathbf{x}^{(m)}, \mathbf{w}_i) + \{ \frac{1}{M-1} \sum_{j, j \neq i} \phi_j(\mathbf{x}^{(m)}, \mathbf{w}_j)^\gamma \}^{1/\gamma}, \quad \gamma > 0 \tag{4.28}$$

where ϕ is assumed to be positive. Note that, when $\gamma \to \infty$, Eq. 4.28 will
closely approximate Eq. 4.27. (See Problem 4.10.)

Two scenarios are of interest. (1) When d is positive, then the associated
pattern would be *misclassified* to the challenger Ω_j. In fact, the larger the

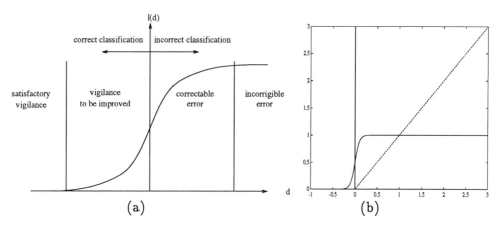

Figure 4.13: (a) For DBNN, only two regions are of interest: misclassification vs. correct classification. In contrast, for FDNN, four regions are distinguished: 1) correct with satisfactory vigilance, 2) correct with vigilance to be improved, 3) error on which correction will be attempted, and 4) error to remain uncorrected. (b) The difference between the penalty functions of a hard-decision DBNN (linear line) and a fuzzy-decision neural network.

magnitude of d, the greater the error. In this case, just like DBNN, the updating process is desirable. (2) When d is negative, then the pattern can be correctly classified to Ω_i. Nevertheless, if d is only a small negative value, then the correct choice Ω_i would win over the challenger Ω_j only by a narrow margin. In this case, unlike DBNN, it may still advisable to invoke the learning process so as to enhance the vigilance. A better vigilance margin is guaranteed as the magnitude of d gets larger,

Penalty functions which lead asymptotically to a minimum error classification (cf. Figure 4.13) are of most interest. For example,

$$\ell(d) = \frac{1}{1 + e^{-d/\xi}} \tag{4.29}$$

$$\ell(d) = \begin{cases} 0 & d \leq -\xi/2 \\ (d + \xi/2)/\xi & -\xi/2 < d < \xi/2 \\ 1 & \xi/2 \geq d \end{cases} \tag{4.30}$$

In particular, when the parameter ξ approaches zero, these penalty functions approach the step function

$$\ell(d) = \begin{cases} 0 & d < 0 \\ 1 & d \geq 0. \end{cases} \qquad (4.31)$$

Note that a complete denotation for the penalty function for an individual training pattern $x^{(m)}$ should have been $\ell(x^{(m)}, w) = \ell(d^{(m)}(x^{(m)}, w))$; and the overall cost-function is $E(w) = \sum_{m=1}^{M} \{\ell(d^{(m)})\}$. If the step penalty function in Eq. 4.31 is adopted, this cost function would be the same as the recognition error count Even with the differentiable forms of Eq. 4.29 or Eq. 4.30, the cost function still represents a good approximation of total number of errors. Figure 4.13(b) compares the soft penalty function, such as Eq. 4.29, with the corresponding penalty function used in the DBNN:

$$\ell(d) = \zeta d \qquad (4.32)$$

Note that the linear penalty function imposes too excessive a penalty for patterns with large margins of error, thus the sigmoid function is more appealing. It effectively treats the errors with equal penalty once the magnitude of error exceeds a certain threshold. Consequently, these errors may be given up for the interest of the majority of training patterns. This strategy is in agreement with the so-called "minimum-error-rate" classifier defined by Duda[61]. Furthermore, now the gradient descent method can be applied to minimize the overall cost function. The soft penalty function provides a means to minimize the number of recognition errors, at least approximately.

Algorithm 4.5 (Fuzzy Decision Learning Rule) *Suppose that the m-th training pattern* $x^{(m)}$ *is known to belong to class* Ω_i; *and that the leading challenger is denoted* $j = \arg\max_{j \neq i} \phi(x^{(m)}, w_j)$. *The learning rule is*

Reinforced Learning: $\quad w_i^{(m+1)} = w_i^{(m)} + \eta \ell'(d) \nabla \phi(x^{(m)}, w_i)$

Antireinforced Learning: $\quad w_j^{(m+1)} = w_j^{(m)} - \eta \ell'(d) \nabla \phi(x^{(m)}, w_j)$

where $\ell'(d)$ *is the derivative of the penalty function evaluated at d.* ∎

Simulation results confirm that the FDNN works more effectively than the DBNN when the the training patterns are not separable. Indeed, the FDNN yields a very smoother decision boundary for the aforementioned Gaussian-mixture problem; cf. Figure 4.12(b). Theoretically speaking, the DBNN is biased, while the FDNN is less biased. If the window size ξ is large, however, the FDNN will be more prone to bias [314]. Therefore, a learning method with adjustable window size, such as that which is used in simulated annealing, may be considered. More precisely, in the beginning phase, the window size should be large enough so that the decision boundary can move rapidly to a correct neighborhood. In order to to reduce bias, the window size should gradually decrease. It may also be argued that the selection of window size will depend on the tradeoff between bias and variance. Therefore, the window size cannot be too small because it may cause a larger variance.

In summary, the FDNN can tolerate misclassification for some patterns, while encouraging greater vigilance for others. By properly imposing vigilance and/or tolerance in the training phase, a better generalization can be attained by the FDNN. Also, under idealistic circumstances, the minimum error rate can be yielded. The FDNN can be applied to both static and temporal recognition problems. The possible discriminant functions for the static problems include LSE and likelihood function. Examples of temporal discriminant functions are likelihood function, prediction error, and DTW distance. In other words, the FDNN formulation can be effectively blended into traditional recognizers. It leads to, for example, a prediction-error based classifier, a hidden Markov model (HMM), or a dynamic time warping (DTW) based system. For more details, see Section 4.4.3 and Chapters 6 and 7.

4.4   Applications to Signal/Image Classifications

In order to demonstrate the applicability of DBNNs, one temporal example (ECG recognition) and two static recognition examples (OCR and texture classification) are studied.

4.4.1   Texture Classification

The DBNNs perform very well in texture-classification applications. Some texture samples are given in Figure 4.14. The performances of several DBNNs, including RBF and EBF subclustering DBNNs (HiPer(R_s) and HiPer(E_s)) and an LBF hidden-node DBNN (HiPer(L_H)) are compared in the study.

Feature Extraction   The texture feature used here is based on a compressed representation of the *texture spectrum* originally proposed by [297]. The texture vector associated with a pixel is characterized by 8 ternary values, $\{0, 1, \text{or } 2\}$, labeling the relative level between the central pixel and its 8 immediate neighbors. More precisely, if a neighbor pixel level is relatively lower (equal, or higher, respectively), then its corresponding value will be labeled 1 (0, or 2, respectively). For each central pixel, the total number of

Figure 4.14: Sample textures used in the texture-classification experiments.

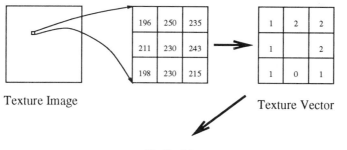

Texture Image   Texture Vector

$(\, 4 \, , \, 3 \, , \, 1 \,)$

Simplified Representation

Figure 4.15: An example of texture vector and its simplified representation. (Note that there are 4 1's, 1 0, and 3 2's in the texture vector.)

possible *texture vectors* is 3^8; cf. Figure 4.15. Because the input dimension (3^8) is too large, we adopt a simplified representation in order to save computation time and storage. It is based on three integers $\{x,y,z\}$ defined as the numbers of 0's, 1's, and 2's in a texture vector, respectively. With the new representation, there are now only 45 possible combinations of $\{x,y,z\}$. Thus the *reduced spectrum* with dimension 45 can be obtained by calculating the histogram of such representation of the texture vectors in that block; cf. Figure 4.16. The texture vector (and thus the texture spectrum) contains the information of the local texture structure of the image. One advantage of the texture spectrum lies in its insensitivity to the variation of the background intensity and noise because only the relative grey level is relevant.

Example 4.2 (DBNNs for Texture Classification)
In the simulation study, a total of 12 Brodatz textures (texture numbers 3, 16, 28, 33, 34, 49, 57, 68, 77, 84, 93, and 103) are used. For each texture image,

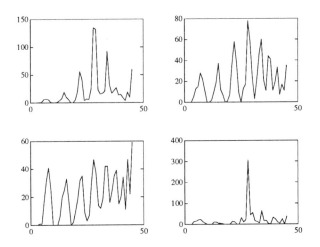

Figure 4.16: Sample reduced-texture spectrum from different classes.

529 32×32 blocks are sampled uniformly across the entire image. Their reduced spectra are then computed which in turn are used as the training data. By a similar method, additional 200 blocks are randomly chosen from the same texture image to form the test set. The linear-basis hidden-node structure, HiPer(L_h), and two subcluster structures, HiPer(R_s) and HiPer(E_s), have been tried. The training is very fast as shown in Figure 4.17. The classification performance is summarized in Table 4.2, showing very satisfactory convergence speeds and classification accuracies. The generalization performance of HiPer(E_s) is slightly better than that of HiPer(R_s), with the HiPer(L_h) as a distant third. Additional experiments indicate that the linear perceptron fails to separate the 12 classes and the approximation-based BP method has very slow speed and persistently large mean-squares error (after 500 sweeps).

4.4.2   Optical Character Recognition (OCR) Application

The problem is to recognize a rectangular pixel array as one of the 26 capital letters in the English alphabet. The character images were based on 20 different fonts, and each letter within these 20 fonts was randomly distorted to produce a file of 20,000 stimuli. Some sample characters used in the OCR classification experiments are given in Figure 4.18. Each character was converted into 16 primitive numerical attributes (in terms of statistical moments

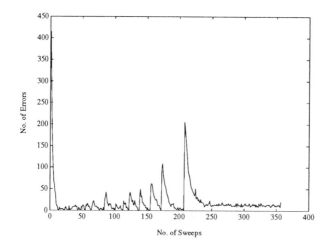

Figure 4.17: Training curves for texture-classification experiment using reduced-texture spectrum as a feature. When the number of errors drops to zero, the vigilance level can be slightly raised. (This is why there are abrupt jumps of the number of errors.)

and edge counts) that were then scaled to fit into a range of integer values from 0 through 15. (The source file of the letter image recognition data was generated by Slate, cf. [70].) The first 16,000 patterns are used as the training patterns and the remaining 4000 serve as the test patterns.

Several Holland-style adaptive classifiers were experimented in [70], obtaining an accuracy of a little over 80%. On the other hand, the simulation results on the DBNNs, summarized in Table 4.3, are considerably better. In this simulation, 10-subcluster $HiPer(E_s)$ performs better than 20-subcluster $HiPer(R_s)$. (Note that the two nets have approximately the same number of weight parameters.) Both DBNNs yield better performance than the results reported in [70].

4.4.3 DTW Temporal Networks for Speech Recognition

A well-known conventional approach for speech recognition is the dynamic time warping(DTW) technique. Speech recognition represents another important potential application of neural networks. For example, it is natural to explore some combination between DBNN and DTW for speech or other temporal signal recognition, cf. Figure 4.19. The mutual training incorporated into the DTW decision-based neural network should help enhance the

Network	Noise Tolerance	Test Set
HiPer(L_h)(20)	0(200 sweeps)	3.25%
HiPer(R_s)(4)	0(20 sweeps)	2.88%
HiPer(R_s)(4)	0.13	2.42%
HiPer(R_s)(8)	0(7 sweeps)	3.54%
HiPer(R_s)(8)	0.2	2.92%
HiPer(E_s)(1)	0(200 sweeps)	3.04%
HiPer(E_s)(4)	0(17 sweeps)	2.46%
HiPer(E_s)(4)	0.15	2.08%

Table 4.2: Comparison of various DBNNs for the texture-classification. The numbers in the parentheses denote the numbers of subnodes in the subnets. The classification rates on the training set are 100% for all models. The exceptions are 99.5% for HiPer(E_s)(1) and 98.4% for HiPer(L_h)(20). We have also observed that, with some additional adjustment of learning rate, the HiPer(E_s)(4) can achieve as low as 1.4% in the error rate.

network performance.

Dynamic Time Warping(DTW)   A temporal speech vector can be formed by, for example, the cepstral coefficients of the speech waveforms. The reference signal, represented by such a sequence of vectors, is denoted by $\mathbf{w}(q)$. (The integer in the parenthesis ( ) denotes the original time index.) Similarly, a training signal is also represented by a sequence of vectors denoted

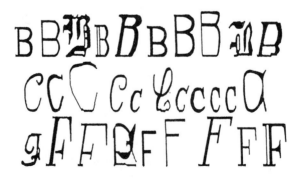

Figure 4.18: Sample characters used in the OCR classification experiments.

Algorithm	No. of Clusters	Training Set	Test Set
HiPer(E_s)	10	0.0375%	6.2%
HiPer(R_s)	20	0.025%	7.5%

Table 4.3: Comparison of two DBNNs for the OCR classification.

by x(q). It is practical to assume that both the training and test signals are inherently warped. So the best "distance" between the two sequences cannot be derived from a direct comparison of the two vectors based on the original time indexing (i.e., template matching). Instead, the distance should be based on a new indexing which takes the warping effect into account. The DTW distance measure provides an effective means to cope with such a time variability problem. The time-warping factor is carefully decoded during the preprocessing phase.

The objective of the DTW is to find a scheme to reindex the reference and training signal sequences so that the best match between two sequences can be attained [250]. The total length of the warping path is denoted by $\hat{Q}$. One example warping path is depicted in Figure 4.20(a). In this example, $\hat{Q} = 14$. The newly indexed reference and training sequences are respectively denoted by w_q, and x_q. Corresponding to the warping path in Figure 4.20(a), the new indexing is displayed in Figure 4.20(b). After the reindexing, the distance measure is obtained as

$$\sum_{q=1}^{\hat{Q}} \bar{p}_q \|(w_q - x_q)\|^2$$

where $\bar{p}_q$ denotes proper weighting factors on each segment of the path

$$\bar{p}_q = p_q / \sum_{q=1}^{\hat{Q}} p_q$$

where $p_q = \alpha$, β, or γ, as illustrated in Figure 4.21.

DBNN With DTW Criterion   The conventional DTW technique does not have a training phase so it incurs high computational cost in preprocessing. This could severely hamper real-time recognition speeds. In this respect,

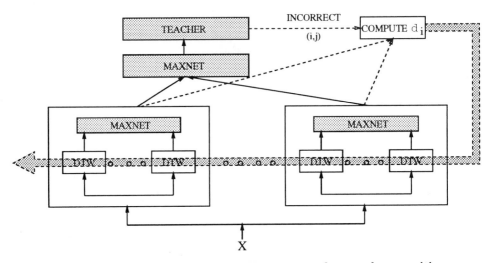

Figure 4.19: A possible DTW DBNN structure for speech recognition.

some training process should be incorporated into the DTW technique in order to alleviate the computational burden in the recognition phase. In order to to apply the DBNN learning rule to a DTW-based model, the discriminant function ϕ is naturally chosen to be (the negative of) the DTW distance function. That is

$$\psi_j(x, \mathbf{w}) = -\sum_{q=1}^{\hat{Q}} \overline{P}_q \delta_q \tag{4.33}$$

where we denote

$$\delta_q = \|(\mathbf{w}_q - x_q)\|^2$$

as the Euclidean distance between two (warped) vectors.

With reference to the (subcluster) DBNN structure in Figure 4.19, the learning rule is described below. Suppose that there are L categories of signals to be classified, and that each category is represented by a number of reference vectors (i.e., the centroids of the subclusters). The distance function between an utterance x and a word (or a class) Ω^j is determined by the local winner among the subclusters in the class,

$$\phi_j(\mathbf{x}, \mathbf{w}) = \max_{s_j} \psi_j(\mathbf{x}, \mathbf{w}_{s_j}) \tag{4.34}$$

where the discriminant function is characterized by Eq. 4.33 with the weight

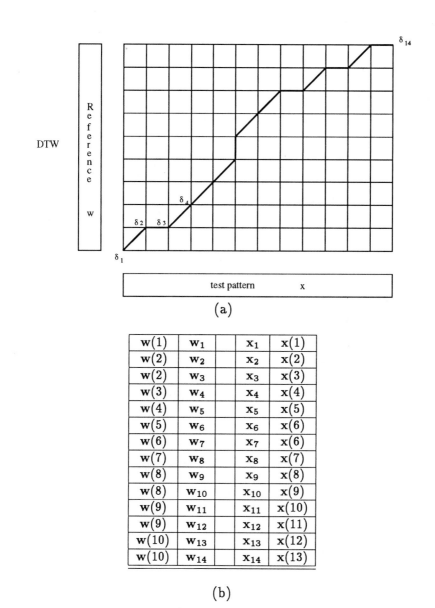

(a)

$w(1)$	w_1		x_1	$x(1)$
$w(2)$	w_2		x_2	$x(2)$
$w(2)$	w_3		x_3	$x(3)$
$w(3)$	w_4		x_4	$x(4)$
$w(4)$	w_5		x_5	$x(5)$
$w(5)$	w_6		x_6	$x(6)$
$w(6)$	w_7		x_7	$x(6)$
$w(7)$	w_8		x_8	$x(7)$
$w(8)$	w_9		x_9	$x(8)$
$w(8)$	w_{10}		x_{10}	$x(9)$
$w(9)$	w_{11}		x_{11}	$x(10)$
$w(9)$	w_{12}		x_{12}	$x(11)$
$w(10)$	w_{13}		x_{13}	$x(12)$
$w(10)$	w_{14}		x_{14}	$x(13)$

(b)

Figure 4.20: (a) A possible DTW path. (b) The corresponding indices between the reference and input sequences

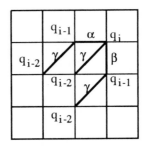

Figure 4.21: Three kinds of permissible local paths leading to the position q_i and their weights are denoted (1) $\gamma - \alpha$, (2) γ, and (3) $\gamma - \beta$.

vector $\mathbf{w}_{s_j}$. More precisely,

$$\psi_j(x, \mathbf{w}_{s_j}) = -\sum_{q=1}^{\hat{Q}_{s_j}} \overline{P}_q \delta_{s_j, q} \tag{4.35}$$

Suppose that the correct class of a given training pattern $\mathbf{x}$ is Ω^i but it is (mis)classified into the Ω^j, that is

$$j = Arg\max_l \phi_l(\mathbf{x}; \mathbf{w}_l)$$

According to the DBNN learning rule, the local winners in Ω^i and Ω^j are updated by the reinforced and antireinforced learning:

$$\mathbf{w}_{s_i, q}^{m+1} = \mathbf{w}_{s_i, q}^m + \eta_m \, \pi_i \tag{4.36}$$

$$\mathbf{w}_{s_j, q}^{m+1} = \mathbf{w}_{s_j, q}^m - \eta_m \, \pi_j \tag{4.37}$$

where

$$\pi_i = \nabla\phi(\mathbf{x}, \mathbf{w}_i) = 2(\mathbf{w}_{s_i, q} - \mathbf{x}_q)p_q / \sigma_{s_i}$$

$$\sigma_{s_i} = \sum_{q=1}^{\hat{Q}_{s_j}} p_q \tag{4.38}$$

$$\tag{4.39}$$

It is possible to adaptively adjust the path weights $p_k, k = 1 \cdots 3$, by making the calculation of the gradients include these extra free parameters.

FDNN With DTW Criterion   According to Algorithm 4.5, the DBNN learning rules Eq. 4.36 and Eq. 4.37 can be modified to become

$$\mathbf{w}_{s_i,q}^{m+1} = \mathbf{w}_{s_i,q}^m + \eta_m \, \nu_i \, \pi_i \tag{4.40}$$

$$\mathbf{w}_{s_j,q}^{m+1} = \mathbf{w}_{s_j,q}^m - \eta_m \, \nu_i \, \pi_j \tag{4.41}$$

where $\nu_i = \ell'(d_i)$. Note that *only* the local winner of the global winning class and that of the correct class are updated. Multiple best paths in the DTW procedure could be combined to produce the word distance. In [43], the more general cost measure in Eq. 4.28 is adopted. A series of speaker-independent recognition experiments (using the English E-set as the vocabulary data base) were conducted based on this technique. It reportedly achieved a high recognition rate, 84%, which is a remarkable improvement over the 64% attained by the traditional template clustering technique.

4.5   Concluding Remarks

This chapter demonstrates that DBNNs can be used as effective classifiers. Linear *perceptron*, which can be regarded as the pioneering DBNN, adopts a single-layer structure with a linear basis function. Multilayer and hierarchical network structures with nonlinear basis functions inherently offer a broader application domain. DBNNs have a modular and hierarchical architecture plus a competition-based credit-assignment scheme that decides which subnets and subnodes should be trained or used. Based on simulation performance comparison, the DBNNs appear to be very effective for many signal/image-classification applications. The hierarchical structure provides a unified framework for other better-known models (e.g., perceptron and LVQ), and offers a better understanding of the structural richness of decision-based neural networks. This structure can also be embedded naturally in fuzzy-decision neural networks.

4.6   Problems[3]

Exercise 4.1 (Linear Programming: Simplex Algorithm)
Show that the decision-based learning algorithm can be reformulated in a *linear programming* format.
Comment: In fact, the simplex algorithm is known to be very effective for minimization of any cost function under the given constraints. It has finite convergence in both the linearly separable and linearly nonseparable cases. The algorithm gives a correct solution when the problem is linearly separable, while providing a useful solution even for the linearly nonseparable case. For more details, see [61, chapter 5].

Exercise 4.2 To prove the finite convergence by the optimal learning rate in Eq. 4.7, it must be shown that the total squared error does decrease with each update. Show that

$$\|\mathbf{w}^{(m+1)} - \mathbf{w}^*\|^2 = \|\mathbf{w}^{(m)} - \mathbf{w}^*\|^2 - \frac{(|\mathbf{w}^{*T}\mathbf{z}^{(m)}| + |\mathbf{w}^{(m)^T}\mathbf{z}^{(m)}|)^2}{\|\mathbf{z}^{(m)}\|^2} \qquad (4.42)$$

Exercise 4.3 Assuming that $\mathbf{w}^{(m)}$ is normalized, prove that the normalized perceptron algorithm with the learning rate η_{norm} in Eq. 4.11 can guarantee the total squared error in Eq. 4.6 to decrease.

Exercise 4.4 Two patterns, (1,1) and (4,4), and another two, (2,2) and (3,3), are not linearly separable. Show that they are separable by a valid RBF discriminant function. Find the function by the LVQ method and show each weight update with a small learning step, for example, $\eta = 0.2$. (Set the initial weights to zero.)

Exercise 4.5 Show that the finite convergence of the perceptron learning rule remains valid for an arbitrary learning rate η.

Exercise 4.6 (Energy Function Criterion)
(a) Show that the perceptron criterion minimizes the cost function

$$E_p(\mathbf{w}) = \sum_m (t^{(m)} - d^{(m)})\mathbf{w}^T\mathbf{z}^{(m)}$$

(b) Show that the relaxation method in Equation 4.10 minimizes the cost function

$$E_r = 1/2 \sum |t^{(m)} - d^{(m)}| \frac{(\delta - \mathbf{w}^{(m)^T}\mathbf{z}^{(m)})^2}{\|\mathbf{z}^{(m)}\|^2}$$

---

[3]The basic problems in this chapter are Problems 4.1 to 4.8. The remaining of the problems are more advanced.

Exercise 4.7 (Linear Separability for Random Patterns [61])
Consider a P-dimensional space and N patterns scattered randomly in this space. We assume that any $P+1$ of these patterns will not fall in a $(P-1)$-dimensional subspace (because this would be very coincidental, that is, with probability 0). In that case, we say that the patterns are in **general position**. Assume that these patterns are assigned randomly in either one of two classes, C_1, C_2. Of all the possible 2^N assignments (also called *dichotomies*), a certain fraction $f(N, P)$ is linearly separable. Show that this fraction is given by the formula

$$f(N, P) = \begin{cases} 1 & N \leq P+1 \\ \dfrac{2}{2^N} \displaystyle\sum_{i=0}^{P} \binom{N-1}{i}, & N > P+1 \end{cases} \qquad (4.43)$$

Notice that for $N = P+1$ patterns or less, the fraction is 1. This simply means that the problem is not overdetermined in this case and a single hyperplane can always perform the separation correctly. Even for $N = 2(P+1)$ (sometimes called the *capacity* of the hyperplane), half of the dichotomies are linear. However, in most real applications, the number of samples will be many times larger than the dimensionality.

Exercise 4.8 Use 4 patterns in a 2-dimensional feature space. Show that 7/8 of all the labeling possibilities (into one of the two classes) are linearly separable.

Exercise 4.9 (a) Write down the explicit form of elliptic basis function (EBF) in both the upright and general versions.
(b) Derive the gradient of a Gaussian EBF discriminant function.

Exercise 4.10 It is plausible to modify Eq. 4.27 into

$$d_k(\mathbf{x}; \mathbf{w_k}) = -\phi_k(\mathbf{x}; \mathbf{w_k}) + \{ \frac{1}{M} \sum_j \phi_j(\mathbf{x}; \mathbf{w_j})^{\gamma} \}^{1/\gamma}, \qquad \gamma > 0 \qquad (4.44)$$

(a) Show that, when $\gamma \to \infty$, it will asymptotically approximate Eq. 4.26.
(b) Show the drawback that if Eq. 4.27 or Eq. 4.44 is adopted as the loss function, then all the subnets will be updated upon each training pattern, instead of the key winner and loser only.

Exercise 4.11 Given two classes of patterns with distributions $p_1(x, y)$ and $p_2(x, y)$, as described in Eqns. 4.24 and 4.25, respectively. The key parameters are
(1) $s = 0.1$, $\mu_x = 1.188s$, and $\mu_y = 2.325s$
(2) $s = 0.1$, $\mu_x = 2s$, and $\mu_y = 4s$
(3) $s = 0.1$, $\mu_x = 1$, and $\mu_y = 5s$ Study by simulation the classification results of the RBF DBNN, HiPer(R_s). For each simulation, first generate 1000 patterns for each class as the training set from the distributions. Generate another 1000 patterns for each class as the test set. What are the computer run time and the training and test accuracies? Repeat the same experiment with the EBF DBNN, HiPer(E_s).

Exercise 4.12 (Constant Learning Rate)

In order to derive a constant learning rate, we have to drop the term $|\mathbf{w}^{(m)T}\mathbf{z}^{(m)}|$ from Eq. 4.9. This leads to a very conservative constant learning rate:

$$\hat{\eta} = \frac{\delta}{\bar{N}}$$

where $\bar{N} \equiv \max_m \|\mathbf{z}^{(m)}\|^2$. Without loss of generality, let us assume that $\mathbf{w}^{initial} = 0$ and set $\|\mathbf{w}^*\| = 1$ (i.e., normalized). This problem shows that the number of (nonzero) corrections will be less than

$$\ell = \left\lceil \frac{\bar{N}}{\delta^2} \right\rceil \tag{4.45}$$

(a) Show that if

$$\hat{\eta} = \frac{|\mathbf{w}^{*T}\mathbf{z}^{(m)}| + |\mathbf{w}^{(m)T}\mathbf{z}^{(m)}|}{max\|\mathbf{z}^{(m)}\|^2}$$

then we have

$$\|\mathbf{w}^{(m+1)} - \mathbf{w}^*\|^2 \leq \|\mathbf{w}^{(m)} - \mathbf{w}^*\|^2 - \hat{\eta} max\|\mathbf{z}^{(\mathbf{m})}\|^2$$

It follows that the number of (nonzero) corrections is no more than

$$\ell = \left\lceil \frac{\|\mathbf{w}^{initial} - \mathbf{w}^*\|^2}{\hat{\eta}^2 \max_m \|\mathbf{z}^{(m)}\|^2} \right\rceil \tag{4.46}$$

(b) Substituting Eq. 4.7 into Eq. 4.42, we have

$$\ell = \left\lceil \frac{\bar{N}\|\mathbf{w}^{initial} - \mathbf{w}^*\|^2}{\delta^2} \right\rceil$$

Show that this equation leads to Eq. 4.45.

Exercise 4.13

Continuing Exercise 4.12, suppose that all the training patterns are normalized by preprocessing. (Therefore, $\bar{N} \equiv \max_m \|\mathbf{z}^{(m)}\|^2 = 1$.) Figure 4.22 depicts the possible angles for the feasible solution vector $\mathbf{w}^*$, where $\mathbf{w}_1$ and $\mathbf{w}_2$ are the two extreme solution vectors, separated by the angle θ (i.e., $\mathbf{w}_1^T\mathbf{w}_2 = \cos\theta$). Show that if the constant learning rate is set to $\hat{\eta} = \sin\frac{\theta}{2}$, then

$$l \leq \frac{1}{\sin^2\frac{\theta}{2}}$$

Hints:

1. Suppose both $\mathbf{z}^{(m)}$ and $\mathbf{w}$ are normalized. Moreover, for simplicity and without loss of generality, we assume that for a correct solution $\mathbf{w}^*$, $\mathbf{w}^{*T}\mathbf{z}^{(m)} < 0$ for all m.

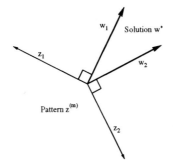

Figure 4.22: The solution region of $\mathbf{w}^*$.

2. Notations: $\mathbf{w}_1^T \mathbf{z}_1 = \mathbf{w}_2^T \mathbf{z}_2 = 0$, and $\mathbf{w}^{*T} \mathbf{w}_1 = \cos \phi$.

3. Show that

$$
\begin{aligned}
\delta &\equiv \min_m |\mathbf{w}^{*T} \mathbf{z}^{(m)}| \\
&= \min(|\mathbf{w}^{*T} \mathbf{z}_1|, |\mathbf{w}^{*T} \mathbf{z}_2|) \\
&= \min\{|\cos(90^\circ + \phi)|, |\cos(90^\circ + \theta - \phi)|\}
\end{aligned}
$$

4. Show that

$$
\begin{aligned}
\max_{\mathbf{w}^*} \delta &= \max_{\mathbf{w}^*} \min\{|\cos(90^\circ + \phi)|, |\cos(90^\circ + \theta - \phi)|\} \\
&= \sin \frac{\theta}{2}
\end{aligned}
$$

5. Finally, there exists a $\mathbf{w}^*$ such that $\delta = \sin\frac{\theta}{2}$ and $l = \frac{\bar{N}}{\delta^2} = \frac{1}{\sin^2 \frac{\theta}{2}}$

Exercise 4.14 This problem discusses a learning rule in which weight vectors are normalized at every step. If η is assumed to be extremely small, the perceptron algorithm can be approximated by the following

$$
\mathbf{w}^{(m+1)} = \mathbf{w}^{(m)} + \eta(t^{(m)} - d^{(m)})(\mathbf{z}^{(m)} - \mathbf{w}^{(m)} y^{(m)}) \tag{4.47}
$$

(A serious drawback of this learning rule is that η has to be extremely small so that we could ignore the higher-order $\mathcal{O}(\eta^2)$ terms.)

(a) Derive Eq. 4.47 by the following procedure, assuming that η is extremely small. Start with a perceptron rule:

$$
\begin{aligned}
\tilde{\mathbf{w}}^{(m+1)} &= \mathbf{w}^{(m)} + \eta(t^{(m)} - d^{(m)})\mathbf{z}^{(m)} \\
\mathbf{w}^{(m+1)} &= \tilde{\mathbf{w}}^{(m+1)} / \|\tilde{\mathbf{w}}^{(m+1)}\|
\end{aligned}
$$

Show that by dropping the $\mathcal{O}(\eta^2)$ terms in Taylor's expansion,

$$1/\|\tilde{\mathbf{w}}^{(m+1)}\| \approx 1 - \eta(t^{(m)} - d^{(m)})y^{(m)}$$

Show that by ignoring the $\mathcal{O}(\eta^2)$ terms, the final form in Eq. 4.47 can be derived.

(b) Show that under the learning rule in Eq. 4.47, the update direction ($\mathbf{z}^{(m)} - \mathbf{w}^{(m)}y^{(m)}$) is always orthogonal to the current weight vector $\mathbf{w}^{(m)}$.

Exercise 4.15 Show that the special case of two classes in the multiple classification linear perceptron in Algorithm 4.2 reduces to a single-output-node perceptron.

Exercise 4.16 A *potential function* is used as the discriminant function

$$\phi(\mathbf{x}, \mathbf{w}) = 1/(1 + \| \mathbf{x} - \mathbf{w} \|^2)$$

Show that the corresponding updating equation is

$$\mathbf{w}^{(m+1)} = \mathbf{w}^{(m)} \pm \eta[\phi(\mathbf{x}, \mathbf{w})]^2(\mathbf{x} - \mathbf{w})$$

Exercise 4.17 Derive the elliptic-LVQ learning formula from Eq. 4.16 in Algorithm 4.3.

Exercise 4.18 Find the number of operations for each training pattern for decision-based networks HiPer(R_s), HiPer(E_s), and HiPer(R_h).

Exercise 4.19 (Dynamic Time Warping Distance)
Given the input and reference sequences: $\mathbf{x} = [1\ 2\ 3\ 3\ 1\ ]$ and $\mathbf{w} = [1\ 1\ 3\ 1\ ]$, as shown in Figure 4.20(b). Calculate the DTW distance of the sequences, provided that the path weights are set to be $[p_1\ p_2\ p_3] = [1\ 1\ 2]$.

Exercise 4.20 With reference to Eq. 4.35, the updating rule for the weights used in the DBNN-DTW is

$$p_k^{m+1} = p_k^m + \eta_m \sum_{q=1, q \in P_k}^{\hat{Q}_{s_i}} (\delta_{s_i, q} - \psi_{s_i})\sigma_{s_i} - \eta_m \sum_{q=1, q \in P_k}^{\hat{Q}_{s_j}} (\delta_{s_j, q} - \psi_{s_j})\sigma_{s_j}$$

where P_k, $k = 1, \cdots, 3$ denote the k_{th} kind of weighting of local movements of the the path chosen. (See Figure 4.21.)

Chapter 5

Approximation/Optimization Neural Networks

5.1 Introduction

Depending on the nature of the teacher's information, there are two approaches to supervised learning. One is based on the correctness of the decision and the other based on the optimization of a training cost criterion. Of the latter, the (least-square-error) approximation-based formulation represents the most important special case. The decision-based and approximation-based formulations differ in their teacher's information and the ways of utilizing it. We will now give a brief comparison of them.

Decision-Based Formulation In a decision-based neural network, the teacher only tells the correctness of the classification for each training pattern. The teacher is a set of symbols, $\mathcal{T} = \{t_i\}$, labeling the correct class for each input pattern. Unlike the approximation formulation, the exact values of teachers are not required. *The objective of the training is to find a set of weights that yields the correct classification.* For comparison, here we recall the updating rule for decision-based networks:

$$\Delta \mathbf{w} \propto \pm \frac{\partial \phi(\mathbf{x}, \mathbf{w})}{\partial \mathbf{w}} \tag{5.1}$$

Approximation-Based Formulation An approximation-based formulation can be viewed as an *approximation/regression* for the trained data set. The training data are given in input/teacher pairs, denoted as $[\mathcal{X}, \mathcal{T}] =$

145

{ $[x_1, t_1], [x_2, t_2], \ldots, [x_M, t_M]$ }, where M is the number of training pairs. The desired values at the output nodes corresponding to the input patterns $x^{(m)}$ are assigned as the teacher's values. *The objective of network training is to find the optimal weights to minimize the error between the teacher value and the actual response.* A popular criterion is the minimum-squares error between the teacher and the actual response. To acquire a more versatile nonlinear approximation capability, multilayer networks (together with the back-propagation learning rule) are usually adopted.

The model function is a function of inputs and of weights: $y = \phi(x, w)$, assuming there is a single output. In the basic approximation-based formulation, the training procedure involves finding the weights to minimize the least-squares-error energy function: $E(x, w) = [t - \phi(x, w)]^2$. The weight vector w can be trained by minimizing the energy function along the gradient-descent direction:

$$\Delta w \propto -\frac{\partial E(x, w)}{\partial w} = (t - \phi(x, w))\frac{\partial \phi(x, w)}{\partial w} \qquad (5.2)$$

In the retrieving phase, the "winner" that wins the recognition is the output node that yields the maximum response to the input pattern.

It is easy to convert a classification problem into an approximation-based formulation. The conversion involves the assignment of teacher values: Let t^d denote the scalar binary teacher values for the decision-based approach; let t^a denote the scalar real teacher values for the approximation-based approach. For example, if $t^d = 1$, then we set $t^a = 1$; and if $t^d = 0$, then $t^a = 0$. Similar conversions can be applied to the multiple-classification problem, assuming N classes to be classified by an N-output network. Now we let t^d and t^a denote a scalar N-ary value and an N-dimensional vector respectively. If $t^d = i$, then we set $t^a = [0, 0, \ldots, 1, \ldots, 0]^T$, that is, a vector with only one nonzero element at the ith position. After the conversion, it is ready to employ the approximation formulation.

To highlight their contrast, the configurations for the decision-based and approximation-based networks are depicted in Figure 5.1. According to Eqns. 5.1 and 5.2, there are some noticeable similarities and differences. Both of them adopt the gradient-based updating rules. (Thus the BP algorithm can be applied to either approach.) As to the difference, the information needed for the decision-based neural net is barely minimum. As long as the correct neuron is known, neither the information on the exact output values nor a specific cost-function criterion will be needed. *Moreover, only the misclassified patterns in each sweep can incur the actual update. Thus, the frequency*

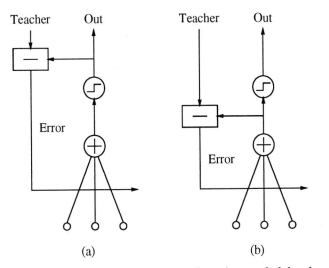

(a)   (b)

Figure 5.1: Difference between perceptron learning and delta learning. (a) For perceptron learning, the teacher is available after the nonlinear unit. Only binary information is provided. (b) For delta learning, the teacher is introduced before the nonlinear unit. Therefore, the exact value of the teacher is a vital reference.

of actual updating will decrease significantly as the network converges closer to the final solution.

On the other hand, approximation/optimization based formulations are very versatile. There are many applications, for example, curve-fitting or signal-restoration problems, for which the decision-based formulation may not be suitable. It can be very beneficial to take advantage of the prior knowledge of the desired output values provided by the teacher. Moreover, the user can exploit the freedom of choosing a proper cost function (energy function) pertaining to the specific application need. Still more, various numerical nonlinear optimization methods are available to facilitate the computations for optimization problems.

Optimization-Based Formulation The approximation and optimization formulations are very intimately related. Relatively, the optimization formulations are appealing to a broader application domain, including signal/image restoration, data compression, noise reduction/removal, and combinatorial optimization. The energy function $E(\mathbf{x}, \mathbf{w})$ must be specifically chosen for the application. Again the weight vector $\mathbf{w}$ can be trained by a gradient-descent updating rule:

$$\Delta \mathbf{w} \propto -\frac{\partial E(\mathbf{x}, \mathbf{w})}{\partial \mathbf{w}} \tag{5.3}$$

For example, the (maximum) likelihood function $Prob(\mathcal{X}|\lambda_i(\mathbf{w}))$ is a popular criteria function for stochastic neural networks. Therefore,

$$\Delta \mathbf{w} \propto \frac{\partial Prob(\mathcal{X}|\lambda_i(\mathbf{w}))}{\partial \mathbf{w}}$$

where $\mathcal{X}$ denotes the training set for the i-th class. In the retrieving phase, the class with $max_j Prob(\lambda_j|x)$ corresponding to the test pattern x will be declared the winner.

Chapter Organization

In Section 5.2, basic linear approximation networks are introduced. Section 5.3 presents the back-propagation algorithm, useful for training any multi-layer network for both approximation and optimization formulations. Convergence of the networks hinges upon the numerical methods used for the BP algorithm. Second-order methods offer favorable numerical performance when compared with first-order alternatives. A prominent example is the (second-order) conjugate-gradient method, which is treated in great detail. Section 5.4 highlights the approximation and generalization theory, while avoiding rigorous mathematical treatment. We also elaborate the radial-basis-function (RBF) approach to the regularization problem. The effect of the network size (i.e., the number of layers and hidden units) on approximation/generalization is discussed. Section 5.5 explores some key application examples of the BP multi-layer networks.

Based on the approximation/optimization formulations, there are *deterministic networks* and *stochastic networks*. They involve very different kinds of energy functions for training the networks. This chapter is devoted mostly to the deterministic networks. Further explorations on the stochastic networks is postponed until Chapter 9.

5.2   Linear Approximation Networks

In this section, linear and nonlinear approximation networks are introduced. Linear networks are easier to analyze, but nonlinear networks are much more useful for practical applications.

5.2.1 Delta Learning Rule: ADALINE

The simplest approximation formulation is one based on the linear least-squares-error criterion. Indeed, one of the pioneering neural models is a linear network, named ADALINE (ADAptive LINear Element), proposed by Widrow [305]. As shown in Figure 5.1(b), ADALINE is a linear single-layer network with a net value

$$y = \sum_{j}^{N_0} w_j x_j + \theta$$

where N_0 is the number of input nodes. Without loss of generality, it is more convenient to regard the threshold θ just as an extra weight, that is, $\theta = w_{N_0+1}$. The net value can be rewritten as

$$y = \mathbf{w}^T \mathbf{z} \tag{5.4}$$

where $\mathbf{w} = [w_1 \ w_2 \ldots w_{N_0} \ \theta]^T$ and $\mathbf{z} = [x_1 \ x_2 \ldots x_{N_0} \ 1]^T$. Note that $\mathbf{z}$ is the augmented pattern $\mathbf{x}$.

Least-Squares-Error Criterion   The weight vector $\mathbf{w}$ can be obtained by minimizing the *least-squares-error* criterion:

$$\text{minimize } E = \frac{1}{2} \sum_{m=1}^{M} (y^{(m)} - t^{(m)})^2$$

The *delta learning rule* adopted in ADALINE is a data-adaptive technique for deriving a least-squares-error solution. It is based on an iterative gradient-descent algorithm. The gradient is defined as the first partial derivative of E_s with respect to $w_j^{(m)}$:

$$\frac{\partial E}{\partial w_j^{(m)}} = -(t^{(m)} - y^{(m)}) z_j^{(m)}$$

In a vector form:

$$\frac{\partial E}{\partial \mathbf{w}^{(m)}} = -(t^{(m)} - y^{(m)}) \mathbf{z}^{(m)}$$

In order to minimize E, the weights should be updated in the direction opposite to that of the gradient, that is,

$$\mathbf{w}^{(m+1)} = \mathbf{w}^{(m)} + \eta(t^{(m)} - y^{(m)}) \mathbf{z}^{(m)}$$

Compare ADALINE and Perceptron   For comparison, the perceptron and delta learning networks are depicted in Figures 5.1(a) and 5.1(b). For the perceptron learning, the teacher is binary-valued (1/0). It is compared with the result of the nonlinear threshold function of y to verify correctness. The decision is used as a feedback in the learning process. In the delta learning rule, the teacher has a real value, and so does the difference $(t-y)$, which is fed back in weight learning. The delta learning rule in ADALINE is formulated as a least-squares-error *approximation* problem. It differs from perceptron training in that the updating amount is now dependent on the exact amount of the output error.

5.2.2   Kaczmarz Projection Method and Learning Rates

Since the model function is linear, $y = \mathbf{w}^T\mathbf{z}$, there exists an iterative projection scheme that allows a simple rule to determine the learning step size. This is known as the Kaczmarz's projection method [42, 268], and it originated from a *row action* scheme used for solving huge and sparse linear systems [42]. The method starts with an initial vector $\mathbf{w}^{(0)}$ and iteratively converges to a final solution vector $\mathbf{w}^*$. In one iteration step, vector $\mathbf{w}^{(m)}$ is refined into a new vector $\mathbf{w}^{(m+1)}$

$$\mathbf{w}^{(m+1)} = \mathbf{w}^{(m)} + \eta(t^{(m)} - \mathbf{z}^{(m)^T}\mathbf{w}^{(m)})\mathbf{z}^{(m)} \tag{5.5}$$

The learning rate η of the projection method is defined as

$$\eta^{(m)} = \frac{\lambda^{(m)}}{\|\mathbf{z}^{(m)}\|^2} = \frac{\lambda}{\sum_{q=1}^{N_0+1}(z_q^{(m)})^2} \tag{5.6}$$

and λ is the relaxation parameter, $0 < \lambda < 2$.

The new vector represents a closer match with respect to the m-th row of the linear system in Eq. 5.4. This can be illustrated by Figure 5.2, which shows a geometric interpretation of the projection method for the case $\lambda = 1$. Given a (N_0+1)-dimensional vector $\mathbf{w}^{(m)}$, then $\mathbf{w}^{(m+1)}$ is the orthogonal projection of $\mathbf{w}^{(m)}$ onto the P-dimensional hyperplane subspace $\mathcal{H}_m$ (see Figure 5.2), where the m-th hyperplane $\mathcal{H}_m$ is defined as

$$\mathcal{H}_m = \{\mathbf{w} \in R^{N_0+1} \mid \, <\mathbf{w}^{(m)}, \mathbf{z}^{(m)}> \, = t^{(m)}\} \tag{5.7}$$

When $\lambda = 1$, the projection method follows a *minimum-perturbation principle*. The exponential convergence behavior of the iterated weight vector

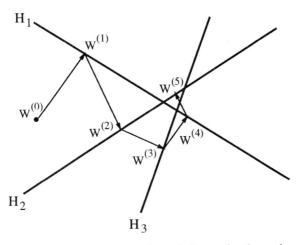

Figure 5.2: The geometric interpretation of the projection scheme for solving a 3×2 linear system. Here the relaxation parameter λ is 1.

$\mathbf{w}^{(m+1)}$ using the projection method is similar to the normalized LMS techniques in adaptive signal processing [31, 131, 304]. Actually, it can be shown [188, 268] that Eq. 5.5 converges to the exact solution when Eq. 5.4 is a consistent linear system. It converges to a minimum-squared-error solution when an inconsistent or singular system is involved. For the former, a consistent (exact) solution $\mathbf{w}^*$ can be obtained for $\mathbf{A}\mathbf{w}^* = \mathbf{t}$, where

$$\mathbf{A} = [\mathbf{z}^{(1)}, \mathbf{z}^{(2)}, \cdots, \mathbf{z}^{(M)}]^T, \quad \text{and} \quad \mathbf{t} = [t^{(1)}, t^{(2)}, \cdots, t^{(M)}]^T$$

Define the *difference variable* $\mathbf{v}^{(m+1)} \equiv \mathbf{w}^* - \mathbf{w}^{(m+1)}$, then

$$
\begin{aligned}
\mathbf{v}^{(m+1)} &= \mathbf{w}^* - \mathbf{w}^{(m+1)} \\
&= \mathbf{w}^* - \mathbf{w}^{(m)} - \lambda \left(t^{(m)} - \mathbf{z}^{(m)^T} \mathbf{w}^{(m)} \right) \frac{\mathbf{z}^{(m)}}{\|\mathbf{z}^{(m)}\|^2} \\
&= \mathbf{v}^{(m)} - \lambda \left(\mathbf{z}^{(m)^T} \mathbf{w}^* - \mathbf{z}^{(m)^T} \mathbf{w}^{(m)} \right) \frac{\mathbf{z}^{(m)}}{|\mathbf{z}^{(m)}|^2} \\
&= \mathbf{v}^{(m)} - \lambda \, \mathbf{z}^{(m)^T} \mathbf{v}^{(m)} \frac{\mathbf{z}^{(m)}}{|\mathbf{z}^{(m)}|^2} \\
&= \left(\mathbf{I} - \lambda \frac{\mathbf{z}^{(m)} \mathbf{z}^{(m)^T}}{\|\mathbf{z}^{(m)}\|^2} \right) \mathbf{v}^{(m)} \quad\quad\quad (5.8)
\end{aligned}
$$

The matrix $\frac{\mathbf{z}^{(m)} \mathbf{z}^{(m)^T}}{\|\mathbf{z}^{(m)}\|^2}$ has one eigenvalue (or singular value) equal to 1 and the other eigenvalues are 0, therefore, the magnitude of $\mathbf{v}^{(m)}$ monotonically decreases if $0 < \lambda < 2$. If there exists no consistent solution, then a minimum-squared-error solution is the best possible alternative, which incurs a residual vector

$$\mathbf{r} = [r^{(1)},\ r^{(2)},\ \cdots,\ r^{(M)}]^T$$

and $\mathbf{A}\mathbf{w}^* + \mathbf{r} = \mathbf{t}$. Now Eq. 5.8 can be rewritten as

$$
\begin{aligned}
\mathbf{v}^{(m+1)} &= \mathbf{w}^* - \mathbf{w}^{(m+1)} \\
&= \mathbf{w}^* - \mathbf{w}^{(m)} - \lambda \left(t^{(m)} - \mathbf{z}^{(m)^T} \mathbf{w}^{(m)} \right) \frac{\mathbf{z}^{(m)}}{|\mathbf{z}^{(m)}|^2} \\
&= \mathbf{v}^{(m)} - \lambda \left(\mathbf{z}^{(m)^T} \mathbf{w}^* - \mathbf{z}^{(m)^T} \mathbf{w}^{(m)} \right) \frac{\mathbf{z}^{(m)}}{|\mathbf{z}^{(m)}|^2} - \lambda\, r^{(m)} \frac{\mathbf{z}^{(m)}}{|\mathbf{z}^{(m)}|^2} \\
&= \mathbf{v}^{(m)} - \lambda\, \mathbf{z}^{(m)^T}\, \mathbf{v}^{(m)} \frac{\mathbf{z}^{(m)}}{|\mathbf{z}^{(m)}|^2} - \lambda\, r^{(m)} \frac{\mathbf{z}^{(m)}}{|\mathbf{z}^{(m)}|^2} \\
&= \left(\mathbf{I} - \lambda\, \frac{\mathbf{z}^{(m)}\mathbf{z}^{(m)^T}}{|\mathbf{z}^{(m)}|^2} \right)\mathbf{v}^{(m)} - \lambda\, r^{(m)} \frac{\mathbf{z}^{(m)}}{|\mathbf{z}^{(m)}|^2} \quad (5.9)
\end{aligned}
$$

The estimation residual (the second term on the right-hand side) prevents the weights from reaching the desired solution $\mathbf{w}^*$. To reduce its effect, a narrower range of λ, $0 < \lambda \leq 1$, is preferred. Moreover, in the final converging stage, λ must be set to be gradually decreasing, for example, inversely proportional to m. For comparison, a more conservative convergence analysis as discussed in Problem 5.4 would yield a slower learning rate.

5.3   Nonlinear Multilayer Back-Propagation Networks

It can be shown that [196] single-layer nets based on linear model functions have very limited classification and approximation capabilities. More precisely,

1. Linear approximation networks are too restrictive and nonlinear approximation networks offer much greater capacity.

2. In order to enhance the approximation capabilities, it is critical to expand a single-layer structure to a multilayer network.

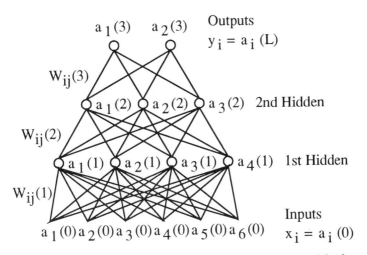

Figure 5.3: The multiple-layer network shown here is a net with three weight layers. The weight layers support linear transformations. The neuron layers perform (local) nonlinear transformations.

The number of nonlinear layers of a multilayer network is defined to be the number of weight layers, instead of neuron layers. For example, the network depicted in Figure 5.3 is called a three-layer network because it has *three* weight layers. In linear systems, there is no real benefit to cascading multiple layers of *linear networks*. The equivalent weight matrix for the total system is simply the product of the weight matrices of different layers.

The situation is quite different if nonlinear *hidden neuron units* are inserted between the input and output layers. In this case, it seems natural to assume that the more layers used, the greater power the network possesses. However, it is not the case in practice. An excessive number of layers often proves to be counterproductive. It may cause slower convergence in the back-propagation learning. Two possible reasons are that the error signals may be numerically degraded when propagating across too many layers and that extra layers tend to create additional local minima. Thus, it is essential to identify the proper number of layers. Generally speaking, two-layer network should be adequate as universal approximators of any nonlinear functions, cf. Theorems 5.1 and 5.2. It was further demonstrated in [174] that a three-layer network suffices to separate any (convex or nonconvex) polyhedral decision region from its background. In summary, two or three layers should be adequate for most applications.

5.3.1   Back-Propagation Algorithm

The back-propagation (BP) algorithm offers an effective approach to the computation of the gradients. This can be applied to any optimization formulation (i.e., any type of energy function) as well as the DBNN formulation introduced in Chapter 4.

A linear basis function (LBF) multilayer network is characterized by the following dynamic equations

$$u_i(l) = \sum_{j=1}^{N_{l-1}} w_{ij}(l)a_j(l-1) + \theta_i(l) \tag{5.10}$$

$$a_i(l) = f(u_i(l)) \quad 1 \le i \le N_l; \quad 1 \le l \le L \tag{5.11}$$

where the input units are represented by $x_i \equiv a_i(0)$, the output units by $y_i \equiv a_i(L)$, and where L is the number of layers. The activation function is very often a *sigmoid function:*

$$f(u_i) = \frac{1}{1 + e^{-u_i/\sigma}}$$

Other dynamic equations are also of possible interest. For example, it is very popular to use Gaussian activation function on radial basis functions (RBF).

The back-propagation algorithm, independently proposed by Werbos [301], Parker [216], and Rumelhart [246], offers an efficient computational speed-up for training multilayer networks. The objective is to train the weights w_{ij} so as to minimize E. The basic gradient-type learning formula is

$$w_{ij}^{(m+1)}(l) = w_{ij}^{(m)}(l) + \Delta w_{ij}^{(m)}(l) \tag{5.12}$$

with the mth training pattern, $\mathbf{a}^{(m)}(0)$, and its corresponding teacher $\mathbf{t}^{(m)}$, $m = 1, 2, \cdots, M$, presented. The derivation of the BP algorithm follows a chain-rule technique:

$$\Delta w_{ij}^{(m)}(l) = -\eta \frac{\partial E}{\partial w_{ij}^{(m)}(l)} \tag{5.13}$$

$$= -\eta \frac{\partial E}{\partial a_i^{(m)}(l)} \frac{\partial a_i^{(m)}(l)}{\partial w_{ij}^{(m)}(l)}$$

$$= \eta \, \delta_i^{(m)}(l) \, f'(u_i^{(m)}(l)) \, a_j^{(m)}(l-1) \tag{5.14}$$

where the error signal $\delta_i^{(m)}(l)$ is defined as

$$\delta_i^{(m)}(l) \equiv -\frac{\partial E}{\partial a_i^{(m)}(l)}$$

Back-Propagation Rule for Approximation-Based Networks   The aforementioned algorithm can be applied to training approximation-based networks. In this case, the objective is to train the weights w_{ij} and the thresholds θ_i, so as to minimize the least-squares-error between the teacher and the actual response [246]. That is,

$$E = \frac{1}{2} \sum_{m=1}^{M} \sum_{i=1}^{N} [t_i^{(m)} - a_i^{(m)}(L)]^2 \tag{5.15}$$

where M is the number of training patterns and N is the dimension of the output space. The back-propagation algorithm can be summarized in two steps:

I. The error signal $\delta_i^{(m)}(l)$ can be obtained recursively by back propagation:

- **Initial (Top) Layer** For the recursion, the initial value (of the top layer), $\delta_i^{(m)}(L)$, can be easily obtained as follows:

$$
\begin{aligned}
\delta_i^{(m)}(L) &\equiv -\frac{\partial E}{\partial a_i^{(m)}(L)} \\
&= t_i^{(m)} - a_i^{(m)}(L) \tag{5.16}
\end{aligned}
$$

For an energy function other than the LSE, the initial condition can be similarly derived.

- **Recursive Formula** The general BP recursive formula for the error signal $\delta_i^{(m)}(l)$ can be derived as follows:

$$
\begin{aligned}
\delta_i^{(m)}(l) &\equiv -\frac{\partial E}{\partial a_i^{(m)}(l)} \\
&= -\sum_{j=1}^{N_{l+1}} \frac{\partial E}{\partial u_j^{(m)}(l+1)} \frac{\partial u_j^{(m)}(l+1)}{\partial a_i^{(m)}(l)}
\end{aligned}
$$

$$\tag{5.17}$$

in the sequence of $l = L - 1, \ldots, 1$.

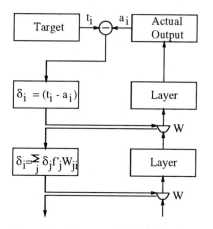

Figure 5.4: The schematic diagram for the back-propagation process.

From Eq. 5.11, it follows that

$$\delta_i^{(m)}(l) = \sum_{j=1}^{N_{l+1}} \delta_j^{(m)}(l+1) \, f'(u_j^{(m)}(l+1)) \, w_{ji}^{(m)}(l+1) \quad (5.18)$$

II. Based on Equations 5.12 and 5.14, the synaptic weights between the (lth and ($l-1$)th) layers can be updated recursively (in order of $l = L, L-1, \ldots, 1$)

$$w_{ij}^{(m+1)}(l) = w_{ij}^{(m)}(l) + \eta \delta_i^{(m)}(l) \, f'(u_i^{(m)}(l)) \, a_j^{(m)}(l-1) \qquad (5.19)$$

The recursive formula is the key to back-propagation learning. It allows the error signal of a lower layer $\delta_j^{(m)}(l)$ to be computed as a linear combination of the error signal of the upper layer $\delta_j^{(m)}(l+1)$. In this manner, the error signals $\delta_j^{(m)}(\cdot)$ are back propagated through all the layers from the top down. This also implies that the influences from an upper layer to a lower layer (and vice versa) can only be effected via the error signals of the intermediate layer.

5.3.2   Numerical Back-Propagation Methods

The goal of training is to minimize the sum-of-squares-error energy function

$$E = \sum_{m=1}^{M} E^{(m)} \qquad (5.20)$$

where

$$E^{(m)} = \frac{1}{2} \sum_{i=1}^{N_L} \left\{ t_i^{(m)} - y_i^{(m)} \right\}^2 \tag{5.21}$$

We need to define *iterations* and *sweeps*. An *iteration* involves a single training datum to the system. A *sweep* covers the presentation of an entire block of training data. In most training practices, multiple sweeps are used and the training patterns are repeatedly presented in a cyclic manner. Assume for convenience that the number of input units, the number of hidden units, and the number of output units are all equal to N. For the two-layer case, the conventional gradient-descent BP requires $\mathcal{O}(5N^2)$ per iteration. For three-layer networks, the conventional BP method requires $\mathcal{O}(7N^2)$ operations per iteration. See Problems 5.5 and 5.6.

The approximation formulation can be viewed as a numerical optimization problem. The numerical method adopted has a direct effect on the performance of the BP algorithm. The rich literature on the study of numerical methods for optimization should be fully explored and utilized [182]. The numerical performance of the BP method depends on the following key factors.

- **Frequency of Update: Data-Adaptive vs. Block-Adaptive:** The choice is between block-adaptive methods (one update per block) and data-adaptive methods (one update per datum). The data-adaptive methods update the weights at each iteration, as opposed to the block methods, which execute the update upon the completion of each sweep. The back-propagation learning algorithm can be executed in either mode. The two approaches have exhibited significantly different numerical performances. Block-adaptive methods are known to be more robust since the training step is averaged over all the training patterns. In contrast, data-adaptive methods can be appealing for some on-line adaptation applications. They are more sensitive to the noise effect on individual patterns. Block methods are recommended for applications where real-time learning is not necessary.

- **Direction of Update: First-Order vs. Second-Order:** For both the first-order and second-order methods, the BP algorithm's sole role is as an effective tool for computing the gradients. Second-order gradients are numerically sensitive to compute. Therefore, data-adaptive methods are usually based on first-order gradients. Block-adaptive methods

– being numerically more robust – often adopt a second-order technique. The second-order methods in general deliver superior numerical performance, although such a comparison is neither conclusive nor universally valid.

5.3.2.1   Data-Adaptive Methods

Without loss of generality, let us focus on a single-output neural network with the model function $\phi(\mathbf{x}, \mathbf{w})$. The output response for each pattern $\mathbf{x}^{(m)}$ is denoted by

$$y^{(m)} = \phi(\mathbf{x}^{(m)}, \mathbf{w}^{(m)})$$

We assume that there are M pairs of input and target training patterns $\{\mathbf{x}^{(m)}, \, \mathbf{t}^{(m)}\}$. The mth input training pattern is denoted $\mathbf{x}^{(m)} = [x_1^{(m)}, \, x_2^{(m)}, \, \ldots, \, x_{N_0}^{(m)}]^T$, where N_0 denotes the number of input dimensions. The least-squares-error criterion in Eq. 5.21 then becomes

$$E^{(m)} \quad = \quad \frac{1}{2}\left(t^{(m)} - \phi(\mathbf{x}^{(m)}, \mathbf{w}^{(m)})\right)^2 \tag{5.22}$$

For data-adaptive updating, it is natural to adopt the (first-order) gradient-descent direction. The weights change from the present point toward the direction of the local basin of the energy function.

$$
\begin{aligned}
\Delta \mathbf{w}^{(m)} \quad &= \quad -\eta \frac{\partial E}{\partial w^{(m)}} \\
&\equiv \quad -\eta E_w'^{(m)} \\
&= \quad \eta\left(t^{(m)} - \phi(\mathbf{x}^{(m)}, \mathbf{w}^{(m)})\right)\phi_w'(\mathbf{x}^{(m)}, \mathbf{w}^{(m)}) \tag{5.23}
\end{aligned}
$$

Moreover, by a first-order Taylor series expansion around $\mathbf{w}^{(m)}$,

$$\phi(\mathbf{x}^{(m)}, \mathbf{w}^{(m+1)}) \approx \phi(\mathbf{x}^{(m)}, \mathbf{w}^{(m)}) + \{\phi_w'(\mathbf{x}^{(m)}, \mathbf{w}^{(m)})\}^T \Delta \mathbf{w}^{(m)}$$

which is expected to closely approach the teacher value $t^{(m)}$, that is

$$t^{(m)} \approx \phi(\mathbf{x}^{(m)}, \mathbf{w}^{(m)}) + \{\phi_w'(\mathbf{x}^{(m)}, \mathbf{w}^{(m)})\}^T \Delta \mathbf{w}^{(m)}$$

Substituting Eq. 5.23 into this equation yields

$$t^{(m)} - \phi(\mathbf{x}^{(m)}, \mathbf{w}^{(m)}) \approx \eta^{(m)}\left(t^{(m)} - \phi(\mathbf{x}^{(m)}, \mathbf{w}^{(m)})\right)\|\phi_w'(\mathbf{x}^{(m)}, \mathbf{w}^{(m)})\|^2$$

which, in turn, leads to the following estimate of an (idealistic) learning rate

$$\eta^{(m)} = \frac{1}{\|\phi'_w(\mathbf{x}^{(m)}, \mathbf{w}^{(m)})\|^2}$$

Practically speaking, however, the rate must be further scaled down by another factor λ:

$$\eta^{(m)} = \frac{\lambda}{\|\phi'_w(\mathbf{x}^{(m)}, \mathbf{w}^{(m)})\|^2}$$

The choice of scaling factor λ depends on the model function chosen.

The conventional wisdom is to keep η very small so as to assure eventual convergence. Convergence speed is of only secondary consideration. Notwithstanding, there have been several conjectures on the choice of the learning rate η. It can be chosen to decrease in proportion to $1/N_0$ (based on a fan-in argument [227]), or even faster than $1/N_0$ (based on the empirical case studies in [97, 273]). Such conjectures are consistent with the learning rate in Eq. 5.24, derived specifically for models with linear basis function and sigmoid activation function:

$$\phi(\mathbf{x}, \mathbf{w}) = \frac{1}{1 + e^{-\mathbf{w}^T \mathbf{z}}}$$

It follows that

$$\phi'_w(\mathbf{w}^T \mathbf{z}) = \phi'_u(u)\mathbf{z}$$

where $u = \mathbf{w}^T \mathbf{z}$. Therefore, the learning rate formula (setting $\lambda = 1$) becomes

$$\eta^{(m)} = \frac{1}{(\phi'_u(u))^2 \|\mathbf{z}^{(m)}\|^2}$$

The learning rate can be estimated by taking the *expectation value* of η. If each $\{z_i^{(m)}\}$ is treated as a random variable with equal probability of being 0 or 1, then the expectation

$$\mathbf{E}\{\|\mathbf{z}^{(m)}\|^2\} = (N_0 + 1)\,\mathbf{E}\{(z_i^{(m)})^2\} = \frac{N_0 + 1}{2} \approx \frac{N_0}{2}$$

Assume further that $\phi(u)$ is uniformly distributed between 0 and 1, the expectation value of $\phi'_u(u)$ is approximately $\frac{1}{6}$. The estimated learning rate is

$$\bar{\eta} = \mathbf{E}\{\eta\} = \mathbf{E}\{\phi'_u\}^{-2}\,\mathbf{E}\{\|\mathbf{z}\|^{-2}\} \approx \frac{72}{N_0} \tag{5.24}$$

This learning rate results in rapid training in the simulations reported in [162].

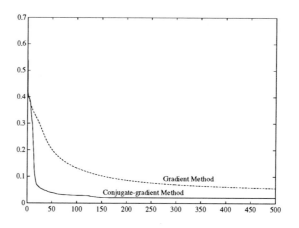

Figure 5.5: Comparison of the (first-order) gradient and (second-order) conjugate-gradient methods in terms of the sweeps needed for convergence. In this simulation, a two-layer (5-5-5) network is used for classifying five Gaussian clusters. For both methods, the line-search technique is applied to find the best learning rates.

5.3.2.2   Block-Adaptive Methods

The first-order data-adaptive gradient methods do not in general yield consistently robust numerical performance. It is therefore desirable to seek other alternatives, such as second-order or block-adaptive methods. The block-adaptive method updates the weights after the entire block of training data is presented. In general, data-adaptive methods are more aggressive and block-adaptive methods tend to be more prudent. A prominent second-order method is the conjugate-gradient technique, whose numerical superiority over the first-order gradient method is exemplified by their convergence speeds depicted in Figure 5.5. When there is no need for real-time training, the block-adaptive methods are preferred since they alleviate some sensitivity problems. In addition, they offer significant improvement in terms of parallel and pipelined computation. (The parallel computational aspects will be explored further in Chapter 10.)

For the block-adaptive method, the energy function becomes

$$E = \frac{1}{2} \sum_{m=1}^{M} \sum_{i=1}^{N_L} \left\{ t_i^{(m)} - y_i^{(m)} \right\}^2 \tag{5.25}$$

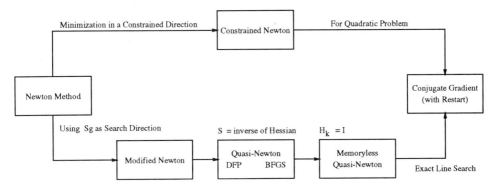

Figure 5.6: Relationships between some second-order methods.

where N_L is the number of output nodes, and M is the block size, that is, the number of training data in one block. The first-order (block) gradient method is a modified version of Eq. 5.13:

$$\Delta \tilde{w} = -\eta \sum_{m=1}^{M} E'_{\tilde{w}}{}^{(m)} \qquad (5.26)$$

For convenience, we use a (long) vector $\tilde{w}$ to denote the set of all weights in all layers.

The effectiveness of any learning algorithm lies in the selection of an optimal update direction. The direction of update depends on whether a first-order or second-order gradient method is adopted. In block-adaptive methods, it could be useful to involve a second-order or momentum term in determining the direction of update. It often involves a direct or indirect computation of the Hessian matrix and its subsequent inversion. Simulation and other numerical studies suggest that the second-order update direction seems to be more effective than its first-order counterpart. In the following, major second-order techniques are introduced and their relationships highlighted.

There exists an intimate relationship among all the second-order methods shown in Figure 5.6. It also provides a natural organization for our discussion of the subject. First, following the upper path, we introduce the Newton method, the constrained Newton method, and the conjugate-gradient method. Next, we follow the lower path and introduce the modified Newton method, the quasi-Newton method, and the memoryless Newton method. In our **notation**, $E'_{\tilde{w}}$ denotes the *gradient vector* and $E''_{\tilde{w}}$ the Hessian matrix.

Newton Method

The Newton method is based on minimizing the energy function $E(\mathbf{w})$ given in Eq. 5.27:

$$E(k+1) = E(k) + E_{\tilde{w}}'(k)^T \Delta \tilde{\mathbf{w}}_k + \frac{1}{2} \Delta \tilde{\mathbf{w}}_k^T E_{\tilde{w}}''(k) \Delta \tilde{\mathbf{w}}_k \qquad (5.27)$$

A heuristic optimal condition (i.e., one that minimizes E) is to choose Δw so that $\frac{\partial E(k+1)}{\partial \Delta w} = 0$. It follows that

$$E_{\tilde{w}}'(k) + E_{\tilde{w}}''(k) \Delta \tilde{\mathbf{w}}_k = 0$$

from which we obtain

$$\Delta \tilde{\mathbf{w}}_k = -[E_{\tilde{w}}''(k)]^{-1} E_{\tilde{w}}'(k)$$

It is common practice to incorporate a small positive learning rate η_k into this equation, leading to the so-called Newton method:

$$\Delta \tilde{\mathbf{w}}_k = -\eta_k [E_{\tilde{w}}''(k)]^{-1} E_{\tilde{w}}'(k) \qquad (5.28)$$

Constrained Newton Method

The derivation of the Newton method can be extended to derive the conjugate-gradient method. The problem is to minimize the Eq. 5.27, given that

$$\Delta \tilde{\mathbf{w}}_k = \eta_k \mathbf{d}_k \qquad (5.29)$$

where

$$\mathbf{d}_k = -E_{\tilde{w}}'(k) + \beta_{k-1} \mathbf{d}_{k-1}$$

In other words, the weight-update direction is a linear combination of the current gradient and the previous update direction.

By substituting Eq. 5.29 into Eq. 5.27 and setting the derivatives with respect to η and β to zero, we can determine the optimal parameters that minimize $E(k+1)$:

$$\eta_k = -\frac{E_{\tilde{w}}'(k)^T \mathbf{d}_k}{\mathbf{d}_k^T E_{\tilde{w}}''(k) \mathbf{d}_k} \qquad (5.30)$$

$$\beta_k = \frac{N(k)}{D(k)} \qquad (5.31)$$

where

$$
\begin{aligned}
N(k) &= (E'_{\tilde{w}}(k+1)^T E'_{\tilde{w}}(k+1))(E'_{\tilde{w}}(k+1)^T E''_{\tilde{w}}(k+1)\mathbf{d}_k) \\
&\quad -(\mathbf{d}_k^T E'_{\tilde{w}}(k+1))(E'_{\tilde{w}}(k+1)^T E''_{\tilde{w}}(k+1)E'_{\tilde{w}}(k+1)) \\
D(k) &= (E'_{\tilde{w}}(k+1)^T E'_{\tilde{w}}(k+1))(\mathbf{d}_k^T E''_{\tilde{w}}(k+1)\mathbf{d}_k) \\
&\quad -(\mathbf{d}_k^T E'_{\tilde{w}}(k+1))(E'_{\tilde{w}}(k+1)^T E''_{\tilde{w}}(k+1)\mathbf{d}_k)
\end{aligned}
$$

Conjugate-Gradient Methods

The conjugate-gradient (CG) algorithm [182, 229] has become very popular for training BP networks. Just like all the second-order methods, the CG algorithm is implemented as a block-adaptive method. The CG algorithm can search the minimum of a multivariate function faster than the (conventional) gradient-descent procedure for BP networks. Each conjugate-gradient step is at least as good as the steepest-descent method from the same point. The formula is simple and the memory usage is on the same order as the number of weights. Most important, the CG technique obviates the tedious tasks of determining optimal learning parameters [229]. Moreover, the CG technique has a very reliable convergence behavior as compared with the (first-order) gradient method, cf. Figure 5.5.

When the problem is quadratic (i.e., $E(k) = w^T E''_{\tilde{w}} w - w^T b$), the constrained Newton method can be reduced to the conjugate-gradient method. In this case, it is critical to exploit the following orthogonality between $E'_{\tilde{w}}(k)$ and $\mathbf{d}_{k-1}$:

$$
\begin{aligned}
\mathbf{d}_k^T E'_{\tilde{w}}(k+1) &= \mathbf{d}_k^T (E''_{\tilde{w}} \tilde{w}_{k+1} - b) \\
&= \mathbf{d}_k^T E'_{\tilde{w}}(k) + \eta \mathbf{d}_k^T E''_{\tilde{w}} \mathbf{d}_k \\
&= 0
\end{aligned}
$$

By this orthogonality, Eq. 5.31 can be simplified to

$$
\beta_{k-1} = \frac{E'_{\tilde{w}}(k)^T E''_{\tilde{w}}(k)\mathbf{d}_{k-1}}{\mathbf{d}_{k-1}^T E''_{\tilde{w}}(k)\mathbf{d}_{k-1}} \tag{5.32}
$$

Further, it can be proved that

$$
\beta_{k-1} = \frac{E'_{\tilde{w}}(k)^T E'_{\tilde{w}}(k)}{E'_{\tilde{w}}(k-1)^T E'_{\tilde{w}}(k-1)} \tag{5.33}
$$

which is used in the following conjugate-gradient procedure.

Conjugate-Gradient Procedure   Start from any initial point $\tilde{w}_0$ and compute $d_0 = -E'_{\tilde{w}}(0)$. The conjugate-gradient algorithm begins with $k = 1$ and for each increment of k performs the following:

1. **Compute** $E'_{\tilde{w}}(k)$.

2. **Update direction vector d:**

$$d_k = -E'_{\tilde{w}}(k) + \beta_{k-1}d_{k-1}$$

where β_{k-1} can be computed by one of the following:

(a)

$$\beta_{k-1} = \frac{E'_{\tilde{w}}(k)^T E'_{\tilde{w}}(k)}{E'_{\tilde{w}}(k-1)^T E'_{\tilde{w}}(k-1)}$$

If this is adopted, a restart will be required.

(b) *In order to avoid restart, the following can be adopted instead:*

$$\beta_{k-1} = E'^T_{\tilde{w}_k}(E'_{\tilde{w}_k} - E'_{\tilde{w}_{k-1}})/\|E'_{\tilde{w}_{k-1}}\|^2 \qquad (5.34)$$

which is equivalent to Eq. 5.33 when the problem is quadratic.

3. **Update the $\tilde{w}$ vector:**

$$\tilde{w}_{k+1} = \tilde{w}_k + \eta_k d_k$$

A line-search algorithm is used to find η_k [182]. Under the ideal quadratic cost function, the line search yields

$$\eta_k = \frac{E'_{\tilde{w}}(k)^T E'_{\tilde{w}}(k)}{d_k^T E''_{\tilde{w}}(k)d_k}$$

In the conjugate-gradient method, Eq. 5.33 is used to find β_{k-1} and a line-search algorithm is used to find η_k [182]. Therefore, the explicit computation of the Hessian matrix $E''_{\tilde{w}}(k)$ can be avoided.

A Remark on Restart Powell observed that if a search direction $\mathbf{d}_k$ is almost orthogonal to the steepest-descent direction $-E_{\tilde{w}}'(k)$, then the β formula in Eq. 5.33 will not produce an effective search direction. This is explained in what follows. Define θ_k to be the angle between $\mathbf{d}_k$ and $-E_{\tilde{w}_k}'$. Then from the definition of $\mathbf{d}_k$, we have

$$\|\mathbf{d}_k\| = \sec\theta\|E_{\tilde{w}_k}'\| \tag{5.35}$$

If the index is increased by 1, we can get

$$\beta_{k+1}\|\mathbf{d}_k\| = \tan\theta_{k+1}\|E_{\tilde{w}_{k+1}}'\| \tag{5.36}$$

Using the previous two equations and the definition in Eq. 5.33, we can eliminate $\|\mathbf{d}_k\|$ and get

$$\tan\theta_{k+1} = \sec\theta_k\|E_{\tilde{w}_{k+1}}'\|/\|E_{\tilde{w}_k}'\| > \tan\theta_k\|E_{\tilde{w}_{k+1}}'\|/\|E_{\tilde{w}_k}'\|$$

If θ_k is already close to $\pi/2$, this iteration brings about only a small change between ($\|E_{\tilde{w}_{k+1}}'\|$ and $\|E_{\tilde{w}_k}'\|$). As a result, the ratio $\|E_{\tilde{w}_{k+1}}'\|/\|E_{\tilde{w}_k}'\|$ is close to 1, and θ_{k+1} is close to $\pi/2$. This represents a very slow progress, which will recur in the subsequent iterations. *Thus, a restart of the algorithm is necessary in order to speed up convergence.*

However, if β_{k-1} in Eq. 5.34 is used instead, such an undesirable updating direction will not be chosen, and the restart will no longer be necessary. This can be explained briefly. Now we have $\beta_{k+1} \leq \|E_{\tilde{w}_k}'\|\cdot\|E_{\tilde{w}_k}' - E_{\tilde{w}_{k-1}}'\|/\|E_{\tilde{w}_k}'\|^2$. This inequality, combined with Eq. 5.35 and Eq. 5.36, yields the following

$$\tan\theta_{k+1} \leq \sec\theta_k\|E_{\tilde{w}_{k+1}}' - E_{\tilde{w}_k}'\|/\|E_{\tilde{w}_k}'\|$$

Therefore, if θ_k is close to $\pi/2$ and the change $\|E_{\tilde{w}_{k+1}}'\| - \|E_{\tilde{w}_k}'\|$ is small, then $\tan\theta_{k+1}$ will become much smaller than $\sec\theta_k$. Thus, the search direction is tilted more toward the steepest-descent direction. Very favorable simulation results are reported by Powell [229].

Modified Newton Method

A major numerical difficulty associated with the Newton method lies in the computation of the Hessian matrix $E_{\tilde{w}}''(k)$. It is numerically sensitive to compute the second-order derivative (Hessian matrix) and its subsequent inversion. Several modified Newton methods have been developed, in which approximate iterations are used instead of the actual inversion of the Hessian matrix. The simplest is the so-called modified Newton method, which can be derived by substituting the inverse of Hessian matrix $E_{\tilde{w}}''(k)^{-1}$ in Eq. 5.28 by a matrix S_k.

$$\Delta \tilde{\mathbf{w}}_k = -\eta_k S_k E_{\tilde{w}}'(k)$$

where matrix S_k can be computed by an iterative formula. A special case sets $S_k = I$ and results in the ordinary gradient method. Several other examples, such as the quasi-Newton method and the memoryless quasi-Newton method, are discussed in what follows.

Quasi-Newton Method

Two key examples of quasi-Newton methods are the Davison-Fletcher-Powell (DFP) method and the Broyden-Fletcher-Goldfarb-Shannon (BFGS) method. Numerical experiments have indicated that the BFGS method, in general, performs better than the DFP method. We focus the following discussion on the BFGS method. Motivated by the (approximate) equality that $E_{\tilde{w}}'' \Delta \mathbf{w} = \Delta E_{\tilde{w}}'$, the updating formula for the BFGS method is based on the following:

$$H_{k+1}\mathbf{p}_i = \mathbf{q}_i, \quad 0 \le i \le k \tag{5.37}$$

where

$$\mathbf{p}_k = \Delta \mathbf{w}_k = \mathbf{w}_{k+1} - \mathbf{w}_k$$

and

$$\mathbf{q}_k = \Delta E_{\tilde{w}_k}' = E_{\tilde{w}_{k+1}}' - E_{\tilde{w}_k}'$$

Matrix H_{k+1} is an approximation of the Hessian matrix and is iteratively computed as

$$H_{k+1} = H_k + \frac{\mathbf{q}_k \mathbf{q}_k^T}{\mathbf{q}_k^T \mathbf{p}_k} - \frac{H_k \mathbf{p}_k \mathbf{p}_k^T H_k}{\mathbf{p}_k^T H_k \mathbf{p}_k} \tag{5.38}$$

It can be shown by induction that H_{k+1} indeed satisfies Eq. 5.37, given that H_k is a good approximation of the Hessian matrix.

Then by the matrix-inversion formula, the inverse of the Hessian matrix (denoted S_{k+1}) can also be iteratively computed:

$$S_{k+1} = S_k + \frac{1 + \mathbf{q}_k^T S_k \mathbf{q}_k}{\mathbf{q}_k^T \mathbf{p}_k} \frac{\mathbf{p}_k \mathbf{p}_k^T}{\mathbf{p}_k^T \mathbf{q}_k} - \frac{\mathbf{p}_k \mathbf{q}_k^T S_k + S_k \mathbf{q}_k \mathbf{p}_k^T}{\mathbf{q}_k^T \mathbf{p}_k} \tag{5.39}$$

Memoryless Quasi-Newton Method

A special version of the BFGS quasi-Newton method can be obtained by setting the previous approximation of the inverse Hessian matrix to the identity matrix $(S_k = I)$. In each iteration, search direction $\mathbf{d}_k$ is set to $-S_k E'_{\hat{w}_k}$ and line search is used to minimize $f(\mathbf{w}_k + \eta_k \mathbf{d}_k)$. It can be shown that if the line search were exact, the method coincides with the conjugate-gradient method. The storage required is the same as that in the conjugate-gradient method. However, when the line search is not exact, the memoryless quasi-Newton approach is preferred [182].

5.4   Training Versus Generalization Performances

The distinction between *training* and *generalization* accuracies lies in the test patterns adopted. For *training accuracy*, the test patterns are simply samples drawn from the original training patterns, namely *memorization*. For *generalization accuracy*, in contrast, the test patterns are not necessarily from the original training patterns. Instead, they are drawn arbitrarily based on the same distribution function that originally generated the training patterns. This distinction leads to different training criteria and strategies. Although high training accuracy guarantees good memorization capability, it does not necessarily yield good generalization accuracy.

1. **Training Accuracy** Good training accuracy can be achieved by forming very complex decision boundaries, which in turn requires a large network size. The approximation theorems in Section 5.4.1 confirm the universal approximation capability by two-layer networks. The theorems are of theoretical interest only, because they cannot predict the number of hidden units required for a given desired accuracy. An insufficient number of hidden units may result in an inadequate capability to separate the categories.

2. **Generalization Accuracy** Generalization accuracy offers a more critical criterion for the determination of the number of hidden units. When too many hidden units are used, it may lead to spurious decision boundaries or cause overfitting of the model and poor interpolation [56]. In other words, if one pushes too hard on the training accuracy, the *overtraining* may result in degraded generalization. This suggests a fundamental tradeoff between training and generalization accuracies, which

will be elaborated in Section 5.4.2. A reduced number of hidden nodes (or subclusters) may improve generalization accuracy at the expense of training accuracy. So does incorporation of some tolerance on errors of the training data, for example, noise, shift, and warping. (For examples, see Section 4.4.) Yet another alternative is via the regularization formulation, which ensures a graceful curve fitting of the training samples. This subject is discussed in Section 5.4.3.

To prevent overtraining, an important controlling parameter is the number of hidden units of the multilayer network, which dictates the network's discriminating capability. Pruning and growing methods may be used to adaptively adjust the number of hidden units. This will be discussed in Section 5.4.4.

5.4.1 Approximation Analysis and Training Performance

There are *nonparameterized* and *parameterized* approaches to the approximation problem. The *nonparameterized* approach involves more than just training the parameters in a fixed function. It involves finding the best function ϕ to minimize a cost function $H[\phi]$. Both the function type and the parameters of the optimal ϕ are to be determined. A typical example of the *nonparameterized* approach is the so-called regularization problem in Section 5.4.3. In contrast, the *parameterized* approach is relatively simple: The activation function, net function, and net topology are all predetermined. This implies that the *model function* $\phi(\mathbf{x}, \mathbf{w})$ is fixed beforehand, leaving only the weights to be adapted to best match the teacher values. Because a *finite* number of parameters are allowed to curve fit the training patterns, a certain degree of smoothness is assured. A typical example of the *parameterized* approach is the back-propagation multilayer network.

For the time being, we focus our approximation analysis on the single-output case. However, it can be easily extended to the multiple-output case. The nonlinearity of the network is attributed to (1) *nonlinear activation function* and/or (2) *nonlinear basis function*. Let us consider a two-layer network in Figure 5.7, whose output can be expressed as

$$y = \phi(\mathbf{x}, \mathbf{w}) = \sum_{i=1}^{K} c_i f(u(\mathbf{x}_i, \mathbf{w}_i))$$

where $\mathbf{w}_i = [w_{i1}, w_{i2}, \cdots, w_{iN}]^T$. The *net function* (or *basis function*) $u(\mathbf{x}_i, \mathbf{w}_i)$ can be either a linear basis function $u = \sum_{j=1}^{n} w_{ij} x_j + \theta_i$ or a radial basis

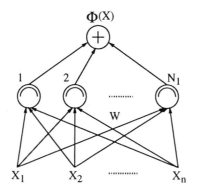

Figure 5.7: A two-layer network for nonlinear approximation. In some application, a constant threshold may be implicitly incorporated into the output node.

function $u = \sum_j^n (x_j - w_{ij})^2$. The neuron function $f(\cdot)$ can be sigmoidal, Gaussian, or others.

Linear-Basis Functions (LBF)

Many neural models, such as perceptron, ADALINE, and back-propagation networks, are based on *linear-basis functions* (LBFs) which have the form $f(\sum_j w_{ij}x_j + \theta_i)$. *The LBF is popular due to its numerical simplicity, which facilitates the implementation of the back-propagation method.* A critical disadvantage associated with the LBF is that it creates a global separating hyperplane function. In other words, it is not inherently effective for forming local clusters. If the training patterns are from a distribution based on one or more local clusters, then the LBF is as appealing as the radial basis function.

Cybenko [57] and Funahashi [76] have provided a useful approximation theorem showing that any input-output mapping can be approximately realized by a two-layer network with a linear-basis function.

Theorem 5.1 (Approximation by Linear-Basis Function (LBF))
Let $f(x)$ be any nonconstant, bounded, and monotonously increasing real continuous function. (The sigmoid function satisfies this condition.) Let S be a compact subset (bounded closed subset) in R^n and $t(\mathbf{x})$ be a continuous target function on S. Then for any $\epsilon > 0$, there exists an integer K and real parameters c_i, w_{ij}, θ_i such that

$$\phi(\mathbf{x}, \mathbf{w}) = \sum_{i=1}^{K} c_i f(\sum_{j=1}^{n} w_{ij} x_j + \theta_i)$$

satisfies $|\phi(\mathbf{x}, \mathbf{w}) - t(\mathbf{x})| < \epsilon$ *for all* $\mathbf{x} \in S$. ∎

Radial-Basis Functions (RBF)

For many applications, a radial-basis function $\sum_{j}^{n}(x_j - w_{ij})^2$ is very amenable to the locality nature of the feature patterns. The Gaussian function can be used as the activation function of RBF. This is denoted

$$g(\sum_{j}^{n}(x_j - w_{ij})^2)$$

In other words, the Gaussian function is an exponential function of the square of radius r:

$$g(r^2) = ce^{-r^2/\sigma^2}$$

It is less effective to apply the fast back-propagation algorithm to the RBF than it is to the LBF. However, the local clustering power of RBF offers great classification and/or approximation capabilities. Just as in sigmoid LBF networks, the Gaussian RBF network is a good function approximator.

Theorem 5.2 (Approximation by Radial-Basis Function (RBF))
Let S be a compact subset (bounded closed subset) in R^n and $t(\mathbf{x})$ be a continuous target function on S. Then for any $\epsilon > 0$, there exists K centroids $\mathbf{o}_i = [w_{i1}, w_{i2}, \cdots, w_{in}]$, and K constants c_i such that

$$\phi(\mathbf{x}, \mathbf{w}) = \sum_{i=1}^{K} c_i g(\sum_{j=1}^{n}(x_j - w_{ij})^2)$$

satisfies $|\phi(\mathbf{x}, \mathbf{w}) - t(\mathbf{x})| < \epsilon$ *for all* $\mathbf{x} \in S$. ∎

The RBF approximation theorem can be derived immediately from the classic Stone-Weierstrass theorem [54]. The detail is left as an exercise, cf. Problem 5.13. As reported in [180], it is also an immediate corollary of the Wiener approximation theory, cf. [2]. From a theoretical estimation perspective, it is closely related to Parzen's approximation theory [219]. Still more, it can also be rederived via a regularization formulation [228]. (See Section 5.4.3 and Problem 5.19.)

In summary, Theorems 5.1 and 5.2 confirm the universal approximation capability by these types of LBF or RBF two-layer networks. However, despite their theoretical success, they do not shed much light on how the networks can be effectively trained or used. The weakness lies in that they cannot determine the number of hidden units required for a desired accuracy.

As for the sigmoid LBF approximation, a technique proposed in [40] suggests explicit methods for constructing two-layer nets using the Radon transform. In [22], a theoretical bound on the approximation error is derived. Assume that the teacher function $t(x)$ has a Fourier transform $\tilde{t}(\omega)$ that satisfies the condition $\int |\tilde{t}(\omega)||\omega| d\omega \leq c$ for some positive constant c. Then the superposition of sigmoid functions can theoretically achieve an integrated squared error of order $\mathcal{O}(c/K)$, where K is the number of hidden units. Similar results can be obtained for the Gaussian RBF approximation. In Section 5.4.3, we look into the role of the Gaussian RBF network from the regularization perspective. Additionally, in Section 5.4.4, this subject is studied from the perspective of network growing techniques (i.e., gradually expanding the hidden layer) and network pruning techniques (i.e., gradually shrinking the hidden layer). The common objective of pruning and growing techniques is to control the number of hidden nodes so that the optimal approximation/generalization accuracy is delivered. The criterion for pruning is such that it does the least damage on the approximation accuracy, while the criterion for growing is such that it best enhances the accuracy.

5.4.2 Generalization Performance

For generalization, the trained networks must be judged according to the cross-validation performance. In cross-validation, the test patterns are drawn from the patterns not encountered in the training phase. A theoretical approach may be adopted, from either an *identification* or *capacity* perspective, which must touch bases on numerical analysis, learning time, network size, weight decay, bias and variance of parameter estimation. Due to its mathematical involvement, we introduce only the key results in the field and omit their detailed derivation.

From the system identification perspective, a proper training criterion is the *validity measure*:

$$\overline{V}(\mathbf{w}) = \lim_{M \to \infty} \mathbf{E} V_M(\mathbf{w}, Z^M)$$

where $Z^M = \{ [\mathbf{x}_1, \mathbf{t}_1], [\mathbf{x}_2, \mathbf{t}_2], \ldots, [\mathbf{x}_M, \mathbf{t}_M] \}$ denotes the vector space represented by the training input/teacher pairs. For generalization, the network is evaluated by its average performance, $\mathbf{E}\overline{V}(\hat{\mathbf{w}}_M)$, where $\hat{\mathbf{w}}_M$ represents the estimated weights trained by the network. Here the expectation is taken over the entire sample space (not only the training patterns) so it statistically represents the generalization space. A series of asymptotic approximations lead to the following *key equation* by Ljung [177]:

$$\mathbf{E}\overline{V}(\hat{\mathbf{w}}_M) = V_M(\hat{\mathbf{w}}_M, Z^M) + \frac{1}{M}tr\{\overline{V}''(\mathbf{w}^*)P_{\mathbf{w}}\} \qquad (5.40)$$

where $(1/M)P_{\mathbf{w}}$ is the asymptotic covariance matrix of $\hat{\mathbf{w}}_M$. For more details, see Problem 5.14. The *key equation* can be illustrated by two important examples:

- **Maximum Likelihood Criterion**

  Suppose that the criterion $V_M(\mathbf{w}, Z^M)$ is defined as the averaged log likelihood function, denoted by $-\frac{1}{M}L_M(\mathbf{w}, Z^M)$, the key equation becomes

  $$\mathbf{E}\overline{V}(\hat{\mathbf{w}}_M) = -\frac{1}{M}L_M(\mathbf{w}, Z^M) + \frac{d}{M} \qquad (5.41)$$

  where d is the dimension of the network as defined in [177].

- **MSE Criterion**

  If a model function $\phi(\mathbf{w}, \mathbf{x}(m))$ closely approximates the desired output $t(m)$, then it is plausible to consider $t(m)$ as a random process

  $$t(m) = \phi(t, \mathbf{x}(m)) + v(m)$$

  with $\phi(\mathbf{w}, \mathbf{x}(m))$ denoting its mean value and $\{v(m)\}$ assumed to be a white noise with variance ρ. The training criterion $V_M(\mathbf{w}, Z^M)$ becomes

  $$V_M(\mathbf{w}, Z^M) = \frac{1}{M}\sum_{t=1}^{M}|y(m) - \phi(\mathbf{w}, \mathbf{x}(m))|^2 \qquad (5.42)$$

  In this case, Eq. 5.40 reduces to

  $$\mathbf{E}\overline{V}(\hat{\mathbf{w}}_M) = \rho(1 + \frac{d}{M}) \qquad (5.43)$$

The above equations are often referred to as the *Akaike Information Criterion* [8]. Their goal is to obtain a good fit using as few parameters as possible. Note that a network with a large number of parameters can always be able to yield a high likelihood function. Eq. 5.41 suggests that the optimal solution must be a compromise between increasing the likelihood and reducing the complexity of network. Similarly, Eq. 5.43 shows that the error measure criterion increases linearly with the network size. Although a large network in general fits the training data better, an excessively large net may cause overfitting. Both equations further suggest that more training patterns (larger M) afford us a larger network (larger d) without sacrificing the cost criterion.

Generalization Perspective   If the minimization problem of Eq. 5.42 is ill conditioned, it would be advisable to *regularize* the criterion function $V_M(\mathbf{w})$. (See, e.g., Golub's formulation on regularization [81].) The regularization formulation involves a moderated energy function:

$$E = V_M(\mathbf{w}) + \lambda P(\phi, \mathbf{w})$$

where $P(\phi, \mathbf{w})$ stands for the regularization factor and λ is a positive regularization parameter. One example is the linear shift-invariant constraint proposed by Poggio [228]:

$$E = V_M(\mathbf{w}) + \|\lambda \nabla \phi\|^2$$

This regularization formulation leads to radial-basis-function (RBF) models. Another possible constraint is imposed on the norm of the weight vectors [178]. The cost criterion then becomes

$$E = V_M(\mathbf{w}) + \lambda \|\mathbf{w} - \mathbf{w}^\#\|^2 \tag{5.44}$$

where $\mathbf{w}^\#$ is some nominal parameter value and λ is a positive regularization parameter. With specially chosen initial conditions, Eq. 5.44 can be simplified into (cf. [178, 262])

$$E \approx \rho(1 + \frac{d(\lambda)}{M}) \tag{5.45}$$

where

$$d(\lambda) = \sum_{i=1}^{d} \frac{\sigma_i^2}{(\sigma_i + \lambda)^2} \tag{5.46}$$

and σ_i are the eigenvalues of $\overline{V}''(\hat{\mathbf{w}}_M^{(i)})$ or the Jacobian matrix.

Recall that, from Eq. 5.43, an unregularized formulation would yield an unnecessarily large AIC unless the redundancy of network is trimmed first.

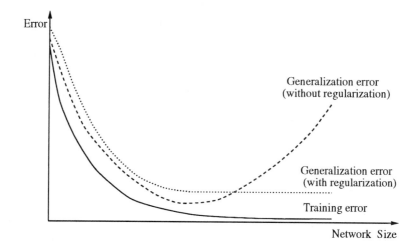

Figure 5.8: The training and generalization errors versus the network size.

More pragmatically, we can think of $d(\lambda)$ as "the efficient number of parameters". That is, those with eigenvalues larger than λ contribute more to the effective dimensionality. If regularization is incorporated, the penalty due to a large number of parameters may be avoided. Thus the network could still yield reasonable performance despite the presence of many redundant parameters. (In other words, it is penalized on network complexity only, but not on generalization.)

In summary, based on the system identification theory, the following error bound on generalization can be established:

$$\mathbf{E}\overline{V}(\hat{\mathbf{w}}_M) = V_M(\hat{\mathbf{w}}_M, Z^M) + D$$

where D can be regarded as the "effective dimensionality", which is also related to the "confidence interval". To illustrate the bounds between training and generalization accuracies (without or with regularization), they are sketched in Figure 5.8.

Some remarks on recent research progress are in order. Based on the assumption of the statistical independence between the error and input, Moody proposed a simplified *generalized* information criterion. (The assumption is valid provided that complete model information is known.) Larsen [170] relaxed the assumption and proposed a more complex analysis. Sometimes, the concept is useful even though regularization is not explicitly applied. When the training method is known to be ill-conditioned, then stopping the training procedure during the middle of iterations will result in the same effect as regularization [178, 248].

Tradeoffs between training and generalization criteria may also be understood from an estimation theoretical perspective, which bears a strong similarity to the well-known tradeoff between *bias* and *variance* [78]. A nonparametric estimation (i.e., the network is allowed an indefinite size) is in general prone to high variance. If the training set size is small and yet we press too hard on minimizing the approximation error (by increasing the size of the network), it is very likely to result in a high variance of estimation error. On the other hand, for the parametric estimation (i.e., using a fixed-size network), the bias can become very large if the chosen model does not match the underlying distribution function.

Capacity Perspective   The capacity of a neural network is characterized by its ability to separate arbitrarily placed patterns in feature space. From this perspective, the following bound of the generalization error may be established [264],

$$E_L \leq E_G \leq E_L + D$$

where the *learning error* E_L is the averaged error of the training set, and the *generalization error* E_G is the expectation value of the error for an arbitrary input/output pair drawn from the original (unknown) distribution and the "confidence interval" D now depends on the VC dimension proposed by [286]. (For a detailed definition of E_L, E_G, and D, see [264].) By a simple (single-layer net) experiment, it is shown that E_L and E_G, as functions of the "effective dimension", have a striking similarity with Figure 5.8. More precisely, Figure 5.8 can also be used to depict training and generalization errors (as the y-axis) with respect to the network capacity (as the x-axis). That is, E_L and E_G, respectively, exhibit similar curves to the training and generalization errors (without regularization) derived from the system identification perspective. Therefore, an optimal learning strategy would yield a capacity large enough to suppress E_L and at the same time avoid incurring a very large D.

In conclusion, the identification and capacity (risk minimization) theories lead to very similar generalization behaviors, cf. Figure 5.8. In fact, it is further observed by Vapnik [285] that the two disciplinaries together could represent a complete theoretical footing for the generalization theory.

5.4.3   RBF Regularization Networks

In this section, we discuss a *regularization* formulation, proposed by Poggio [228]. Without loss of generality, we discuss only the single-output case.

Let $S = \{(\mathbf{x}_i, t_i) \in R^n \times R \mid i = 1, \ldots, N\}$ be the training set and $\phi(\cdot, \mathbf{w})$ denote the *unknown* model function with the weight vector $\mathbf{w}$ also *unknown*. The learning phase of a regularization problem involves finding ϕ **and** its parameter $\mathbf{w}$ that minimize the following energy function:

$$H[\phi] = \sum_{i=1}^{N}(t_i - \phi(\mathbf{x}_i, \mathbf{w}))^2 + \lambda \|P\phi\|^2 \tag{5.47}$$

where $\|\cdot\|$ denotes the L^2 norm in the function space. The constraint operator $(P(\cdot))$ in a regularization problem should be carefully selected to ensure the smoothness of the function ϕ; cf. [228]. The positive *regularization parameters* λ_k's indicate the degree of strictness of the constraints. The larger λ is, the stricter the constraints.

To simplify the theoretical derivation, the constraint operator (P) is assumed to be *linear*. Then the solution $\phi(\mathbf{x}, \mathbf{w})$ can be solved based on the *variational principle* [228]. Assume ϕ is the solution that minimizes the energy function $H[\phi]$; then for every $\psi \in L^2(R^n)$, the functional $H[\phi + \alpha\psi]$ of the real variable α has a local minimum at $\alpha = 0$. In other words,

$$\frac{\partial}{\partial \alpha}H[\phi + \alpha\psi]\bigg|_{\alpha=0} = 0 \tag{5.48}$$

for any continuous function ψ. It follows that

$$\begin{aligned}
\frac{\partial}{\partial \alpha}H[\phi + \alpha\psi] &= \frac{\partial}{\partial \alpha}[\sum_{i=1}^{N}(t_i - \phi(\mathbf{x}_i) - \alpha\psi(\mathbf{x}_i))^2 + \lambda\|P(\phi + \alpha\psi)\|^2] \\
&= \frac{\partial}{\partial \alpha}[\sum_{i=1}^{N}(t_i - \phi(\mathbf{x}_i) - \alpha\psi(\mathbf{x}_i))^2 + \lambda\int_{R^n}(P\phi + \alpha P\psi)^2 d\mathbf{x}] \\
&= \sum_{i=1}^{N}2(t_i - \phi(\mathbf{x}_i) - \alpha\psi(\mathbf{x}_i))(-\psi(\mathbf{x}_i)) + \\
&\quad 2\lambda\int_{R^n}(P\phi \cdot P\psi + \alpha(P\psi)^2)d\mathbf{x}
\end{aligned}$$

Setting $\alpha = 0$ in Eq. 5.48, we can derive the following:

$$\sum_{i=1}^{N}2(t_i - \phi(\mathbf{x}_i))(-\psi(\mathbf{x}_i)) + 2\lambda\int_{R^n}P\phi \cdot P\psi d\mathbf{x} = 0 \tag{5.49}$$

Let $<\cdot, \cdot>$ denote the *inner product* operation, $<\phi, \psi> = \int_{R^n}\phi\psi d\mathbf{x}$. Let $\hat{P}$ denote the *adjoint operator* of P, that is $<P\phi, \psi> = <\phi, \hat{P}\psi>$. Eq. 5.49 can now be rewritten as

$$\int_{R^n} \hat{P} P\phi \cdot \psi dx = \frac{1}{\lambda} \int_{R^n} \sum_{i=1}^{N} (t_i - \phi(\mathbf{x})) \delta(\mathbf{x} - \mathbf{x}_i) \psi dx$$

The condition for this equation to hold valid for any arbitrary function is that

$$\hat{P} P\phi = \frac{1}{\lambda} \sum_{i=1}^{N} (t_i - \phi(\mathbf{x})) \delta(\mathbf{x} - \mathbf{x}_i) \qquad (5.50)$$

Let G denote the Green's function for the operator $\hat{P}P$, that is,

$$\hat{P} P G(\mathbf{x}; \mathbf{t}) = \delta(\mathbf{x} - \mathbf{t}) \qquad (5.51)$$

By the superposition principle, the solution for the differential equation, Eq. 5.50 can be derived as

$$\phi(\mathbf{x}) = \frac{1}{\lambda} \sum_{i=1}^{N} [t_i - \phi(\mathbf{x}_i)] G(\mathbf{x}; \mathbf{x}_i) = \sum_{i=1}^{N} c_i G(\mathbf{x}; \mathbf{x}_i) \qquad (5.52)$$

where

$$c_i = \frac{1}{\lambda} [t_i - \phi(\mathbf{x}_i)] \qquad (5.53)$$

Radial-Basis Function (RBF) Models

To derive the complete solution, we need to tackle two tasks: (1) find the Green function, G, and (2) find the c_i coefficients.

(1) Find the Green Function Suppose that the linear constraint operator P is chosen as a differential operator and

$$\|P\phi\|^2 = \int_{R^n} dx \sum_{m=0}^{\infty} a_m (D_m \phi(\mathbf{x}))^2 \qquad (5.54)$$

where a_m are real positive coefficients. Moreover, for any integer $k \geq 0$, we define operators: $D_{2k} = \nabla^{2k} = (\frac{\partial^2}{\partial x_1^2} + \cdots + \frac{\partial^2}{\partial x_n^2})^k$ and $D_{2k+1} = \nabla \nabla^{2k} = (\frac{\partial}{\partial x_1} \nabla^{2k}, \ldots, \frac{\partial}{\partial x_n} \nabla^{2k})$, where ∇^2 is the Laplacian operator and ∇ is the gradient operator.

Because the differential (constraint) operator is translationally invariant, the Green function has a special form

$$G(\mathbf{x}; \mathbf{t}) = G(\mathbf{x} - \mathbf{t})$$

Based on Eq. 5.51, the Green function G must satisfy

$$\hat{P}PG(\mathbf{x};\mathbf{t}) = \sum_{m=0}^{\infty}(-1)^m a_m D_{2m} G(\mathbf{x}-\mathbf{t}) = \delta(\mathbf{x}-\mathbf{t}) \qquad (5.55)$$

Taking the Fourier transform on both sides of Eq. 5.55, we have

$$\sum_{m=0}^{\infty} a_m (\omega \cdot \omega)^m \tilde{G}(\omega) = 1$$

and it follows that

$$\tilde{G}(\omega) = \frac{1}{\sum_{m=0}^{\infty} a_m (\omega \cdot \omega)^m}$$

By the inverse Fourier transform,

$$G(\mathbf{x}) = \int_{R^m} \frac{e^{i\omega \cdot \mathbf{x}}}{\sum_{m=0}^{\infty} a_m (\omega \cdot \omega)^m} d\omega \qquad (5.56)$$

The fact that there are only even-order terms of ω implies that $G(\mathbf{x})$ must be a symmetric function around the origin $\mathbf{x} = 0$. More precisely, $G(\mathbf{x}-\mathbf{x}_i)$ must be a *radial basis function*, that is, a function of $\|\mathbf{x}-\mathbf{x}_i\|^2$ [228].

To derive the popular Gaussian RBF model, we need to set [309]

$$a_m = \frac{\sigma^{2m}}{m!2^m}$$

then

$$G(\mathbf{x}) \propto e^{-\frac{\|\mathbf{x}\|^2}{2\sigma^2}}$$

It follows that

$$\phi(\mathbf{x}) = \sum_{i=1}^{N} c_i e^{-\frac{\|\mathbf{x}-\mathbf{x}_i\|^2}{2\sigma^2}} \qquad (5.57)$$

where the coefficient c_i is derived in Eq. 5.58.

(2) Find the c_i Coefficients. Assuming that the matrix $(\mathbf{G}+\lambda\mathbf{I})$ is non-singular, then there is a unique solution:

$$\mathbf{c} = (\mathbf{G}+\lambda\mathbf{I})^{-1}\mathbf{t} \qquad (5.58)$$

where $\mathbf{G} = \{G(\mathbf{x}_i,\mathbf{x}_j)\}$ is an $N \times N$ matrix, $\mathbf{I}$ is an $N \times N$ identity matrix, and $\mathbf{c} = [c_1,\ldots,c_N]^T$, and $\mathbf{t} = [t_1,\ldots,t_N]^T$. This can be verified by substituting the solution into Eq. 5.52.

Generalized Radial-Basis Function (GRBF)

The aforementioned Gaussian RBF network needs exactly N hidden neurons, whose centers correspond to the N training points. (See Figure 5.7.) This is not feasible when N is very large. To reduce the size of the network, an approximation by a smaller number of centers must be adopted.

$$\phi(\mathbf{x}) = \sum_{i=1}^{K} c_i G(\mathbf{x}; t_i)$$

where K is the number of centers t_i, $K << N$.

In order to achieve fast learning speed, several variants of RBF network structures that combine self-organization, supervised learning, and hierarchical clustering have been proposed [101, 185, 198]. For example, the network proposed by Holdaway [101] employs Kohonen's self-organizing feature map for data preprocessing and a feedforward multilayer for classification. Furthermore, in order to achieve a better approximation, different effective radii for each center can be adopted:

$$\phi(\mathbf{x}) = \sum_{i=1}^{K} c_i e^{-\frac{\|\mathbf{x}-t_i\|^2}{\sigma_i^2}}$$

where t_i and σ_i^2 can be obtained by clustering and the variance approach proposed in [198]. This variant is called a *generalized radial-based function* (GRBF), which is essentially the same as the *locally receptive field* proposed by Moody and Darken [198]. Although it is not possible to derive such GRBF networks rigorously from the regularization theory, this should not prevent them from being successfully applied to practical applications.

5.4.4 Network Pruning and Growing Techniques

An excessively large hidden-layer in an ACON supernet may cause deterioration of the generalization performance. Moreover, it is very likely to cause serious numerical problems in terms of convergence and local minimum. Thus it is critical to select an optimal number of hidden units, for which two empirical approaches are:

1. *network pruning method*

2. *network growing method*

5.4.4.1   Network Pruning Techniques

In the ACON structure, it is difficult to estimate exactly the number of hidden units so that a satisfactory model can be obtained. Often, it is necessary to use a larger network and a laborious training effort to optimize the training accuracy. After such an initial training phase, the network can be trimmed gradually by the removal of excessive hidden units. The reduced network should facilitate a cost-effective real-time implementation for the recognition phase.

Many pruning techniques have been proposed, with the common objective of causing minimum damage. Sietsma and Dow [260] have demonstrated manual pruning of neural networks by exploiting redundancy among the output of neurons. Rumelhart has proposed a new cost function to enforce weights with small magnitudes that converge to zero so that they can be removed with minimal effect. This approach has since been refined by Weigend et al. [300], Chauvin [45], Lang and Hinton [169], Hanson and Pratt [91], and others. A similar gain-competition approach has been proposed by Kruschke [143, 144]. Mozel and Smolensky [203], and later Le Cun, et al. [56] proposed removing weights that are less sensitive to output error. Similarly, Kung and Hu [160] proposed a subspace approximation approach, improving on an earlier method [108], to selection of the most expendable hidden neurons.

As illustrated in Figure 5.9, the basic idea of this approach is to retain only a subset of the hidden units. When a hidden unit is pruned, all the synaptic weights connected to it will be removed. For the retained hidden units, only their upper-layer weights need to be updated. The lower-layer weights connected to those units will remain temporarily unchanged.

To facilitate discussion of network pruning techniques based on the subspace approximation method, the following notations are introduced:

- M = number of training patterns

- N = number of original hidden units

- r = number of hidden units used in the reduced model ($r < N$)

- $A = [a_1, a_2, \cdots, a_N]$: $M \times N$ matrix formed by activation values of the N hidden units

- $U = [u_1, u_2, \cdots, u_N]$: $M \times L$ matrix formed by net values of the next layer

- $B_r = [b_1, b_2, \cdots, b_r]$: $M \times r$ matrix formed by r selected columns of A

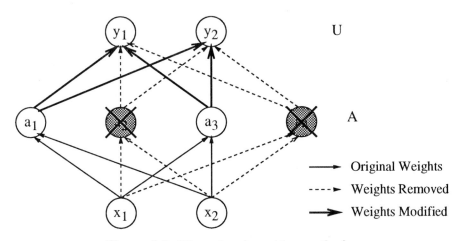

Figure 5.9: The network pruning method.

- $U|B_r \equiv$ projection of U onto the space of B_r (see Figure 5.10)

- $U/B_r \equiv$ projection of U onto the complementary (null) space of B_r (see Figure 5.10)

The problem is to retain only the most representative, say, r, hidden nodes and delete all the others. (See Figure 5.9.) The selection process hinges upon the linear dependency of (i.e., the redundancy between) the nodes. For example, assume that there are three neurons in the same hidden layer having the values a_1, a_2, and a_3; and that there is only a single neuron in the output layer, whose net value is denoted u. If the net value is linearly dependent only on a_1 and a_2, that is,

$$u = w_1 a_1 + w_2 a_2$$

for all the training patterns, then clearly the third hidden unit (a_3) will not be needed. In short, the hidden units should be selected so as to best span the subspace of the net values in the next layer, (i.e., the output layer for the two-layer networks).

The strategy adopted in the Frobenius approximation-reduction method [160] is to recursively search the best r hidden units. Suppose now that the optimal $M \times (k-1)$ matrix B_{k-1} is already determined. The next step is to find a "best" column of A, say, $a_{Index(k)}$, to form a new matrix $B_k \equiv [B_{k-1}, a_{Index(k)}]$ (i.e., $b_k = a_{Index(k)}$), so that $U|B_k$ could most closely approximate U in the Frobenius norm. This "step-by-step" optimality can be accomplished by the following procedure:

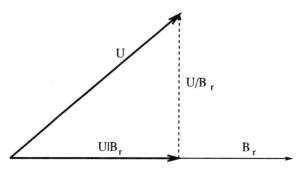

Figure 5.10: The operators "|" ("/") denote the projection operation onto the specified space (the null space).

Search Procedure   Start with $k = 1$:

1. Normalize A (column by column). With a notational abuse, the normalized version is again renamed as A.

2. Compute $||U|a_i||_F = ||U^T a_i||_F$ to select the entry with maximum magnitude, denoted as $Index(k)$. (See Eq. 5.59.) [1]

3. Project (the normalized) A onto the null space of B_k. (Note that because A is orthogonal to B_{k-1}, so $A/B_k = A/a_{Index(k)}$. Update $A \leftarrow A/a_{Index(k)}$.)

4. Set b_k to be the $Index(k)$th column of the *original* A matrix. Increment $k \leftarrow k + 1$ and repeat steps 1 to 3 until $k = r$.

The search process begins with one unit, two units, and completes the selection by induction. (Initially, the B_0 matrix ($r = 0$) is empty.) It can continue until all r columns of B_r are determined. The new upper-layer weights $\hat{W}$ can be solved from $U|B_r = B_r(\hat{W})^T$, which yields

$$\hat{W} = U^T (B_r^T)^\dagger$$

where $(B_r^T)^\dagger$ is the pseudo-inverse of the B_r^T matrix.   ■

---

[1]In deriving steps 1 and 2, we have used the following result

$$||U|a||_F = ||U|\hat{a}||_F = ||U^T \hat{a}||_F \qquad (5.59)$$

where a is any given column vector, and $\hat{a}$ denotes its normalized vector. See Problem 5.22.

Discussion   The computation cost of the search scheme is only $\mathcal{O}(rNM)$; thus, it offers a considerable computational savings compared to a globally optimal solution. simulations suggest that this search scheme leads a result very close to the global optimal solution. Noticeable improvement can be expected if one continues training the reduced network using the obtained weights as an initial condition [108].

The step-by-step optimality of the procedure can be mathematically verified: Suppose that the optimal $M \times (k-1)$ matrix B_{k-1} is already determined and the next step is to find a "best" column of A, say, $a_{Index(k)}$, to form a new matrix $B_k \equiv [B_{k-1}, a_{Index(k)}]$ (i.e., $b_k = a_{Index(k)}$) so that $U|B_k$ optimally approximates U, that is, $\|U|B_k - U\|_F$ reaches the minimum. It is equivalent to finding $Index(k)$ so that $\|U|B_k\|_F$ is maximized. In turn, this is equivalent to maximizing $\|U|(a_{Index(k)}/B_{k-1})\|_F$. It can be verified that $a_{Index(k)}$ is orthogonal to B_{k-1}, so $a_{Index(k)}/B_{k-1} = a_{Index(k)}$. Summing up all the above, the main task required is to maximize $\|U|a_{Index(k)}\|_F$, which is assured by step 2 in the Search Procedure.

5.4.4.2   Network Growing Techniques

Network growing techniques start with a small number of hidden units, and add new hidden units, one by one, to gradually refine the network [17, 44, 64, 103, 158, 272, 302]. They all have a common generic configuration, as shown in Figure 5.11(a). The growing process can stop at the minimum number of hidden neurons to acquire the desired training accuracy. Another important feature is that the newly added neurons can be directed to best compensate the existing neurons. Along this line, Ash [17] proposed adding a new node when a large output error persists for a predefined period. Later, the same idea is used in an online growing technique by Chang [44], in which an effective formula for determining the initial values of the new weights is derived. The scheme reportedly improves both convergence speed and training accuracy. Taking into account the generalization performance, White [302] suggested the use of a cross-validation-based criterion that considers testing performance as well as training performance. This represents an important open research topic.

Laterally growing techniques may be adopted; cf. Figure 5.11(b), which select the hidden nodes with an ordered importance. Two closely related techniques have been independently developed: the *cascaded correlation networks* proposed by Fahlman [64] and the *lateral orthogonalization networks* by Kung and Diamantaras [158]. In the former, the cascaded correlation net

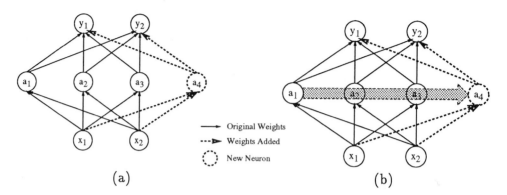

Figure 5.11: Network growing methods. (a) Conventional network growing. (b) Hidden nodes are selected with an ordered importance: the left nodes have more dominant roles than the nodes on the right.

recursively augments the hidden nodes one by one. When a new hidden node is added, its inputs consist of both the original input nodes and the old hidden nodes. When the new hidden-node weights are trained, all the old weights are temporarily frozen. The objective of training is to maximize the covariance between the hidden-node value and the desired output. Subsequently, the output weight will be trained while the newly trained hidden-node weights are frozen.

In the *lateral orthogonalization network*, it is proposed that the new hidden nodes are directed along a direction "orthogonal" to the subspace spanned by the old hidden nodes, cf. Chapter 8. This should help minimize the redundancy between the (old and new) hidden nodes. If the network has over-grown its desired size, a prune-after-grow process may be invoked. If still necessary, the reduced network can grow again and the network may be fully polished by such a intertwined process.

5.5 Applications of Back-Propagation Networks

The approximation/optimization networks are suitable applications which require regression curve fitting, modeling nonlinear functions, or data analysis. Such an application domain is very broad, including adaptive signal processing, robotic control, remote sensing, industrial inspection, image/vision processing (e.g., recognition of a face in a video image), speech/character recognition (e.g., reading hand-printed numbers, text recognition, synthetic speech generation), medical applications (e.g., EKG/ECG processing, test-

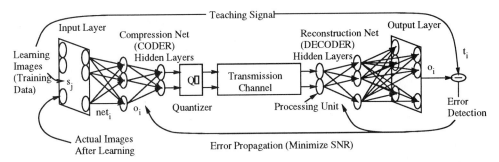

Figure 5.12: The expanded system for the image compression and transmission. Adapted from [265].

ing normal/abnormal heart beats), and banking (e.g., signature verification, consumer loan credit screening, mortgage processing). For examples, see [124, 156].

Energy Function Criteria for Training Networks The most critical characteristic for the design of application-driven neural networks is the training cost criterion or energy function. So the selection of an energy function must be given the highest priority. The primary computational goal in a neural model is to optimize a given energy function. Although the least square error training criterion is very popular, it is definitely not the only choice. The models should freely exploit a tailored training criteria to best satisfy the specific application requirements. A good energy function E should satisfy several of the following criteria: (1) The optimal solution of that energy function must ensure a good classifier, (2) It should enhance the regularization and/or generalizability (see, e.g., cf. Section 5.4), (3) It can sufficiently highlight certain special features (e.g., robustness or shape contour in Section 5.5.2). The optimal solution can be calculated via the first-order or second-order gradient updating techniques. Among them, the most effective is the (conjugate-gradient) back-propagation algorithm.

5.5.1   Approximation Formulation: Image Compression

The BP network can be applied to image compression applications [265]. As shown in Figure 5.12, images are fed to the input and output layers as training pairs, that is, the inputs and teacher values are identical. The number of hidden units is purposely kept very small so that the left-half of the network is forced to learn some data-compression transform, and the right-half learns right-half learns the inverse transformation rule. In other words, the model is designed for image compression/transmission applications. Simulations were conducted to evaluate the compression and generalization performances. The results suggested that the BP network recalled well the learned images (in terms of SNR), but generalized rather poorly for unlearned images. The BP network's overall performance was compatible with or slightly inferior to the conventional DCT (discrete cosine transform) technique. The *lateral orthogonalization network*, designed for extracting the principal component of the images, offers an attractive alternative for data compression/transmission applications. Details are postponed to Chapter 8.

5.5.2   Optimization Formulation: Surface Reconstruction

The surface reconstruction problem has a broad domain of applications, for example, manufacturing automation, terrain mapping, and vehicle guidance. Given a set of data points $\{x\}$ (in $\mathcal{R}^2$ or $\mathcal{R}^3$) that lie on or close to the 2D contour or 3D surface of an object, the goal is to reconstruct the contour or surface. The contour (or surface) is often expressed by the (continuous) roots of $\phi(x) = 0$. The training set ($\mathbf{B} = \{x^{(i)}, i = 1, \ldots, n\}$) is given as sample root points of $\phi(x)$. Therefore, the desired teacher values corresponding to the training (root) points are $t^{(i)} = 0$. If the standard (least-squares-error) energy function is minimized:

$$E = \frac{1}{2} \sum_{x \in \mathbf{B}} [t - \phi(x)]^2 = \frac{1}{2} \sum_{x \in \mathbf{B}} \phi^2(x)$$

then the trained network will result in a trivial solution $\phi(x) \equiv 0$. Obviously, an alternative cost function is needed. In reconstructing a contour, the value of the 2-dimensional function $\phi(x)$ must be positive on one side of the contour and negative on the other. An additional criterion is required that forces the 2-dimensional function $\phi(x)$ to have large gradients at the root points [270]. The following cost function incorporates two important criteria at the roots (i.e., $x \in \mathbf{B}$): (1) small values of $\phi(x)$ and (2) large gradients ($\|\nabla_{\mathbf{x}}\phi(x)\|$) [110, 114].

$$E = \frac{1}{2} \sum_{x \in \mathbf{B}} \frac{\phi^2(x)}{\|\nabla_{\mathbf{x}}\phi(x)\|^2} + \text{regularization terms} \qquad (5.60)$$

With the first cost term, the root points on the contour will be more likely to lie on or near a large-gradient steep cliff. The extra regularization terms are necessary to discourage the presence of false contours exterior to a certain reasonable object region. (See examples in [110].) Furthermore, the first term alone is sensitive to outlying noise, which would unduly suppress the magnitude of the gradient of outlying points. To tackle these two problems, two regularizing terms are used in Eq. 5.60 [114]. One serves to discourage zero-crossing exterior to a designated object region, and the other forces a smoother gradient along the radial direction of the object boundary, cf. Figure 5.13(d). Figure 5.13(c) shows the reconstructed airplane contour from very spare sample points (Figure 5.13(b)) based on the proposed regularized cost function [114].

5.5.3   OCON Applications: OCR, Speech, and Texture

In this subsection, individual training strategies based on the OCON structures are applied to practical applications such as OCR, speech recognition, and texture classification. In these experiments, it was found that very few hidden nodes per subnet are needed in the OCON approach. Yet its performance compares very favorably with the ACON approach in terms of both convergence speed and classification accuracy.

Discriminative Training

As discussed in Chapter 1, the **discriminative training** strategy uses *all* the training patterns (both the positive and negative examples) to train each subnet. For the positive samples, the teacher values are "1". For the negative samples, the teacher values are "0". This discriminative training strategy provides a clearer definition of the decision boundaries. Therefore, as demonstrated by the following application examples, it is a reliable technique.

Character Recognition   In this example, handwritten characters (10 Arabic numerals and 26 lower-case English letters of the alphabet) are recognized. There are a total of 432 training patterns for the 36 categories. (Thus each class has 12 positive training patterns.) The OCON approach achieves faster training, about 4 times speedup compared to the ACON approach. Moreover, it shows a number of improvements over the ACON in training and generalization performances, cf. Table 5.1.

Speech Recognition   Two examples of speech recognition are discussed here. In the first example [120], a 408-subnet OCON network is constructed

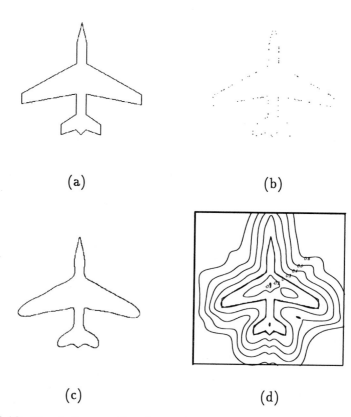

(a)   (b)

(c)   (d)

Figure 5.13: Simulation results of a surface-reconstruction problem. (a) The original airplane contour. (b) The 100 random samples from the airplane boundary. (c) The surface reconstructed airplane ($\phi(\mathbf{x}) = 0$ contour) with 24 hidden neurons after 100 training iterations. (d) The slope representation of the reconstructed airplane in terms of equi-potential contours.

	Training Accuracy	Generalization Accuracy	Training Time
ACON (BP)	405/432 = 94%	324/396 = 82%	normalized = 1.00
OCON (BP)	430/432 = 99.5%	344/396 = 87%	about = 0.25

Table 5.1: Performance comparisons between the ACON and OCON models on handwritten character recognition.

to classify 408 Mandarin speech syllables. The input features are extracted from 10th order LPC-driven cepstra with 256 points per frame. Adaptive time-shift is adopted to normalize input pattern into 40 frames per utterance at 8-kHz sampling rate. Accordingly, the total number of input units is very large, $10 \times 40 = 400$. Fortunately, the experiment also indicates that as few as 3 hidden nodes per subnet are sufficient. Therefore, in the OCON approach, there are a total of 408 subnets, and each subnet has a 400-3-1 two-layer structure. In the training phase, 8 different speakers are sampled and there are $3264 (= 408 \times 8)$ training patterns. In addition, $816 (= 408 \times 2)$ (outside) test patterns are collected. According to the simulation results reported in [120], most of the subnets converged very rapidly, within several tens of sweeps. The training accuracy was 100% (3264/3264), and the generalization accuracy exceeded 83% (678/816). In a separate experiment on isolated English speech recognition [111], the OCON discriminative training approach also produced significant performance improvement over several well-known methods.

Independent Training

In contrast to discriminative individual training, the independent training model is trained *only* by positive examples, cf. Chapter 1. It has relatively limited discrimination power. We focus on the Gaussian-mixture model, in which a class is modeled by a set of clusters, each represented by a Gaussian distribution. The probability distribution function (*pdf*) of the input patterns is represented by a linear combination of Gaussian functions:

$$p(\mathbf{x}|\Lambda) = \sum_{k=1}^{K} c_k^2 \frac{1}{(\sqrt{2\pi}\sigma)^n} e^{-\|\mathbf{x}-\mu_k\|^2/2\sigma^2}$$

with the normalization constraint $\sum_{k=1}^{K} c_k^2 = 1$. According to Parzen's classic approximation theory [219], it can approximate any *pdf* as closely as desired. Given training patterns $\mathbf{x}^{(1)}, \cdots, \mathbf{x}^{(m)}$, the objective of the **maximum likelihood estimator** [61] is to find a model Λ for each class such that

$$\max_{\Lambda} \sum_{m=1}^{M} \ln P(\mathbf{x}^{(m)}|\Lambda)$$

An adaptive maximum likelihood estimator can be obtained via the gradient-updating rule, cf. Problem 5.29. As a simple example, let us consider two nonseparable training sets, each with a Gaussian-mixture *pdf*. The distribution function and decision boundary obtained by the optimal Bayes decision rule is shown in Figure 5.14(a) and the classification accuracy is 94.70% (for 3000 training samples). The distribution and boundary obtained by the maximum likelihood estimator are shown in Figure 5.14(b), for which three clusters are used for each class and the training accuracy reaches 94.47%, which is very close to the optimal Bayes decision.

Texture Classification In this experiment, three satellite image texture blocks representing city, forest, and fields are extracted to form three classes of mosaics. Image blocks are drawn from the mosaics and 16 principal components (cf. Chapter 8) are computed as feature patterns. For each class, 256 patterns are obtained. Of the 256 patterns, 171 are used as the training set and the rest as the test set. The simulation results are summarized in Table 5.2. It was found that the discriminatively trained networks (DBNN and hybrid) produced better (up to 100%) training accuracies. The independent-trained network produced much poorer training performance. Nevertheless, it yielded very compatible generalization accuracy. We attribute the poor training performance to its inability to create intricate decision boundaries. However, its smooth decision boundaries do not appear to adversely affect its generalization performance.

5.5.4   Control Application: Robotic Path Control

With a specified trajectory in the path planning level, the task of path control is to generate the motor control signal (torques and forces) so that the

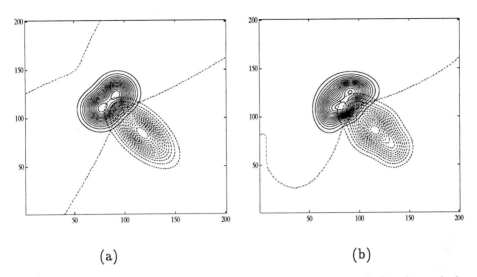

(a)   (b)

Figure 5.14:   (a) Two Gaussian-mixture distributions and the theoretical minimum-error-rate decision boundary. (b) The distribution and boundary obtained by the independent training maximum likelihood estimator. Each class is modeled by 3 Gaussians.

robot may be driven to follow the trajectory. Based on some physiological model [130, 232], the dynamic movement of a robot or a manipulator can be controlled by a feed-forward neural net controller that consists of three major components: two *identical* inverse dynamics systems ($IDS_1 = IDS_2$) and the robot or manipulator, cf. Figure 5.15. The IDS_1 receives the desired trajectory information $\mathbf{\Pi}_d$ and produces the corresponding desired motor command $\mathbf{T}_d$ to drive the robot so the actual movement of the robot (denoted as $\mathbf{\Pi}$) follows the desired trajectory $\mathbf{\Pi}_d$ as closely as possible. The IDS_2, on the other hand, takes the actual movement $\mathbf{\Pi}$ and produces the reference motor command $\mathbf{T}_r$ as shown in Figure 5.15.

Two stages of learning procedure can be adopted [130, 231]. The first stage is called *generalized learning*, with its configuration shown in Figure 5.16(a). The second stage is called *specialized learning*, with a different configuration shown in Figure 5.16(b). Multilayer neural nets have been proposed by [232] to implement the IDS in both a generalized learning system and a specialized learning system. In generalized learning, a set of desired motor commands, denoted as $\{\mathbf{T}_d\}$, is used to drive the robot, and the set of resulting trajectories is denoted as $\{\mathbf{\Pi}\}$. Then the IDS receive $\{\mathbf{\Pi}\}$ as input

Neural Model	Training Accuracy	Test Accuracy
Mutual Training: DBNN(E_s)(8)	100%	87.45%
Independent Training	95.71%	89.02%
Hybrid Training	98.24%	87.45%

Table 5.2: Performance comparisons of the mutual, independent, and hybrid training strategies for texture classification.

and yield a set of reference motor commands, denoted as $\{\mathbf{T}_r\}$. The goal of the generalized learning is to minimize the errors between $\{\mathbf{T}_r\}$ and $\{\mathbf{T}_d\}$ in the least-square sense [232]. After the *IDS* are well trained, if a real input $\mathbf{\Pi}'$ is sufficiently close to one trajectory in the set $\{\mathbf{\Pi}\}$, the controller should be able to retrieve a proper motor command $\hat{\mathbf{T}}$, making the actual movement $\hat{\mathbf{\Pi}}$ follow $\mathbf{\Pi}'$ closely.

Due to lack of knowledge about the operating range of the desired motor commands $\{\mathbf{T}_d\}$, an unnecessarily large set of $\{\mathbf{T}_d\}$ may have to be used for training. This difficulty can be overcome by incorporating a specialized learning stage into the controller system. (See Figure 5.16(b).) The *IDS* are trained based on the desired trajectory $\{\mathbf{\Pi}_d = [\Pi_1^{(d)}, \cdots, \Pi_m^{(d)}]\}$ to yield appropriate motor commands $\{\mathbf{T}\}$ to drive the robot. The actual movement trajectory of the robot is a function of $\mathbf{T}$, denoted as $\mathbf{\Pi}(\mathbf{T}) = [\Pi_1, \cdots, \Pi_m]$. When the operating points of the system change or when new training patterns are added, a specialized learning can be used to fine-tune the system. A severe weakness in the specialized learning is that, in the initial step, the training of *IDS* may be very inefficient due to lack of knowledge about the dynamic model of the robot. Therefore, it is advantageous to properly combine generalized and specialized learning.

5.6   Concluding Remarks

This chapter presents several key theoretical issues on approximation/optimization multi-layer networks, including the back-propagation algorithm and generalization theory. The back-propagation algorithm is an important tool for the computation of gradients of multilayer networks. Numerical methods for the first and second-order BP learning rules are discussed. Noting that overtraining could severely degrade the generalization performance, theoret-

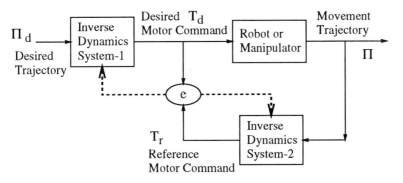

Figure 5.15: A simplified schematic diagram for the feed-forward controller.

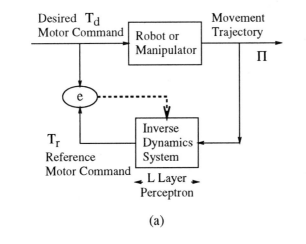

(a)

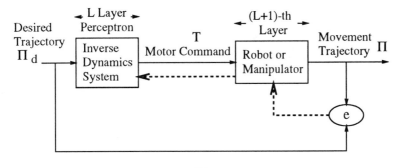

(b)

Figure 5.16: (a) Generalized learning configuration. (b) Specialized learning configuration. Note that the *IDS* can be modeled by an *L*-layer perceptron.

ical approaches for safeguarding the network's generalizability are proposed. Theoretical analysis on the trade-off between the training and generalization accuracies is explored. In practice, several regularization techniques are provided to improve generalization performance at the expense of training accuracy. Further theoretical investigation on this subject is greatly needed.

The optimization formulation is appealing to a very broad application domain. For application-driven neural networks, it is critical to select a proper energy function or cost function. Other key characteristics include network structures, training strategy, etc. A systematic design of application-driven neural models hinges upon a full understanding and a coherent interplay of these key design aspects. To illustrate such design strategies, this chapter provides some examples of neural models for practical application.

5.7   Problems[2]

Exercise 5.1 (Hidden Units and Linear Separable Regions) Suppose that H is the number of hidden units, and d is the dimension of the pattern space. Let M(H,d) denote the number of linear separable regions in the pattern space. Show that [197]

$$M(H, d) = \sum_{k=0}^{d} \left(\begin{array}{c} H \\ k \end{array} \right)$$

In theory, if M(H,d) is given, the optimal number of hidden units H can be found from this formula. However, this is only a theoretically optimal value of H; it does not necessarily guarantee that weights can be numerically computed [197].

Exercise 5.2 (Block Method for Least-Squares Solution) When the training set is available as a block of finite data, it may be advantageous to compute the least-squares-error solution of Eq. 5.15 via a block (batch) method. Show that the least-squares-error solution is given as

$$\mathbf{w}^* = \mathbf{A}^\dagger \mathbf{t}$$

where $\mathbf{A}^\dagger$ is the *pseudoinverse* of $\mathbf{A}$, generally defined as

$$\mathbf{A}^\dagger = \lim_{\epsilon \to 0} [(\mathbf{A}^T \mathbf{A} + \epsilon I)^{-1} \mathbf{A}^T]$$

Also show that $\mathbf{A}^\dagger$ always exists even if the matrix $\mathbf{A}^T \mathbf{A}$ is singular.

---

[2]The basic problems are Problems 5.1 to 5.20. The remaining problems are more advanced.

Also show that $\mathbf{A}^\dagger$ always exists even if the matrix $\mathbf{A}^T\mathbf{A}$ is singular.

Exercise 5.3 The Kaczmarz projection method is a projection technique based on a fundamental "minimum perturbation principle". Carry out (geometrically and quantitatively) at least 5 iterations of the Kaczmarz projection method for

$$\begin{aligned}
\mathbf{z}^{(1)} &= [2\ 1], & t^{(1)} &= 1 \\
\mathbf{z}^{(2)} &= [-1\ 0], & t^{(2)} &= 2 \\
\mathbf{z}^{(3)} &= [1\ 4], & t^{(3)} &= -2
\end{aligned}$$

and an initial weight of

$$w = [1\ 1].$$

Exercise 5.4 The convergence analysis can be simplified if Equation 5.8 is modified into a block-update version. That is, the weights will be updated at the end of each sweep. If k denotes the sweep number, then the recursion has the following form:

$$\mathbf{v}^{(k+1)} = \left(\ \mathbf{I} - \lambda \sum_{m=1}^{M} \frac{\mathbf{z}^{(m)}\mathbf{z}^{(m)^T}}{|\mathbf{z}^{(m)}|^2}\ \right)\mathbf{v}^{(k)}$$

where M is the number of patterns. Denote λ_{max} as the largest eigenvalue of R,

$$R = \frac{1}{M}\sum_{m}\left(\frac{\mathbf{z}^{(m)}\mathbf{z}^{(m)^T}}{|\mathbf{z}^{(m)}|^2}\right)$$

(a) Show that if

$$0 < \lambda < \frac{2}{M\lambda_{max}}$$

then the block-update method converges.

(b) Show that $\lambda_{max} \leq 1$.

(c) It follows that the block-update method converges if

$$0 < \lambda < \frac{2}{M}$$

(Accordingly, a learning rate of $\lambda = \frac{2}{M}$ is suggested.)

Exercise 5.5 Assume that the number of input units, the number of hidden units, and the number of output units are all equal to N. Show that for the two-layers case, the conventional BP requires $\mathcal{O}(5N^2)$ per iteration. Show that for three-layer networks, the conventional BP method requires $\mathcal{O}(7N^2)$ operations per iteration.

Exercise 5.6 Assume that the number of input units is N_0, the number of hidden units N_1, and the number of output units N_2.

(a) For the two-layer case, how many operations (multiply-and-adds) are required by the conventional gradient-descent BP method.

(b) How many operations are required by conjugate-gradient BP method.

(c) Repeat (a) and (b) for the case of three-layer networks.

Exercise 5.7 It is well known that the XOR problem can be classified by a two-layer network with BP learning.

(a) Find the weights by an analytical method. (No computer, please!)

(b) By computer simulation, show how the weights gradually adapt to the training patterns. (An example of weight adaptation is shown in Figure 1.14.)

Exercise 5.8 The nonlinear activation function f of Eq. 5.11 adopts the sigmoid function with unity gain,

$$
\begin{aligned}
a_i(l) &= f(u_i(l)) \\
&= \frac{1}{1 + e^{-u_i(l)}}
\end{aligned}
$$

(a) Show that

$$f'(u_i) = a_i \, (1 - a_i)$$

(b) Show that the expectation value of $f'(u)$ is

$$E[f'(u)] = \frac{1}{6}$$

if $f(u)$ is assumed to be uniformly distributed between 0 and 1, that is, $Pr(f(u)) = 1$.

Exercise 5.9 It is a common perception that the back-propagation algorithm on a two-layer network has local (nonglobal) minima.

(a) Create a set of training samples that numerically shows this phenomenon. (Show that a different initial condition may lead to a different final convergent solution.)

(b) Can this be verified analytically? (Namely, prove or disprove that the solution obtained before is truly a local minimum, instead of a saddle point.)

Exercise 5.10 Perform a simulation study on the effect of nonlinearity of the activation function to training speed.

(a) For the *training phase*, discuss the trade-off between a sharp and a smooth nonlinear function.

(b) For the *retrieving phase*, compare the implementation costs between the sigmoid and step activation functions.

Exercise 5.11 (Back-Propagation for Gaussian RBF Networks)
Derive the back-propagation algorithm for multilayer networks with a Gaussian activation function and a radial basis function.

Exercise 5.12 (Back-Propagation for General Net Functions)
Suppose that the neuron functions have a more general form:

$$a_i(l) = f(\mathbf{w}_i^{(m)}(l), \mathbf{a}(l-1)), \quad l = 1, \dots, L.$$

for each neuron i in layer l, where $\mathbf{a}(l-1)$ denotes the vector with elements $a_i(l-1)$. Show that the gradient-descent updating step is

$$\Delta \mathbf{w}_i^{(m)}(l) = \eta \delta_i^{(m)}(l) f_w^{(l)}(\mathbf{w}_i^{(m)}(l), \mathbf{a}(l-1))$$

Define

$$\phi_{k,i}(l) = f_{a_i(l)}^{(l+1)}(\mathbf{w}_k(l+1), \mathbf{a}(l))$$

Show that $\delta_i^{(m)}(l)$ can be computed by back-propagation as follows

$$
\begin{aligned}
\delta_i^{(m)}(L) &= \{t_i^{(m)} - a_i^{(m)}(L)\}, \quad \text{for the output layer } L \\
\delta_i^{(m)}(l) &= \sum_{k=1}^{N_{l+1}} \delta_k^{(m)}(l+1)\phi_{ki}^{(m)}(l), \quad \text{for all layers } l = L-1, \dots, 1
\end{aligned}
$$

Exercise 5.13 (Stone-Weierstrass Theorem)

Let domain D be a compact space of N dimensions, and let F be a set of continuous real-valued functions on D, satisfying the following criteria:

1. Identity function: The constant function $f(x) = 1$ is in F.

2. Separability: For any two points $x_1 \neq x_2$ in D, there is an $f \in F$ such that $f(x_1) \neq f(x_2)$.

3. Algebraic closure: If f and g are any two functions in F, then fg and $af + bg$ are in F for any two real numbers a and b.

Then F is dense in $C(D)$, the set of continuous real-valued functions in D. In other words, for any $\epsilon > 0$ and any function g in $C(D)$, there is a function $f \in F$ such that $|g(x) - f(x)| < \epsilon$ for all $x \in D$.

Based on the Stone-Weierstrass theorem, show how it can be applied to support the approximation capability of (a) Gaussian RBF and (b) Gaussian EBF (both upright and skewed versions).

Exercise 5.14 Derive Eq. 5.40, using the following hints. For training accuracy, suppose that the minimum solution is $\hat{\mathbf{w}}_M$ given a set of training patterns, that is, $\overline{V}'(\hat{\mathbf{w}}_M, Z^M) = 0$. The Taylor series approximation around the $\hat{\mathbf{w}}_M$ is

$$V_M(\hat{\mathbf{w}}_M, Z^M) \approx V_M(\mathbf{w}^*, Z^M) - \frac{1}{2}(\hat{\mathbf{w}}_M - \mathbf{w}^*)^T V_M''(\mathbf{w}^*, Z^M)(\hat{\mathbf{w}}_M - \mathbf{w}^*)$$

Similarly, the minimum solution for generalization is denoted $\hat{\mathbf{w}}^*$ and $\overline{V}'(\mathbf{w}^*) = 0$. Then the Taylor series approximation around the minimum $\mathbf{w}^*$ is

$$\overline{V}(\hat{\mathbf{w}}_M) \approx \overline{V}(\mathbf{w}^*) + \frac{1}{2}(\hat{\mathbf{w}}_M - \mathbf{w}^*)^T \overline{V}''(\mathbf{w}^*)(\hat{\mathbf{w}}_M - \mathbf{w}^*)$$

Take the expectation values of these two expressions and note that

$$V_M(\hat{\mathbf{w}}_*, Z^M) \approx \overline{V}(\mathbf{w}^*)$$

Finally, Eq. 5.40 will follow after applying the asymptotic relationships below:

$$E\frac{1}{2}(\hat{\mathbf{w}}_M - \mathbf{w}^*)^T \overline{V}''(\zeta_M)(\hat{\mathbf{w}}_M - \mathbf{w}^*) \approx \frac{1}{2}tr\{\overline{V}''(\mathbf{w}^*)P_M\}$$

$$E\frac{1}{2}(\hat{\mathbf{w}}_M - \mathbf{w}^*)^T \overline{V}''_M(\zeta_M, Z^M)(\hat{\mathbf{w}}_M - \mathbf{w}^*) \approx \frac{1}{2}tr\{\overline{V}''(\mathbf{w}^*)P_M\}$$

Exercise 5.15 Show that the approximation $tr\{\overline{V}''(\mathbf{w}^*)P_{\mathbf{w}}\} \approx 2\lambda d$ is useful in the derivation of Eq. 5.43.

Exercise 5.16 Show that the Green function $G(\mathbf{x})$ for Eq. 5.56 is a function of $\|\mathbf{x}\|^2$.

Exercise 5.17 Show that $\mathbf{c} = (\mathbf{G} + \lambda\mathbf{I})^{-1}\mathbf{y}$ is the unique solution to Eq. 5.52 when $\mathbf{G} + \lambda\mathbf{I}$ is nonsingular.

Exercise 5.18 Suppose that the linear constraint operator P over R^2 in Eq. 5.47 is

$$\|P\phi\|^2 = \int_{R^2}[(\frac{\partial^2\phi}{\partial x^2})^2 + (\frac{\partial^2\phi}{\partial x\partial y})^2 + (\frac{\partial^2\phi}{\partial y^2})^2]dxdy$$

Show that the Green function $G(\mathbf{x})$ is a thin-plate spline function:

$$G(r) = r^2 log r$$

where $r = \sqrt{x^2 + y^2}$.

Exercise 5.19 Based on Eq. 5.53 and Eq. 5.58, show that by choosing λ arbitrarily small, we can make $\phi(\mathbf{x}_i)$ arbitrarily close to y_i at a linear rate with respect to λ. (This verifies Theorem 5.2.)

Exercise 5.20 Design a back-propagation network to search for the real roots of a high-order polynomial. Verify your result with a low-order, for example, third-order, polynomial.

Exercise 5.21 (Ho-Kashyap Algorithm) The Ho-Kashyap Algorithm is a hybrid between perceptron-type and ADALINE-type networks. This algorithm uses the sum-of-squares-error criterion. This method allows both $\mathbf{w}$ and $\mathbf{t}$ to change. (Here we assume the teacher has bipolar value $+1$ or -1.) Both $\mathbf{w}$ and $\mathbf{t}$ vectors are updated according to the following: At the kth iteration(sweep),

$$\begin{aligned}
\mathbf{w}(k) &= \mathbf{A}^\dagger \mathbf{t}(k) \\
\mathbf{e}(k) &= \mathbf{A}\mathbf{w}(k) - \mathbf{t}(k) \\
t^{(m)}(k+1) &= t^{(m)}(k) + \eta(e^{(m)}(k) \pm |e^{(m)}(k)|), \quad m = 1, 2 \ldots M
\end{aligned}$$

where, the "+" ("−") sign is chosen if $t^{(m)}$ is negative (positive).

(a) Show that the algorithm converges in a finite number of sweeps if the problem is linearly separable.

(b) Show that when, for some k, all the $e^{(m)}(m)$ have opposite signs with respect to $t^{(m)}(m)$, then the problem is not linearly separable. The algorithm should then be terminated.

Exercise 5.22 Prove Eq. 5.59 in the step-by-step pruning technique, that is, given any column vector a, and its normalized vector $\hat{a}$, then

$$||U|a||_F = ||U|\hat{a}||_F = ||U^T \hat{a}||_F$$

Exercise 5.23 Show that by the step-by-step Search Procedure in Section 5.4.4 the Frobenius norm of the approximation error of the net value can be computed as

$$||U/B_k||_F^2 = ||U||_F^2 - \sum_{i=1}^{k} v(Index(k))$$

Exercise 5.24 Prove the step-by-step optimality theorem by using the following hints.

Note that (cf. Figure 5.10) $U|B_k = U - U/B_k$. By Pascal's Theorem, we have

$$||U||_F^2 = ||U|B_k||_F^2 + ||U/B_k||_F^2 \tag{5.61}$$

Therefore, it is obvious that minimizing the Frobenius approximation error of

$$||U - U|B_k||_F^2$$

is equivalent to maximizing $||U|B_k||_F^2$. Again, by Pascal's Theorem,

$$||U|B_k||_F^2 = ||U|B_{k-1}||_F^2 + ||U|(a_{Index(k)}/B_{k-1})||_F^2$$

so the minimum approximation error can be achieved by finding the Index(k) that maximizes $||U|(a_{Index(k)}/B_{k-1})||_F^2$.

Exercise 5.25 (A MAP Perspective for the Gaussian RBF Model)
This problem shows that regularization is related to the *MAP* approach in *Bayes Estimation* [228]. Basically, different constraints in the problems can be represented as the *a priori* probability $Prob(\phi)$ of mapping function ϕ. The goal is to estimate the mapping function ϕ that can maximize the *a posteriori* probability $Prob(\phi/d)$

of solution ϕ given training data d. This is called the *maximum a posteriori (MAP)* estimation. By the *Bayes theory*,

$$\propto Prob(\phi)Prob(d/\phi)$$

where $Prob(\phi)$ is the prior probability function of the process associated with ϕ, and $Prob(d/\phi)$ is the conditional probability density of data d given solution ϕ. Assume that ϕ is a Gaussian process and

$$Prob(\phi) \propto e^{-\|P\phi\|^2}$$

If we further assume that the noise corrupting the training data d is white, additive, and Gaussian with variance σ^2, then

$$Prob(d/\phi) \propto e^{-\frac{1}{2\sigma^2}\|\phi-d\|^2}$$

where $\phi - d$ represents the noise. Then the MAP is equivalent to minimize

$$\| \phi - d \|^2 + \lambda \| P\phi \|^2$$

Show that this special case of MAP estimation is essentially the same as the regularization formulation.

Exercise 5.26 Show that for the interpolation problem, if

$$f_i(\mathbf{x}) = \frac{sin(\|\mathbf{x}-\mathbf{x}_i\|)}{\|\mathbf{x}-\mathbf{x}_i\|}$$

and the training data are uniformly spaced with interval 1 (i.e., sampling interval $= 1$), then the function

$$\phi(\mathbf{x}) = \sum_i c_i f_i(\mathbf{x})$$

is basically the same as what is derived by the classical sampling theorem.

Exercise 5.27 (Generalization Error) Assume K training samples are drawn independently from a distribution D. Let $Prob(\gamma, \epsilon)$ denote the probability that there exists a network *in F* which can achieve less than $(1-\gamma)\epsilon$ misclassification (in fraction) on the training set and yet the misclassification on the test pattern from the same distribution D is higher than ϵ [284]. The $Prob(\gamma, \epsilon)$ has an upper bound: $Prob(\gamma, \epsilon) < 8\Delta_F(2K)e^{-\gamma^2\epsilon K/4}$, where $\Delta_F(2K)$ is the number of possible assignments which is classifiable by F. Although $\Delta_F(K)$ grows exponentially with K when K is small, it tapers off when K exceeds the so-called VC dimension. (This is the defining characteristic of the VC dimension.) Show that

(a) The larger K the smaller the upperbound of $Prob(\gamma, \epsilon)$ becomes.

(b) The less the number of weights the smaller is the upperbound of $Prob(\gamma, \epsilon)$. (This is because $\Delta_F(K)$ will decrease.)

Exercise 5.28 To design a neural model with fault tolerance, the energy function should be less sensitive to variation of the hidden (input) node values. For example, one possible energy function is that

$$E_{new} = E_{lse} + \beta \sum_{k=1}^{H} [\frac{\partial E_{lse}}{\partial a_k(1)}]^2$$

Based on this energy function, derive the following:

$$
\begin{aligned}
E_{new} &= \sum_{m=1}^{M} \{(t^m - y^m)^2 + \beta \sum_{k=1}^{H} [\frac{\partial(t^m - y^m)^2}{\partial a_k^m(1)}]^2\} \\
&= \sum_{m=1}^{M} \{(1 + 4\beta \sum_{k=1}^{H} w_k^2 [y^m(1-y^m)]^2)(t^m - y^m)^2\}
\end{aligned}
$$

Exercise 5.29 For the maximum likelihood estimator, we want to maximize (given each training pattern $\mathbf{x} = \mathbf{x}^{(m)}$)

$$P(\mathbf{x}|\Lambda) = \sum_{k=1}^{K} c_k^2 \frac{\prod_{n=1}^{N} \rho_{kn}}{(\sqrt{2\pi})^N} exp\{-\sum_{n=1}^{N}(\mathbf{x}(n) - \mu_k(n))^2 \rho_{kn}^2/2\}$$

under the constraint $\sum_{k=1}^{K} c_k^2 = 1$. Show that the following gradient-based method may be adopted to iteratively estimate the parameters

$$
\begin{aligned}
\frac{\partial P(\mathbf{x}|\Lambda)}{\partial \rho_{kn}} &= yc_k\{1/\rho_{kn} - \rho_{kn}(\mathbf{x}(n) - \mu_k(n))^2\} \\
\frac{\partial P(\mathbf{x}|\Lambda)}{\partial \mu_k(n)} &= yc_k \rho_{kn}^2(\mathbf{x}(n) - \mu_k(n)) \\
\frac{\partial P(\mathbf{x}|\Lambda)}{\partial c_k} &= 2y
\end{aligned}
$$

where

$$y = c_k \frac{\prod_{n=1}^{N} \rho_{kn}}{(\sqrt{2\pi})^N} exp\{-\sum_{n=1}^{N}(\mathbf{x}(n) - \mu_k(n))^2 \rho_{kn}^2/2\}$$

After each iteration, renormalization will be performed to comply with the constraint $\sum_{k=1}^{K} c_k^2 = 1$.

Exercise 5.30 Verify the approximation $tr\{\overline{V}''(\mathbf{w}^*)P_{\mathbf{w}}\} \approx 2\lambda d$. Show how to use this for derivation of Eq. 5.43.

PART IV: TEMPORAL MODELS

Chapter 6

Deterministic Temporal Neural Networks

6.1 Introduction

It is important to have a fundamental study on modeling and analysis of temporal neural networks, since temporal pattern recognition is omnipresent in practical applications. *Temporal patterns* and *static patterns* have fundamentally different characteristics. A static pattern is viewed as a random point in, say, an N-dimensional feature space. For example, a static vector formed from the prices of 10 different stocks at the same time is not sensitive to the listing order of the prices in the vector. The coordinates may be arbitrarily permuted without affecting the inherent distribution or the final classification of static patterns. In contrast, being a function of time, a temporal sequence must be order-sensitive. For example, a temporal vector formed from sampled prices of a given stock for 10 consecutive days is sensitive to the order of the prices. Similar concerns arise in many practical situations, such as speech, radar, and medical applications. As another example, suppose that two warped distortions of the same temporal pattern are represented by temporal vectors [0 0 1 1 0 1 1 1 0] and [0 1 1 0 1 1 0 0 0]. If they were treated as static vectors, the two vectors would likely be (mistakenly) classified into two different symbols due to the large Hamming distance (= 6).

In summary, for a neural model to fully exploit transient or contextual information, time must play a prominent role. Memoryless networks discussed in the previous chapters are, in general, inadequate for temporal pattern recognition. Temporal dynamic modeling deserves a totally innovative perspective. The temporal model must be chosen so as to adequately manifest the vital temporal characteristics and remain robust with respect to unpredictable temporal variations such as shift or warping. How to cope with such temporal variations or other distortion remains the most difficult challenge of all.

Memory Mechanisms in Temporal Models   The most crucial consideration is to incorporate some sort of memory unit into temporal neural models. The following are two popular memory mechanisms.

- In **deterministic networks**, the memory can be represented by *time-delay units*. Deterministic temporal networks constitute the main subject of this chapter. Typical examples are linear and nonlinear digital filters, time-delay neural networks(TDNNs), and other temporal dynamic models. In general, a neuron value at a specific time is a function of the present and past states of all the neurons. (In a layered structure, a neural value is a function of the neurons of any lower layers as well as the past states of all neural layers.) It is critical to identify a proper *discriminant function* for the temporal patterns, which dictates the neural model training criteria. The least-squares approximation error criterion is adopted by the TDNNs. The predictive error criterion, in contrast, is effective for capturing transient characteristics of the temporal signals.

- In **stochastic networks**, such as hidden Markov models, the memory mechanism is implicitly manifested by a *state transition matrix*, which is trained to best model the temporal behavior. The most popular training criterion is the *maximum likelihood criterion*. Given a temporal sequence O, find the model Λ which is most likely to have generated the sequence. In other words, now the training criterion is based on the likelihood function, $Prob(O|\Lambda)$. Stochastic networks will be treated in Chapter 7.

Another alternative is to obviate altogether the need for explicit memory units by using proper preprocessing. As discussed in Section 4.4.3, for example, the dynamic-time-warping(DTW) approach needs no explicit delays or other memory mechanisms.

Chapter Organization

This chapter introduces basic linear and nonlinear temporal dynamic models. Section 6.2 introduces the basic linear filter structures, including both non-recursive and recursive filters. A state-space formulation for the filters is proposed. It facilitates the derivation of the adaptive learning recursive filters. For modeling complex system behaviors, in Section 6.3, linear models are extended to nonlinear temporal dynamic models (TDMs). The feedforward (i.e., non-recurrent) time-delay neural networks(TDNNs) and the recurrent neural networks(RNNs) are presented. The training rule for the feedforward time-delay models follows directly the conventional back-propagation algorithm. Similarly, the training rule for RNNs can be derived as a (straightforward) extension of the learning algorithms used for the conventional recursive filters. For most general TDMs, a Hamiltonian-Jacobian learning rule can be adopted. It not only offers a unification framework for the existing learning rules for RNNs but also potentially introduces a fundamental learning principle for dynamic models. Finally, Section 6.4 presents the (independent training) prediction-based networks. The prediction-based neural classifier shares the same theoretical basis as the linear predictive classifier(LPC) well-known in the signal-processing community. It is especially suitable for transient signal recognition and has been successfully applied to ECG and other signal classifications.

6.2   Linear Temporal Dynamic Models

Let us, for simplicity, assume that an OCON approach is adopted. There are as many subnets as there are different classes in the overall classification system. As an example, Figure 6.1 shows a parametric model for one subnet (i.e., for one class), which produces certain estimation values or discriminant functions. The output of the model is denoted by $y(n)$, which can, in general, be expressed as

$$y(n) = \phi[n, y(n-p), \cdots, y(n-1), x(n-q), \cdots, x(n-1), x(n); W]$$

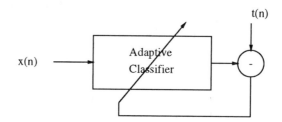

Figure 6.1: Basic schematic diagram for an adaptive classifier.

The teacher value is the desired output of the model, denoted by $t(n)$. The objective of the algorithm is to minimize the least-squares-error criterion:

$$E = \sum_n e(n)^2 \equiv \sum_n [t(n) - y(n)]^2 \tag{6.1}$$

This section is focused on basic structures and adaptive algorithms for linear digital filters. Two important classes are *nonrecursive* and *recursive* filters [212]. They are also referred to as *finite impulse response* (FIR) and *infinite impulse response* (IIR) filters.

1. **FIR Nonrecursive Filter:** For FIR filters, the output $y(n)$ is a function of finite past input values, the present input being either inclusive or exclusive. That is, the output is a weighted running average of the input $x(n)$:

$$y(n) = \sum_{k=0}^{q} \beta_k x(n-k) \tag{6.2}$$

The above FIR filter is also called an **all-zero** filter.

2. **IIR Recursive Filter:** The recursive filters may be divided into all-pole and zero-pole types.

- For the **all-pole** model, the output $y(n)$ is a linear regression of its (finite) past output values and the present input:

$$y(n) = \sum_{k=1}^{p} \alpha_k y(n-k) + x(n)$$

- The **pole-zero** model follows the so-called *autoregressive moving-average* (ARMA) dynamic equation

$$y(n) = \sum_{k=1}^{p} \alpha_k y(n-k) + \sum_{k=0}^{q} \beta_k x(n-k) \qquad (6.3)$$

This model is the most versatile among all the above structures.

In the following, we first discuss the liner prediction method based on the FIR filter. Second, we present a state-space formulation for the adaptive algorithms associated with the recursive (IIR) filters. While linear filters have very limited classification capability compared with nonlinear models, they can serve as effective signal preprocessors. Also, the theoretical ground established here for linear models is easily generalized to the nonlinear models treated in the next section.

6.2.1   Non-recursive Linear Predictive Filter

The structure for a linear classifier can be either FIR or IIR. In the linear prediction method [186], an FIR predictive filter is adopted:

$$y(n) = \sum_{k=1}^{p} \beta_k x(n-k)$$

In the case of a prediction filter, the output cannot be a function of the *present* input value $x(n)$. In fact, $x(n)$ is used as the teacher value, that is, $t(n) = x(n)$. The prediction error is

$$e(n) = x(n) - y(n) = x(n) - \sum_{k=1}^{q} \beta_k x(n-k) \qquad (6.4)$$

The discriminant function is simply the least-squares-error criterion function:

$$
\begin{aligned}
E &= \sum_{n} e^2(n) \\
&= \sum_{n} [x(n) - \sum_{k=1}^{q} \beta_k x(n-k)]^2 \\
&= \sum_{n} [x(n) - \sum_{i=1}^{q} \beta_i x(n-i)][x(n) - \sum_{k=1}^{q} \beta_k x(n-k)]
\end{aligned}
$$

$$= \sum_n [x^2(n) - 2\sum_i \beta_i x(n-i)x(n) + \sum_i \sum_k \beta_i \beta_k x(n-i)x(n-k)]$$

$$= \phi_{00} - 2\sum_i \beta_i \phi_{i0} + \sum_i \sum_k \beta_i \beta_k \phi_{ik}$$

where $\phi_{ik} = \sum_n x(n-i)x(n-k)$. The lower and upper limits of the summing indices are deliberately omitted here. (See Problem 6.1.) Note that the optimal weights must satisfy

$$\frac{\partial E}{\partial \beta_i} = 0 \qquad (6.5)$$

This leads to the Yule-Walker equation:

$$\sum_{k=1}^{p} \beta_k \phi_{ik} = \phi_{i0} \qquad (6.6)$$

for $i = 1, \cdots, p$. Therefore, the optimal weights can be directly computed from the Yule-Walker equation [186]. For this case, the conventional gradient-type learning is not favored.

For many signal generation environments, the linear prediction method matches well with the underlying physical models. In real world applications, it has been an effective technique for speech data compression and image coding [118, 296]. A prominent example is the vocal-tract model for speech generation. The vocal-tract parameters are often represented by either the linear predictive coding (LPC) coefficients or the corresponding reflection coefficients (denoted as $\{k_m\}$). As another example, in coding applications, a quantized (digitized) sequence $y(n)$ can be recovered from the digital sequence $e(n) = \hat{y}(n) - y(n)$, where $\hat{y}(n)$ is the quantized prediction of $y(n)$. The entropy of the prediction error $e(n)$ is generally much less than that of $y(n)$; thus, it can be encoded into fewer bits per sample.

6.2.2 Recursive (IIR) Adaptive Filters

For greater flexibility, the classifier can be modeled by a recursive ARMA filter:

$$y(n) = \sum_{k=1}^{q} \alpha_k y(n-k) + \sum_{k=1}^{p} \beta_k x(n-k)$$

$$= \alpha(D)y(n) + \beta(D)x(n) \qquad (6.7)$$

where

$$\alpha(D) = \sum_{k=1}^{q} \alpha_k D^k \quad \text{and} \quad \beta(D) = \sum_{k=1}^{p} \beta_k D^k$$

denote polynomials of delay operators. The usage of these polynomial operators should be self-explanatory. For example, $D^k y(n) = y(n - k)$.

The training algorithm for a recursive filter structure is more involved. In general, the gradient-type approach is adopted. The filter coefficients are updated with the objective of minimizing the error energy function in Eq. 6.1. Define

$$y'_{\alpha_m}(n) \equiv \frac{\partial y(n)}{\partial \alpha_m} \quad \text{and} \quad y'_{\beta_m}(n) \equiv \frac{\partial y(n)}{\partial \beta_m}$$

then

$$\frac{\partial E}{\partial \alpha_m} = 2e(n)y'_{\alpha_m}(n) \quad \text{and} \quad \frac{\partial E}{\partial \beta_m} = 2e(n)y'_{\beta_m}(n)$$

The gradients $y'_{\alpha_m}(n)$ and $y'_{\beta_m}(n)$ may be directly derived by taking gradients on Eq. 6.7:

$$y'_{\alpha_m}(n) = D^m y(n) + \alpha(D) y'_{\alpha_m}(n)$$
$$y'_{\beta_m}(n) = D^m x(n) + \alpha(D) y'_{\beta_m}(n)$$

Equivalently, in a more conventional notation, we have

$$y'_{\alpha_m}(n) = y(n - m) + \sum_{k=1}^{q} \alpha_k y'_{\alpha_m}(n - k)$$

$$y'_{\beta_m}(n) = x(n - m) + \sum_{k=1}^{q} \alpha_k y'_{\beta_m}(n - k)$$

For these and subsequent gradient equations, all the initial conditions are assumed to be zero.

6.2.3 State-Space Representations

State-Space Realization It is well-known in linear system theory that a high-order filter may be represented by a first-order state-space realization:

$$\mathbf{a}(n) = W\mathbf{a}(n - 1) + \mathbf{u}x(n - 1) \tag{6.8}$$
$$y(n) = \mathbf{v}\,\mathbf{a}(n) + dx(n) \tag{6.9}$$

where W is a $P \times P$ *state-feedback matrix*, and $\mathbf{u}$ and $\mathbf{v}$ are P-dimensional input and output *transformation vectors*. The state vector, comprising the P state variables, $\mathbf{a}(n) = [a_1(n), a_2(n), \cdots, a_P(n)]^T$, must fully reflect the condition of the system at that time. A concise definition of the state was suggested by Kailath [126]: *a state is a sufficient statistic which contains enough information to enable the calculation of the future responses without further reference to the old history of inputs and responses.* The term *minimal realization* refers to a state-space realization using a minimal number of state variables. Therefore, a minimal state is a minimal sufficient statistic which contains just enough information to enable the calculation of the future responses.

Given a (linear or nonlinear) filter structure, it is quite straightforward to describe its dynamic behavior via a state-space formulation. A state vector can be obtained by taking all the (immediate) outputs of the delay nodes as the state variables. The ij-th element of the feedback matrix, w_{ij}, can be obtained by taking into account all the paths (direct and indirect) from the output of i-th delay to input of j-th delay, as long as they do not pass through any delay elements. Barring degenerative situations, [1] such a state-space model is a minimal realization.

Example 6.1 (Canonical State-Space Realization for ARMA Filter)

As an example, the ARMA model in Eq. 6.7 has a canonical realization as shown in Figure 6.2(a). (For simplicity, here we assume $p = q$ and $\beta_0 = 0$.) Let the state variables be the output values of all the delays. Then

$$W = \begin{bmatrix} \alpha_1 & \alpha_2 & \alpha_3 \\ 1 & 0 & 0 \\ 0 & 1 & 0 \end{bmatrix}$$

$$\mathbf{u} = \begin{bmatrix} 1 & 0 & 0 \end{bmatrix}^T$$

$$\mathbf{v} = \begin{bmatrix} \beta_1 & \beta_2 & \beta_3 \end{bmatrix}$$

Note that there exist many other closely related realizations [126].

The state space realizations are not unique. Different realizations can have very different numerical properties of stability and convergence. This raises the question of the design criteria for an optimal filter. A major drawback of the direct form is that some poles of the adaptive filter may become unstable during the adaptation. If this occurs, the output can grow without bound.

---

[1] Degeneration can occur only when there are uncontrollable or unobservable states, using a linear system theoretical terminology.

Therefore, it is critical to have some assurance on the system stability. For the direct form realization (cf. Figure 6.2(a)), however, it is very difficult to monitor and control such instability. Several alternate realizations, for example, (1) cascade form, (2) parallel form, and (3) lattice form, lend themselves more naturally to such stability checking.

Cascade and Parallel Filters   In the **cascade form**, the rational transfer function is first factorized into a product of second-order factors. Each second-order section can be realized in a pole-zero structure. The filter is then constructed by cascading all the second-order sections in tandem. The **parallel form** is derived from a partial fraction expansion (in terms of second-order factors) of the rational transfer function. Now all the second-order sections are arranged in parallel. The filter output is the sum of all outputs of the second-order sections. A common disadvantage of both of these forms is that there are many global minima which can be obtained by reordering the poles among the different sections. It may lead to saddle points on the manifold of equivalent sections that separate the global minima [207]. Furthermore, the cascaded form usually has a slower convergence rate [258]. In that respect, the gradient computation with the parallel form is superior to the cascaded form.

Lattice Filters   The structure of the lattice filter is illustrated in Figure 6.2(b). A lattice filter is characterized by a set of reflection coefficients $\{k_m\}$. The lattice filter is known to be less sensitive to finite-word-length effects. It has a superior numerical stability than the direct form. More importantly, no special effort is needed to monitor the stability of the system. *A system is stable if and only if all the reflection coefficients satisfy $|k_m| < 1$* [186]. Its advantage over the parallel form lies in that the adaptive lattice filter has no saddle points since there is a unique lattice representation corresponding to any given direct form. Consequently, it has a convergence property very similar to that of the direct form [258].

Generalized State-Space Representation   Utilizing the delay operators D, Eq. 6.8 can be rewritten as

$$\mathbf{a}(n) = WD\mathbf{a}(n) + \mathbf{u}Dx(n) \tag{6.10}$$

To provide an extra flexibility in representing a filter structure (e.g., lattice), a *generalized state-space realization* is proposed:

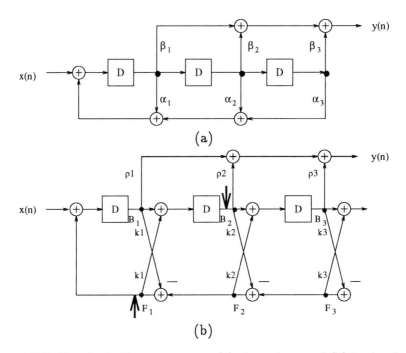

Figure 6.2: Two basic filter structures: (a) direct form and (b) lattice form.

$$\mathbf{a}(n) = W(D)\mathbf{a}(n) + \mathbf{u}(D)x(n) \qquad (6.11)$$
$$y(n) = \mathbf{v}\, \mathbf{a}(n) + dx(n)$$

where $W(D)$ and $\mathbf{u}(D)$ are, respectively, a *first order* polynomial matrix and vector of the delay operator D. The advantage of the generalized state-space realization lies in its flexibility in the state variable assignment. Any output, given in Eq. 6.9, could now be assigned as a (non-hidden) state variable under the generalized formulation. (See Problem 6.8.) The state dimension has to increase since redundant states are introduced. Despite the higher dimensionality, however, it is possible to incur fewer operations because of a sparser state-feedback matrix. This is illustrated in Example 6.2. The generalized representation is equally amenable to nonlinear recurrent neural networks (RNNs), cf. Figure 6.5.

Example 6.2 (Generalized State-Space Realization of Lattice Filter)

We consider, for simplicity, a third-order lattice filter with three lattice sections. The state variables, as labeled in Figure 6.2(b), obey the following relationship:

$$B(n) = \begin{bmatrix} 0 & 0 & 0 \\ D & 0 & 0 \\ 0 & D & 0 \end{bmatrix} B(n) + \begin{bmatrix} D & 0 & 0 \\ k_1 D & 0 & 0 \\ 0 & k_2 D & 0 \end{bmatrix} F(n) + \begin{bmatrix} D \\ 0 \\ 0 \end{bmatrix} x(n)$$

$$F(n) = \begin{bmatrix} -k_1 & 0 & 0 \\ 0 & -k_2 & 0 \\ 0 & 0 & -k_3 \end{bmatrix} B(n) + \begin{bmatrix} 0 & 1 & 0 \\ 0 & 0 & 1 \\ 0 & 0 & 0 \end{bmatrix} F(n)$$

Lumping all the states in a long vector, we have

$$\mathbf{a}(n) = \begin{bmatrix} B(n) \\ F(n) \end{bmatrix}$$

Then the state space of the lattice filter is given as

$$\mathbf{a}(n) = W(D)\mathbf{a}(n) + \mathbf{u}(D)x(n)$$

where

$$W(D) = \left[\begin{array}{ccc|ccc} 0 & 0 & 0 & D & 0 & 0 \\ D & 0 & 0 & k_1 D & 0 & 0 \\ 0 & D & 0 & 0 & k_2 D & 0 \\ \hline -k_1 & 0 & 0 & 0 & 1 & 0 \\ 0 & -k_2 & 0 & 0 & 0 & 1 \\ 0 & 0 & -k_3 & 0 & 0 & 0 \end{array} \right], \quad \mathbf{u}(D) = \left[\begin{array}{c} D \\ 0 \\ 0 \\ \hline 0 \\ 0 \\ 0 \end{array} \right] \qquad (6.12)$$

Note that the generalized state-space realization has a state dimension $P = 2K$, where K denotes the filter order, which doubles the dimension of the minimal realization. The advantage, however, is that the state feedback matrix is very sparse and has only $O(K)$ nonzero parameters. In contrast, a minimal realization has the state dimension $= K$. It can be derived by assigning the outputs of the delays as the (only) state variables, for example, B_1, B_2, and B_3 in Figure 6.2(b). However, the state feedback matrix is not sparse, and there are roughly $\frac{K^2}{2}$ nonzero parameters. (See Problem 6.5.)

Adaptive Algorithm for State Space Representation   The training algorithm for a recursive filter structure has been extensively studied. See [38, 215, 259, 276, 303] for more detailed discussion and references. The adaptive algorithms for both conventional and generalized state space representations can be derived in a very similar fashion. Suppose that $W(D)$ is parameterized by $\gamma_m, \forall m = 1, ..., M$. To compute the gradients with respect to these parameters, we note that

$$\frac{\partial E}{\partial \gamma_m} = \sum_{p=1}^{P} \frac{\partial E}{\partial a_p} \frac{\partial a_p}{\partial \gamma_m}, \quad \forall m = 1, ..., M$$

Denote the gradient vector:

$$\mathbf{a}'_{\gamma_m}(n) \equiv \frac{\partial \mathbf{a}(n)}{\partial \gamma_m}$$

From Eq. 6.11, the gradient vector can be obtained as

$$\mathbf{a}'_{\gamma_m}(n) = W(D)\mathbf{a}'_{\gamma_m}(n) + \frac{\partial W(D)}{\partial \gamma_m}\mathbf{a}(n) + \frac{\partial \mathbf{u}(D)}{\partial \gamma_m}x(n) \qquad (6.13)$$

The dynamic equations for the gradients $(\mathbf{a}'_{\gamma_m})$ are the same as that of the original filter, but with different inputs. Since the poles of the system remain the same, we conclude that the *dynamic system for the gradients is stable as long as the original filter is stable throughout the training phase.*

Example 6.3 (Adaptive Training of Lattice Filter)

Again let us refer to the lattice filter structure in Figure 6.2(b). The gradient vector with respect to k_1, say, can be computed as

$$\mathbf{a}'_{k_1}(n) = W(D)\mathbf{a}'_{k_1}(n) + \begin{bmatrix} 0 \\ DF_2(n) \\ 0 \\ \hline -B_1(n) \\ 0 \\ 0 \end{bmatrix}$$

On the right-hand-side, the first feedback term is identical to that of the original filter (Eq. 6.12) signaling that the same lattice structure (Figure 6.2(b)) is reusable for the gradient filter. The second vector term suggests that the *inputs to the adaptive gradient filter are $F_2(n-1)$ and $-B_1(n)$, which are obtained from the original filter. The proper locations to apply these two values (as inputs) are marked by the "↓" and "↑" signs in Figure 6.2(b). For another example, see Problem 6.6.*

6.3 Nonlinear Temporal Dynamic Models

Linear filters can offer only very limited classification capability. Most real-world applications must involve nonlinear temporal dynamic models (TDMs). Analogous to non-recursive and recursive filters in Section 6.2, nonlinear TDMs are also divided into two categories: non-recurrent time-delay neural networks(TDNNs) and recurrent neural networks(RNNs). The gradient-based training algorithm for non-recurrent TDNNs follows the same scheme as the conventional back-propagation. The adaptive learning algorithms for RNNs and recursive filters have a striking similarity, particularly in their state-space formulations. Consequently, the learning rule also follows the same principle in the state-space model, cf. Eq. 6.8 and Eq. 6.13. Note also that, in the adaptive environment, a thorough analysis on the stability of nonlinear neural models is very critical [52].

6.3.1 Nonrecurrent Temporal Dynamic Model (TDNN)

Nonrecurrent temporal dynamic models have a variety of structures. One early example is a network with delays appearing only on the input layer, A prominent example is NETtalk. A more complex example incorporates delays in the hidden layer(s), as well as the input layer, leading to the so-called time-delay neural network (TDNN).

NETtalk With reference to Figure 6.3(a), the input field comprises several groups of units, connected by time-delay elements. It is shown that the current vector (the center group) is accompanied by two preceding and two succeeding vectors. This arrangement has the purpose of better utilizing the contextual information in the temporal signal. A well-known example is NETtalk, a two-layer TDNN that learns to turn text into speech [255]. Extending the basic structure of Figure 6.3(a), NETtalk is depicted in Figure 6.3(b). NETtalk can be trained to convert graphemes to phonemes. It takes strings of characters forming English text and converts them into strings of phonemes that can serve as an input to a speech synthesizer. NETtalk requires a long training time, roughly 12 CPU hours of training on a DEC

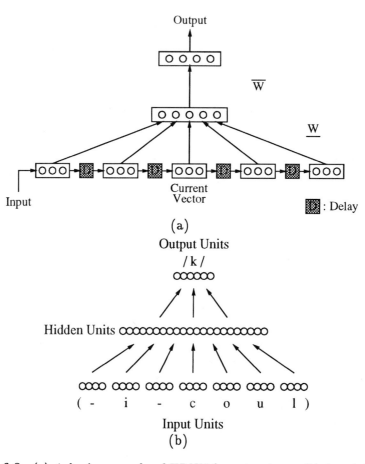

Figure 6.3: (a) A basic example of TDNN is a structure with input delays. (b)NETtalk network. The input has 7 groups with 29 units in each group. For the corpus of continuous speech, there are 80 hidden units and 26 output nodes. A threshold unit is used for each hidden and output unit.

VAX. Its training accuracy is nearly 95%, but test accuracy drops to as low as 78%. Nevertheless, most of the errors are close enough to the correct phonemes so that the synthesized speech is largely comprehensible. DECtalk, a commercial product by Digital Equipment Corporation, uses a complex rule-based expert system developed over a number of years. It yields only a slightly higher accuracy. A comparison study of the same type of TDNN and the hidden Markov model was reported in [35].

TDNN To help capture the salient features in temporal signals, it was proposed by Waibel et al. [295] to expand the hidden layer by adding multiple (orthogonal) delay-lines, one delay-line for each of the original hidden units. As shown in Figure 6.4, this leads to a structure with 2-dimensional delay arrays. Such a network structure is called *Time-Delay Neural Network* (TDNN). The TDNN is non-recurrent and copes with time alignment by explicitly delaying the signal waveform by a fixed time span.

Successful demonstration on TDNN's application to phoneme recognition was reported in [295]. As depicted in Figure 6.4, the ACON neural model constructed from a three-layer TDNN is adopted. The input layer is itself a tapped-delay-line. Both hidden layers are expanded into two-dimensional time-delay arrays. The conventional BP algorithm can be adopted to train the weights. Theoretically speaking, this comprehensive delay structure should enable the capture of vital temporal acoustic-phonetic features. However, in practice, it may not be easy to have the network converge to such an ideal state. Another application experiment was conducted [111], where an OCON TDNN structure was adopted for isolated English speech recognition. The model was trained by the discriminative training method. In addition, a special parametric representation was adopted to fine-tune the decision boundaries. The OCON TDNN yielded a favorable performance over several better known methods.

In terms of real-world applications, the TDNN suffers from several critical drawbacks. The complexity of the structure usually requires a time-consuming training process. The prefixed span of the time-delay-lines renders it less suitable for heavily warped (speech) signals. Moreover, the TDNN is quite sensitive to ambient noise, causing significant performance degradation when speech signals are noise corrupted. The theoretical analysis and empirical remedy pertaining to the TDNN structure remain open research subjects.

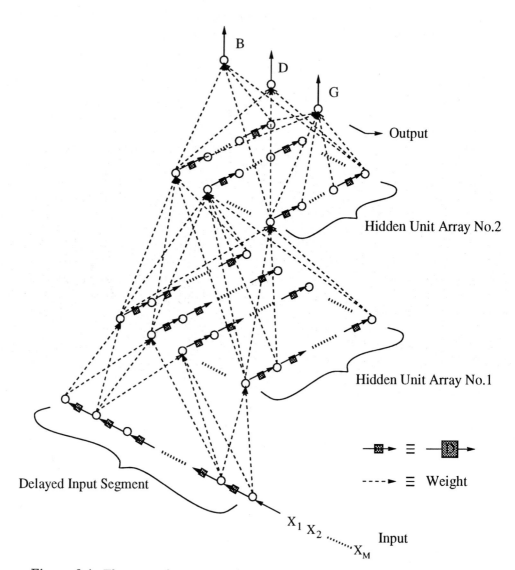

Figure 6.4: The network structure for a TDNN phoneme recognizer for three phonemes "B","D", and "G". The input layer is basically a tapped-delay-line, while the hidden layers contain two-dimensional arrays of time delay units.

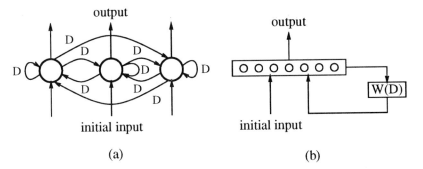

Figure 6.5: Two forms for state-space representation of a single-layer RNN.

6.3.2   Recurrent Neural Networks (RNN)

A major alternative to TDNN is to incorporate delay feedbacks into temporal
dynamic models, making them recurrent. This leads to the so-called *recurrent neural network* (RNN) [242, 246, 299, 306]. For example, a multi-layer
network may be made recurrent by introducing time-delay loops to the input,
hidden, and/or output layers. Another way is to route delay connections from
one layer to another. As a result of such a structural change, the gradient
computation for the RNNs involves a complex back-propagation rule through
both time and space.

A very important class of RNNs is represented by single-layer recurrent
models such as those shown in Figure 6.5(a). This model serves to reduce
the network complexity. The state-space representation again proves very
useful for RNNs. The states can be either fully or sparsely interconnected.
Some direct connections between the neurons (without delay) may also be
accommodated. This is shown in Figure 6.5(b). In this case, the model can
be approximated by "unfolding" the network over a finite time period into
a multi-layer network. Then the conventional back-propagation learning rule
can be applied with the restriction that all the unfolded weights must be
uniform. (See Problem 6.10.) This formulation is similar to the learning
algorithm for the hidden Markov model, cf. Chapter 7.

Learning Algorithm via State Space Representation   The adaptive
learning algorithms for the RNNs and recursive filters share the same theoretical ground. Both derivations benefit greatly from the state-space representation. The state-space nonlinear dynamics for the RNN is represented
by

$$a_i(n) = f(u_i(n-1)) = f(\sum_j w_{ij} a_j(n-1)) \tag{6.14}$$

Using the delay operator D, it follows that

$$a_i(n) = f(\mathbf{u}) = f(\sum_j w_{ij} D a_j(n)) \tag{6.15}$$

Here the vector $\mathbf{u}$ is formed from the net values. The input, which sets the starting state initially, is omitted here. Just as in the recursive filters, a generalized state space realization provides a more versatile representation:

$$\mathbf{a}(n) = f(\mathbf{u}) = f(W(D)\mathbf{a}(n)) \tag{6.16}$$

where $W(D)$ is a first order polynomial matrix of the delay operator D. Suppose, also, that all the entries $\{w_{ij}(D)\}$ are represented by the free parameters $\gamma_m, \forall m = 1, ..., M$. Following the same derivation for Eq. 6.13, the gradients can be computed from

$$\mathbf{a}'_{\gamma_m}(n) = f'(\mathbf{u}) \left[W(D)\mathbf{a}'_{\gamma_m}(n) + \frac{\partial W(D)}{\partial \gamma_m} \mathbf{a}(n) \right] \tag{6.17}$$

Note that the state space representation in Eq. 6.14 can be regarded as a special case, where $w_{ij}(D) = w_{ij}D$. In this case, the weights $\{w_{ij}\}$ are all free parameters. Applying the formula in Eq. 6.17 and replacing $\{\gamma_m\}$ by $\{w_{ij}\}$, we obtain

$$
\mathbf{a}'_{w_{ij}}(n) = f'(\mathbf{u}) \left\{ W D \mathbf{a}'_{w_{ij}}(n) + \begin{bmatrix} 0 & \cdots & & & 0 \\ \vdots & \ddots & & & \vdots \\ 0 & \cdots & D & \cdots & 0 \\ \vdots & & & \ddots & \vdots \\ 0 & & \cdots & & 0 \end{bmatrix} \mathbf{a}(n) \right\}
$$

$$
= f'(\mathbf{u}) \left\{ W D \mathbf{a}'_{w_{ij}}(n) + \begin{bmatrix} 0 \\ \vdots \\ D a_j(n) \\ \vdots \\ 0 \end{bmatrix} \leftarrow i_{th} \right\}
$$

This formula can be rewritten in an explicit form

$$\frac{\partial a_k(n)}{\partial w_{ij}} = f'(u_k(n-1))[\delta_{ki}a_j(n-1) + \sum_j w_{kj}\frac{\partial a_k(n-1)}{\partial w_{ij}}] \qquad (6.18)$$

This is the same as the *real-time recurrent learning* (RTRL) formula proposed by Williams and Zipser [306]. The initial condition for the iterative algorithm is set to be zero; that is, $\frac{\partial a_k(0)}{\partial w_{ij}} = 0$.

The error measure for an individual output node at time t is

$$e_k(n) = \begin{cases} t_k(n) - a_k(n), & \text{if } t_k(n) \text{ is specified at time n} \\ 0, & \text{otherwise} \end{cases}$$

The total cost function is

$$E(N) = \frac{1}{2}\sum_k [e_k(n)]^2$$

By the gradient-descent method, the learning rule is

$$\Delta w_{ij}(n) = -\eta\frac{\partial E(n)}{\partial w_{ij}} = \eta\sum_k e_k(n)\frac{\partial a_k(n)}{\partial w_{ij}}$$

For a fully connected recurrent net with N units, there are N^3 derivatives $(\frac{\partial a_k}{\partial w_{ij}}, 1 \leq i,j,k \leq N)$ to be computed or N^4 total operations for each iteration. (Each actual updating takes only proportional to N operations.) If the nets are sparsely connected (such as digital filters) with M model parameters (γ_m), the number of derivatives to be computed is dramatically reduced to PN, amounting to PN^2 operations for each iteration.

Stability Issue   So far only very scarce results on stability are known, so our treatment, of necessity, is very brief. The stability of the normal recurrent net has a simple stability condition: it is stable if all the eigenvalues of W have magnitude less than 1. As to the stability of the gradient computation, we note that the original feedback matrix is now scaled by a constant $f'(u)$, so as long as $|f'(u)| \leq 1$ the stability condition will remain intact. For the sigmoid function, $f(u) = \frac{1}{1+e^{-u/\sigma}}$, this condition can be met simply by requiring σ to be less than or equal to .25. (See Problem 6.9.) This stability condition is deceptively simple, however, since there is no easy way to monitor the eigenvalues on line. This prompts the use of a sparse, but more structured, network configuration. For some structures, such as lattice filters, it is possible to give explicit stability conditions. More research work is needed on this issue.

6.3.3 Hamiltonian Theoretical Approach to General Learning

There are several training formulations proposed [222, 225, 306] for temporal dynamic models (TDMs) under certain restrictive model assumptions. In order to develop a general learning theory, a fundamental theoretical footing must established for as broad a class of TDMs as possible. This motivates a unification framework based on the Hamiltonian-Jacobian system theory proposed by Ramacher [236]. It leads to a new energy formulation for the learning theory.

The Hamiltonian function (denoted by H) is characterized by a Jacobian *surface function J*:

$$\frac{\partial J}{\partial t} + H(t, a, \Delta) = 0, \quad with \quad \Delta_i \equiv \frac{\partial J}{\partial a_i}$$

where the Jacobian surface function $J(t, a(t); W(t))$ is obtained from

$$\frac{dJ(t, a(t); W(t))}{dt} = E(t, a(t); W(t))$$

where $E(t, a(t); W(t))$ denotes the (time-varying) cost function (e.g., squared-error). As before, { $a(t)$ } denotes the state vector, and $W(t) = \{ w_{ij}(t) \}$ denotes the weights. The function $\Delta_i(t, a(t); W(t))$ has a role very similar to that of the back-propagation error signal, introduced in Chapter 5.

The learning principle is based on finding a weight solution $W(t)$ minimizing the accumulated error E integrated over time

$$J(T) = \int_0^T E(\tau, a(\tau); W(\tau))d\tau + C$$

More precisely, it is based on finding an extremum (i.e., minimum) on the Jacobian surface function, that is, taking the first-order variation of any trajectory $\delta J(t, a(t); W(t))$ with respect to all weight functions { $\delta w_{ij}(t)$ } and making it equal to 0 (i.e., $\delta J = 0$). (See Problem 6.11 and [236].) This leads to the following *Hamiltonian-Jacobian learning rule*:

$$\frac{\partial H}{\partial w_{ij}}(t) = 0 \tag{6.19}$$

with the boundary conditions

$$\sum_k \Delta_k(T) \frac{\delta a_k}{\delta w_{ij}}(T) = 0 \quad \text{and} \quad \frac{\partial J}{\partial w_{ij}}(0) = 0 \qquad (6.20)$$

Eq. 6.19 implies that the convergent solution lies in an extremum (i.e., maximum) of the Hamiltonian surface function. To reach this solution, a gradient-type updating rule can be adopted:

$$\Delta w_{ij}(t) = \eta \frac{\partial H}{\partial w_{ij}}(t) \qquad (6.21)$$

So far we have only highlighted the general principle behind the *Hamiltonian-Jacobian learning rule*. For a better understanding, we now focus on a special *continuous-time* state-space model[2]

$$\frac{d}{dt} a_i(t) = F_i(t) \equiv -a_i(t) + f_i(\sum_{j=-1}^{N} w_{ij}(t) a_j(t)) \qquad \text{for } i = 1, \cdots, N \quad (6.22)$$

For this state-space model, the Hamiltonian function has the following form

$$H = \sum_j \Delta_j F_j(t, a; W) - E(t, a; W)$$

where Δ_i can be solved from

$$\frac{d\Delta_i}{dt} = -\frac{\partial H}{\partial a_i} \qquad (6.23)$$

based on the basic Hamiltonian PDE theory[140]. More explicitly, based on Eq. 6.22 and Eq. 6.23,

$$\frac{d\Delta_i}{dt} = \Delta_i(t) - \sum_j \Delta_j(t) f_j'(t) w_{ji}(t) + \frac{\partial E}{\partial a_i}(t) \qquad (6.24)$$

---

[2]With integral sampling instants $t = n = 0, \pm 1, \pm 2, \cdots$, Eq. 6.22 is approximately (assuming time-invariant case),

$$a_i(n) - a_i(n-1) = -a_i(n-1) + f_i(\sum_{j=-1}^{N} w_{ij} a_j(n-1))$$

So the model is an approximation of the discrete-time system, Eq. 6.14, and vice versa.

Both on-line and off-line learning formulas can now readily be derived [236]. For off-line training, for example, it is necessary to introduce a new training time variable, s, in addition to the original time variable t (for retrieving). With this modification and assuming $\frac{\partial J}{\partial w_{ij}}(0) = 0$ (cf. Eq. 6.20), the off-line learning formulas follow immediately Eqns. 6.21, 6.22, and 6.24:

$$\frac{dw_{ij}}{ds}(t, s) = \eta[\Delta_i(t, s)f_i'(t, s)a_j(t, s) - \frac{\partial E}{\partial w_{ij}}(t, s)]$$

where the (forward) state vector is calculated from

$$\frac{d}{dt}a_i(t, s) = -a_i(t, s) + f_i(\sum_j w_{ij}(t, s)a_j(t, s))$$

and the (back-propagated) error signal is

$$\frac{d\Delta_i}{dt}(t, s) = \Delta_i(t, s) - \sum_j \Delta_j(t, s)f_j'(t, s)w_{ji}(t, s) + \frac{\partial E}{\partial a_i}(t, s)$$

with the boundary condition $\Delta_i(T, s) = 0$.

The Hamiltonian-Jacobian learning rule provides a unified and more general framework to existing learning rules for RNN [146, 222, 225, 306]. For example, assuming that the models have constant weights (during the retrieving phase), then the updating formula becomes

$$\frac{dw_{ij}}{ds}(s) = \frac{1}{T}\int_0^T \frac{dw_{ij}}{ds}(t, s)dt = \frac{\eta}{T}\int_0^T [\Delta_i(t, s)f_i'(t, s)a_j(t, s) - \frac{\partial E}{\partial w_{ij}}(t, s)]dt$$

This is more general than the off-line learning rule, proposed in [222]. The latter applies only to the time-invariant (constant-weight) models, while the new formulation copes well with time-varying model and cost functions. It can also be shown that the "real-time" learning scheme [306] (cf. Eq. 6.17 and Eq. 6.18) is just a special case [236]. Further work (somewhat straightforward) is needed to extend the Hamiltonian analysis to RBF TDMs. Another issue, still open, is the stability of nonlinear neural systems, especially the relationship between stabilities of discrete-time and continuous-time dynamic systems [52].

6.4   Prediction-Based Temporal Networks

Ultimately, the temporal dynamic models must be designed according to the specific application needs. Typical temporal processings, such as differentiation, integration, prediction, smoothing, or harmonic analysis, all require specially tailored model structures. In this section, we propose a prediction-based neural model, for analysis of transient behaviors, and analyze its performance in the ECG recognition applications.

6.4.1 Prediction-Based Independent Training Model

The prediction-based classifier has the same theoretical basis as the linear predictive classifier(LPC). Since it is nonlinear, it offers a much more effective means to model nonlinear behaviors. Also it adopts the independent training scheme, so it is named *prediction-based independent training* (PBIT) model [315]. According to the OCON structure, one PBIT net is assigned to each class. Referring to Figure 6.6, the PBIT model combines a time-delay neural network and a (two-layer) back-propagation model, making it very similar to the NETtalk configuration.

A long sequence x with length $\bar{N}$ is input through a tapped-delay line, cf. Figure 6.6(a), from which a set of N-dimensional vectors ($N << \bar{N}$) are consecutively extracted:

$$\mathbf{x}_j = [x(j+1)\ldots x(j+N)] \tag{6.25}$$

where $x(n)$ denotes the n-th sample value of the signal sequence x. These N-dimensional vectors serve as the inputs to the back-propagation network. Each vector is processed to yield a best prediction for its immediate future sample $x(j + N + 1)$. The prediction function is represented by $f_a(\mathbf{x}_j) = f(\mathbf{x}_j, \mathbf{w})$ − a function of the current input vector $\mathbf{x}_j$ and the weight vector w. The function is usually either sigmoid LBF or Gaussian RBF.

For each training pattern, the discriminant function ϕ is defined as the (negative) squared prediction error,

$$\phi = - \sum_{j=0}^{\bar{N}-N-1} (f_a(\mathbf{x}_j) - x(j+N+1))^2 \tag{6.26}$$

In the **retrieving phase**, just like the DBNN, a pattern is input to *all* the PBIT subnets and is classified into the subnet which yields the largest discriminant function, (i.e., the smallest prediction error). In the **training phase**, the objective is to minimize the sum of the squared prediction errors of all the M training patterns in the same class,

$$E = \sum_{m=1}^{M} \sum_{j=0}^{\bar{N}-N-1} (f_a(\mathbf{x}_j) - x(j+N+1))^2 \tag{6.27}$$

(This complies with the independent training principle.) The gradient-type updating rule can be adopted:

$$\triangle \mathbf{w} = -\eta \frac{\partial E}{\partial \mathbf{w}}$$

As shown in Figure 6.6(a), the tapped-delay line is followed by a multi-layer network. For the latter net, a Gaussian RBF classifier is favored. It offers a natural clustering capability, which is good for approximation/generalization in many applications. (The initial centroids of the hidden nodes can be estimated by the K-mean or VQ clustering algorithm, which usually yields a fast convergence in the subsequent BP learning.) More importantly, the centroids of the Gaussian function can be trained to reflect the salient features in the signal. For example, some sample ECG waveforms are shown in Figure 6.7. It can be demonstrated that (cf. Figure 6.8) the centroids of the hidden nodes in the RBF networks actually capture the key segments in the original waveform. All but 2 of the 15 centroids represent the meaningful curves inherently embedded in the training ECG waveforms. When a test signal from the same class is presented, the trained centroids would be able to produce a close match and, therefore, a minimum prediction error.

We note that the window size for the PBIT model should be properly chosen so that it is robust with respect to time misalignments and uncertainty of the waveform length. Obviously, the window size must be adequate so that the information in each segment is sufficient to facilitate prediction. If the size is too large, it might hamper the network's ability to cope with temporal variations such as time misalignments.

6.4.2   Compare Static and Temporal Models for ECG Analysis

In this ECG classification experiment, there are 10 different classes. Each class has 10 sample waveforms, 5 used for training and the remaining, for testing. Some samples of the ECG pulses are shown in Figures 6.7(a) and (b). Both static and temporal networks are evaluated. Their generalization performance and tolerance to time misalignments are studied.

6.4.2.1   Static Models for ECG Analysis

In static models, the entire input waveform is treated as a long static input vector. For comparison, both decision and approximation based models are tried.

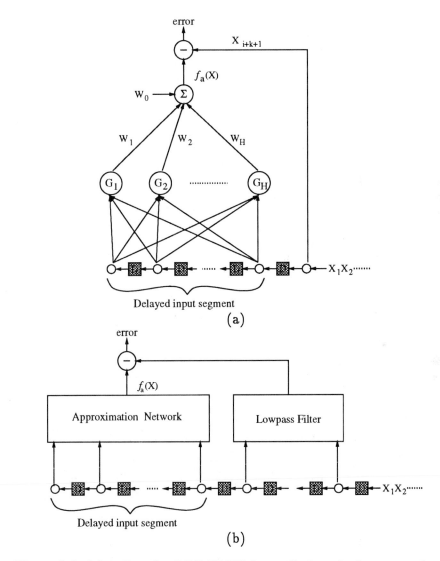

Figure 6.6: (a) A Gaussian RBF TDNN for prediction of a future sample. (b) Using output of a low-pass filter to replace the sample to be predicted.

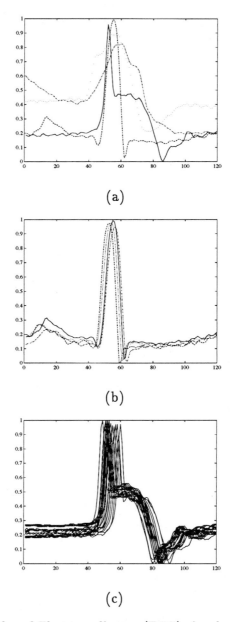

(a)

(b)

(c)

Figure 6.7: Samples of Electrocardiogram(ECG) signals: (a) original ECG waveforms from 4 different classes; (b) four ECG waveforms from the same class; and (c) time-shifted waveforms for the same class.

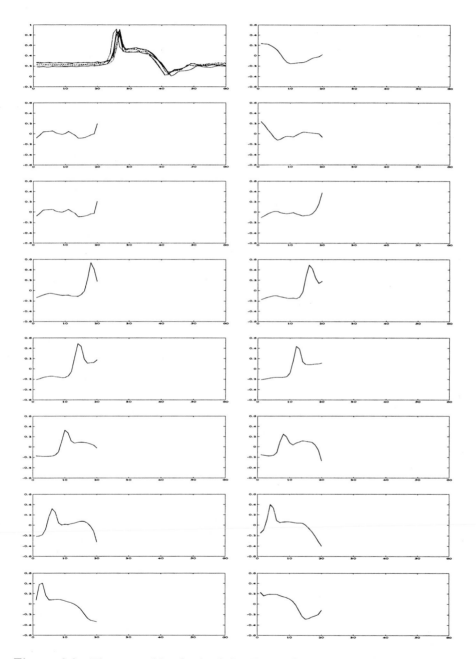

Figure 6.8: The centroids obtained for ECG Class No. 1. The training sequences are shown in the upper-left figure.

	Model	Generalization
Approximation-Based	LBF-ACON(20)	78%
Static Models	RBF-OCON(4)	80%
Decision-Based	DBNN(E_s)(2)	90%
Static Models	DBNN(R_s)(4)	90%

Table 6.1: Comparison of ECG classification by various static models. *All models reach 100% training accuracies.* For the DBNN(E_s)(2), a noise tolerance of 0.5 is adopted.

1. For the *approximation-based networks*, the teacher value is set to be 1 when the input sequence is in the class represented by the network; otherwise it is 0. Both the ACON and OCON models, with the conjugate-gradient algorithm, are adopted. The ACON model, using LBF, has 120 input neurons, 20 hidden neurons, and 10 output neurons. The OCON model has 10 subnets each using 4 (RBF) hidden neurons. Under the approximation-based formulation, the OCON and ACON models have very compatible performance, cf. Table 6.1.

2. For the *decision-based networks*, we adopt subcluster DBNNs with 10 subnets. Similar performances are reported for the DBNN(EBF), with 2 subclusters per subnet; and for the DBNN(RBF), with 4 subclusters per subnet. According to the ECG classification experiments summarized in Table 6.1, decision-based models outperform approximation-based models in convergence speed and training/generalization accuracy.

Tolerance to Temporal Misalignment   Since the ECG segments are extracted from an original long waveform, it is likely that signal segments may be misaligned by an unknown time interval. It is critical that the neural model be made somewhat shift-tolerant. The static models are, unfortunately, not very tolerant. To enhance this, a special training procedure is adopted. First, all the (100) ECG waveforms are shifted forward or backward by one or two time steps. Samples of the shifted ECG waveforms are shown in Figure 6.7(c). Second, the original data set is expanded by 5 fold. Half of the expanded set is randomly chosen as the training set. In the generalization experiments, both the original and shifted signals are used as test sets. The radial basis

Algorithm	Noise Tolerance	Original Test Set(50)	Shifted Test Set(250)
DBNN(E_s)	0 (5 sweeps)	96%	93.6%
DBNN(E_s)	2.25	96%	96.8%
DBNN(R_h)	1.76	96%	97.2%
RBF-OCON	NA	96%	94%

Table 6.2:   Networks are trained with right/left-shifted ECG data. In this simulation, the original set and shifted data, respectively, are used to test the generalization capability of the network. The classification rates of the training set are 100% for all models. The number of subnodes is 4 for each subnet.

model DBNN(R_s) and the elliptic basis model DBNN(E_s) have very close generalization accuracies. For comparison, hidden-node DBNN(R_h) models are also experimented with. The results in Table 6.2 show that generalization performance is indeed improved by using shifted training data.

6.4.2.2   Temporal Models for ECG Analysis

In both training and retrieving phases, in order to smooth the noise in the signal, a small segment of signal is passed through a fixed-weight lowpass filter, and the output of the filter is used as teacher for the prediction network. The modified configuration is shown in Figure 6.6(b). In the ECG analysis, a 4-th order moving average low-pass filter appears to be adequate. To make the classifier tolerant to the DC level of the ECG segment, the values of the input segment and the output of the lowpass filter are both readjusted to have 0 DC-level. For both PBIT(LBF) and PBIT(RBF) networks, a window size of around 20 is found to be adequate. (In fact, the two networks have very similar accuracies.)   All input segments contribute in equal share to the cost-criterion in Eq. 6.27, so the models are fairly robust. As expected, temporal models consistently outperform static models, cf. Table 6.3. In a separate experiment, temporal models (based on sigmoid LBF net with a short window) were successfully applied to model nonlinear time-varying background noise in a ECG QRS detection application [107].

Tolerance to Temporal Misalignment   It can be demonstrated by experiments, that the PBIT nets were inherently tolerant of temporal misalignment of waveforms. They were trained by the original unshifted patterns, and

Classifier	Window Size	Hidden Units	Training Set	Test Set
	30	NA	94%	94%
LPC	40	NA	100%	94%
	45	NA	100%	76%
	20	10	100%	98%
PBIT(LBF)	20	15	98%	98%
	20	20	100%	94%
	20	10	100%	94%
PBIT(RBF)	20	15	100%	98%
	20	20	100%	96%

Table 6.3: Training/generalization accuracies of several temporal models, including LPC, PBIT(LBF), and PBIT(RBF).

there is no need to use time-shifted patterns in the training set. (This is in contrast to the approach previously adopted for the static models.) Only the 50 original waveforms are used as the training set. By waveform time-shift, the original data set is expanded to a total of 500 patterns. Among them, 450 patterns were used as the test patterns. (Those used in the training set are excluded from the testing set.) The results of the experiment are summarized in Table 6.4. It appears that the PBIT nets have high generalization accuracy and were very shift-tolerant. Note that the linear predictive classifier (LPC) is somewhat intolerant to time-shift, although it has a very respectable generalization accuracy without time-shift. In comparison, PBIT(LBF) and PBIT(RBF) were more tolerant to shift. As predicted, the static DBNN(E_s) shows the least tolerance. In comparison with the HMM, the PBIT nets have either comparable or slightly better performance. However, more exhaustive experiments are needed before a more definitive conclusion can be reached.

Hierarchical Training Strategy　With reference to Figure 1.20, the design hierarchy is purposely divided into two stages. In the independent training rule, each model is trained by patterns from its own category. This is very appealing to temporal pattern recognition and offers cost-effective learning in the initial phase. If further training is needed, the mutual training scheme, cf. Figure 1.20(b), can always follow. Either DBNN or FDNN may be adopted to fine-tune the classifier. Note that many other types of recurrent structures (e.g. [53]) and discriminant functions (e.g. smoothing error function) may

Classifier	Original Test Set	Shifted Test Set
DBNN(E_s)	90%	85.2%
LPC	94%	90%
PBIT(LBF)	98%	98%
PBIT(RBF)	98%	98.45%

Table 6.4: Comparison of the shift-tolerance of different static and temporal models. The models were trained by the original data but tested (mostly) by the shifted data.

also be considered in temporal classification models.

6.5   Concluding Remarks

This chapter presents the basic neural models for temporal pattern recognition. The selection of a suitable temporal model hinges upon the intended applications. For example, the prediction-based classifier is effective for capturing temporal transient characteristics, as demonstrated in this chapter. The DTW and HMM networks, in contrast, appear to be more suitable for the time warping problem, cf. Chapter 7. Many theoretical and practical issues on temporal models remain to be investigated. Examples are how to incorporate a practical generalization criterion, or how to best capture the contextual information in temporal data. Furthermore, Giles et al. [89] has recently demonstrated that high-order recurrent nerual networks can be trained to behave like deterministic finte-state automata. Due to the high-orderness of these networks, rule-insertion becomes a straightforward mapping of rules into weights and neurons.

In a broader scope, many conventional techniques are very suitable (and often more so) for temporal signal processing. Prominent candidates include linear techniques such as least squares, constrained least squares, SVD pseudo-inverse filter, Wiener filter, nonrecursive FIR filters, and recursive Kalman filtering [127], as well as iterative nonlinear techniques such as maximum likelihood estimation, maximum entropy estimation [37], maximum a posteriori estimation and minimum variance inverse filtering. It is important to explore the rich theoretical relationship between the nonlinear filtering and identification theory and the neural models.

6.6   Problems

Exercise 6.1 Complete the lower and upper limits of the summing indices which are absent in the derivation of the Yule-Walker equation, Eq. 6.6.

Exercise 6.2 For the signal waveform $[1.1, 1.5, 1.6, 1.2, .8, .6, .4, .3, .3, .2]$, find the weights for the optimal LPC for the window size 4 and 5. Compare their prediction errors.

Exercise 6.3 For an ARMA representation of order (p, q) shown in Eq. 6.3, show how the parameters $\{ a_k, k = 1, ..., p \}$ and $\{ b_k, k = 1, ..., q \}$ can be determined from the covariance function $r(n) = E[y(n)y(0)]$.

Exercise 6.4 Show that a lattice filter is stable if and only if all the reflection coefficients satisfy $|k_m| < 1$.

Exercise 6.5 For the lattice filter structure in Figure 6.2(b) a minimal realization can be obtained by assigning the delay outputs as the (only) state variables (i.e. B_1, B_2, and B_3). Write down its state-space representation. Show that, for a K-order lattice filter, the state feedback matrix has roughly $\frac{K^2}{2}$ nonzero parameters.

Exercise 6.6 For the lattice structure in Figure 6.2(b), for the different states as labeled in Figure 6.9, derive its generalized state-space representation and compute the gradient vector with respect to k_1.
Hint: Note that $\mathbf{u}(D)$ is a function of k_1.

Exercise 6.7 For the states labeled in an alternative lattice structure in Figure 6.10, derive its generalized state-space representation. Compute the gradient vector with respect to k_2.
Hint: The state space of the lattice filter is given as

$$\mathbf{a}(n) = W(D)\mathbf{a}(n) + \mathbf{u}(D)x(n)$$

where

$$W(D) = \begin{bmatrix} 0 & 0 & 0 & 0 & 1 & 0 & 0 & 0 \\ D & 0 & 0 & 0 & k1 & 0 & 0 & 0 \\ 0 & D & 0 & 0 & 0 & k_2 & 0 & 0 \\ 0 & 0 & D & 0 & 0 & 0 & k_3 & 0 \\ -k_1 D & 0 & 0 & 0 & 0 & 1 & 0 & 0 \\ 0 & -k_2 D & 0 & 0 & 0 & 0 & 1 & 0 \\ 0 & 0 & -k_3 D & 0 & 0 & 0 & 0 & 1 \\ 0 & 0 & 0 & 0 & 0 & 0 & 0 & 0 \end{bmatrix}, \quad \mathbf{u}(D) = \begin{bmatrix} 0 \\ 0 \\ 0 \\ 0 \\ 0 \\ 0 \\ 0 \\ 1 \end{bmatrix}$$

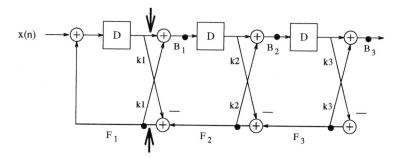

Figure 6.9: The different states in the lattice structure.

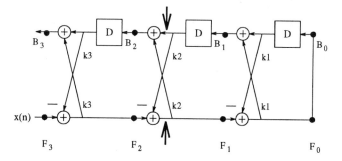

Figure 6.10: Another lattice filter structure.

Exercise 6.8 Show that under the generalized state space formulation, the output $y(n)$ in Eq. 6.9 can be represented as a (non-hidden) state variable. Write down the expanded state-feedback matrix.

Exercise 6.9 Show that, if $\sigma < .25$ for the sigmoid function $f(u) = \frac{1}{1+e^{-u/\sigma}}$, then $|f'(u)| \leq 1$. Is this condition sufficient to guarantee the stability of the adaptive learning system, assuming the original state-feedback matrix has all the eigenvalues with magnitude less than 1?

Exercise 6.10 The recurrent network can be approximated by an L-layer feedforward network with uniform weights. Namely, the synaptic weights are the same for all the layers, $w_{ij}(l) = w_{ij}$, $\forall l$, [97, 245]. Verify that all the derivations from Eqns. 5.10, 5.11, 5.15, and 5.14, are still applicable to the uniform back-propagation network. In addition, show that

$$\frac{\partial E}{\partial w_{ij}} = \sum_{l=1}^{L} \frac{\partial E}{\partial w_{ij}(l)} \frac{\partial w_{ij}(l)}{\partial w_{ij}}$$

$$= \sum_{l=1}^{L} \frac{\partial E}{\partial w_{ij}(l)}$$

This is equivalent to taking an average on Eq. 5.12:

$$w_{ij} \longleftarrow w_{ij} - \eta \sum_{l=1}^{L} \frac{\partial E}{\partial w_{ij}(l)}$$

$$= w_{ij} - \eta \sum_{l=1}^{L} \delta_i(l) f_i'(u_i(l)) a_j(l-1)$$

As before, $\delta_i(l)$ is the computed by the back propagation rule, cf Eqns. 5.16 and 5.18.

Exercise 6.11 For the state-space model Eq. 6.22, show that, by taking the first-order variation of $\delta J(t, a(t); W(t))$ with respect to $\delta W(t)$, one can obtain

$$\delta J = \sum_{i,j} \left(-\int_0^T \frac{\partial H}{\partial w_{ij}}(t) \delta w_{ij}(t) dt + \sum_k \Delta_k(T) \frac{\delta a_k}{\delta w_{ij}}(T) \delta w_{ij}(T) + \frac{\partial J}{\partial w_{ij}}(0) \delta w_{ij}(0) \right)$$

Show also that, by making $\delta J = 0$, the learning rules (and the boundary conditions) in Eq. 6.19 can be derived.

Exercise 6.12 Consider the design of prediction-based mutual training networks:
    (a) Design a decision-based neural network(DBNN).
    (b) Define a proper loss function and then derive the learning rule for a fuzzy-decision neural network.

Exercise 6.13 (Neural Networks Based on Smoothing Filter Design)
Instead of a prediction-based model, a smoothing network may be appealing for noncausal (e.g. imaging) systems. Derive a proper formulation for the smoothing neural network. (Hint: Recall the denotation $x_j = [x(j+1) \ldots x(j+N)]$. Denote also $\bar{x}_j = [x(j-1) \ldots x(j-N)]$, find the best smoothing function of x_j and $\bar{x}_j$ to estimate $x(j)$.)

Chapter 7

Stochastic Temporal Networks: Hidden Markov Models

7.1 Introduction

Stochastic models represent a very promising approach to temporal pattern recognition. An important class of the stochastic models is based on *Markovian state transition*. Two typical examples are the *Markov model* (MM) and the *hidden Markov model* (HMM). The following are some reasons for adopting the MM or HMM.

- *Temporal Variability*
  The HMM is suitable for modeling temporal patterns. In contrast, the multilayer feedforward networks are suitable for static patterns.

- *OCON Structure with Independent Training*
  As depicted in Figure 7.1, HMM subnets are used as the building blocks in the OCON (one-class-one-net) structure. For example, $L = 26$ subnets are used for the English alphabet recognition. There is one HMM for each alphabet, and each HMM is independently trained. This *independent training* strategy significantly distinguishes the HMM approach from other OCON approaches based on the mutual or discriminant training strategy.

- *Stochastic State Transition Model for Each Subnet*
  In the training phase, the model is trained to be the generative model,

237

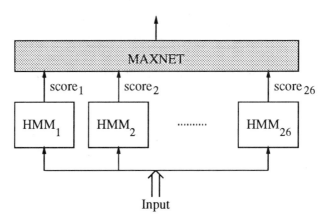

Figure 7.1: The overall HMM network uses an OCON structure. In general, L subnets are used, one for each class. Here $L = 26$.

which is most likely to have created the temporal training pattern. In the retrieving phase, the subnet that has the maximum likelihood of generating the given test pattern is recognized. The generative model can be either a Markov model (MM) or a hidden Markov model (HMM). The former uses a singly stochastic model, whereas the latter involves a doubly stochastic process. The dynamics of the temporal sequences is governed by a Markov state-transition shown in Figure 7.2(a), which resembles the RNN structure in Figure 6.5.

- *Learning Phase: Baum-Welch's BP-Type Training Algorithm*
  A gradient-type formulation resembling that of the BP algorithm can be adopted to maximize the likelihood function. A unification between the BP and HMM learning rules [112, 113] can be established according to the mathematical correspondence in Table 7.2. This conceptually simplifies the derivation of the (BP-type) HMM learning rule.

- *Retrieving Phase: Viterbi Nets for Pattern Recognition or Completion*
  Viterbi networks are effective, in computation as well as storage, for recognizing and/or completing a given temporal pattern.

Chapter Organization

This chapter focuses on the hidden Markov models for temporal pattern classification. Section 7.2 discusses the traditional *Markov model* (MM). The stochastic sequence of the state is modeled by a Markovian process, whose state transition is governed by the *state-transition probabilities*. The Markov model is extended to the *hidden Markov model* (HMM) by introducing a doubly stochastic process [234]. Section 7.3 presents the learning algorithms for both the MM and HMM networks. A unified perspective of BP and HMM learning rules (i.e., the Baum-Welch reestimation algorithm) is provided. Section 7.4 explores the retrieving phase for the hidden Markov models. The Viterbi net is adopted for two important retrieving problems: model-scoring and pattern-completion. Section 7.5 presents application examples for speech, ECG, and character recognitions.

7.2 From Markov Model to Hidden Markov Model

7.2.1 Markov Model

In a Markov model, the transition between states is governed by the *transition probabilities*, that is, the state sequence is a Markovian process; cf. Figure 7.2. The observable state is then directly observed as the output feature, for example, a stroke in character pattern recognition. Let us for simplicity assume that the features are all the straight lines shown in Figure 7.3, where there are 18 feature states representing all possible orientations. Under the Markov Model, there is an underlying state-transition diagram, cf. Figure 7.2(a), which governs the likelihood of one feature following another. For example, in capital letter L, the probability of observing a horizontal line following a vertical line is high . For each particular letter, there corresponds a unique distribution accounting for the variation of the features. Under simple circumstances, the problem can be formulated by a pure Markov model.

Description of Markov Model   A basic block diagram for the Markov model is illustrated in Figure 7.2.

Notations   Suppose that there are L classes represented by L corresponding subnets. Each subnet is modeled by $\Lambda = \langle A, \pi \rangle$ described below:

$\mathbf{Q} = \{q_1, q_2, \ldots, q_N\}$ denotes the set of N possible states.

$\pi = \{\pi_1, \pi_2, \ldots, \pi_N\}$, where $\pi_j = Pr(q_j \text{ at } t = 1)$ is the initial state distribution. Here $Pr(\cdot)$ denotes the probability of an event.

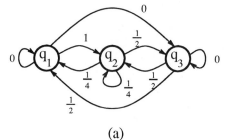

(a)

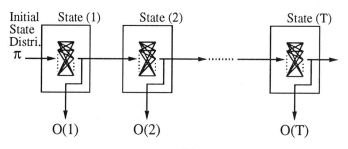

(b)

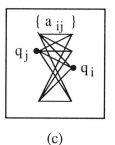

(c)

Figure 7.2: In a pure Markovian model (MM), the observed symbol is a deterministic output of the state. (a) A state-transition diagram for MM. (Here we assume 3 states; cf. Example 7.2.) By this diagram, the MM can be regarded as a single-layer recurrent neural network. (b) An MM contains a cascade of multiple layers of state-transition stages. By this configuration, the MM now can be considered as a multiple-layer feedforward network. (c) Each state-transition stage is characterized by $\{a_{ij}\}$.

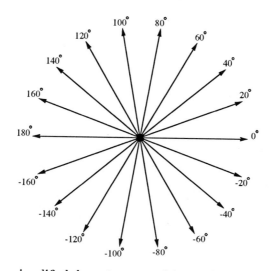

Figure 7.3: In a simplified character-recognition problem, 18 states are used to represent all the possible orientations in (-180°,+180°). In the Markov model, since one state is mapped to one feature; only 18 features can be represented.

$\mathbf{A}=$ the state-transition matrix $\{a_{ij}\}$, where $a_{ij}(t) = Pr(q_i$ at $t+1 \mid q_j$ at $t)$ is the state-transition probability. Here, "q_j at t" means the event that the *state* is q_j at time t.

$\mathbf{O}=$ $\{O(1),\ldots,O(T)\}$, the observation sequence, with the total length T and $O(t)$ is one of the states in $Q = \{q_1, q_2, \ldots, q_N\}$.

Given a Markov model, $\Lambda = \langle A, \pi \rangle$, where $\{a_{ij}\}$ and $\{\pi_j\}$ are to be specified. There are N possible states $\{q_j, j = 1, 2, \ldots, N\}$ in a Markov model. At time $t = 1$ the *initial state-distribution probability* is given as π_j, that is,

$$\pi_j = Pr(\ q_j \text{ at } t = 1)$$

The new state is entered at time $t+1$ based upon a *state-transition probability* a_{ij}, which depends on the previous state at time t (the Markovian property), that is,

$$a_{ij}(t) = Pr(\ q_i \text{ at } t+1 \mid q_j \text{ at } t)$$

By this, an observation sequence $O = \{O(1), O(2), \ldots, O(T)\}$ is generated.

7.2.2   Hidden Markov Model

The HMM model is based on a doubly stochastic process. *It involves two stochastic processes, one producing an (unobservable) state and another producing an observable feature sequence based on the (unobservable) state.* The HMM has been successfully applied, for example, to speech-recognition tasks [18, 119, 234], English spelling checkers [109], and character recognition [290].

The basic HMM block diagram is shown in Figure 7.4(a). The state-transitions of the Markov model and hidden Markov model are both governed by the Markovian state transition function. The difference is that the Markov model has explicit states while the hidden Markov model has hidden states. More precisely, the mapping from a state to the actual observation in HMM is not unique, unlike the Markov model. The basic HMM block diagram is illustrated in Figure 7.4(b), wherein each state is mapped to many features with nonzero probabilities. Likewise, different states may be mapped to the same feature with varying probabilities. This feature of *multiple mappability* offers additional flexibility in modeling variation in temporal patterns, as illustrated by the following example.

Example 7.1 (Hidden States and Observable Features)

The doubly stochastic process is useful in coping with unpredictable variation of the observed patterns. For example, the same character can be written in various forms. A horizontal line can, in actuality, have varying appearances (i.e., features). For example, cf. Figure 7.5, an ideal horizontal line can be tilted by, say, -10°,-5°,0°,5°, or 10°. Each tilted line has a nonzero probability to appear (as the observed feature) on behalf of the horizontal line. On the other hand, an ideal 20°-line can be similarly tilted to lines with 10°,15°,20°,25°, or 30°. Therefore, when a 10°-line feature is observed, it could be interpreted as being originated either from the horizontal state or the 20°-state. The multiple mappability of the double stochastic process is designed for such situations. In Figure 7.5, for example, although only 18 states are used, the total number of features possibly covered by the HMM is 72. To reduce computational complexity for tracking the state-transition function, the number of states should be as small as permitted by the application.

Notations   The notations largely follow the exposition by Juang and Rabiner [125]. For each of the L models, $\Lambda = \langle A, B, \pi \rangle$, we have the following parameters:

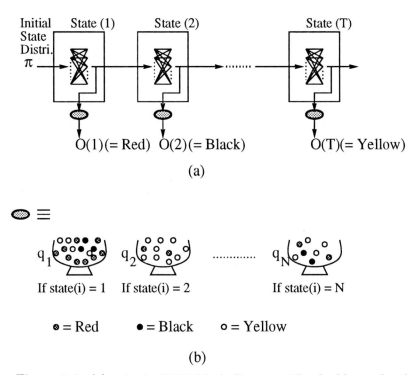

$O(1)(= \text{Red})\ \ O(2)(= \text{Black})$ $\quad\quad\quad O(T)(= \text{Yellow})$

(a)

If state(i) = 1   If state(i) = 2   If state(i) = N

$\circledcirc$ = Red $\bullet$ = Black $\circ$ = Yellow

(b)

Figure 7.4: (a) A basic HMM block diagram. The doubly stochastic process in HMM means that, in contrast to the regular Markovian model, the observed symbol is a random output dependent on the value of the current state. (b) The second stochastic unit is characterized by $\{b_{ik}\}$. For example, if State(i) = 1, then $Pr(O(i) = \text{Yellow}) = 4/16$, $Pr(O(i) = \text{Red}) = 9/16$, and $Pr(O(i) = \text{Black}) = 3/16$.

Q,π,A denote, respectively, the possible states, the initial state distribution, and the state-transition matrix $\{a_{ij}\}$ in the same way as the Markov model.

V= $\{v_1, v_2, \ldots, v_M\}$ is a set of M possible feature observations. The features are directly observable. (For example, they could be particular orientations of arcs and lines in an OCR application, or an English letter in word recognition.)

B= the *emission-distribution matrix* $\{b_{ik}\}$, where

$$b_{ik} \equiv b_i(v_k) = Pr(v_k \text{ at } t \mid q_i \text{ at } t)$$

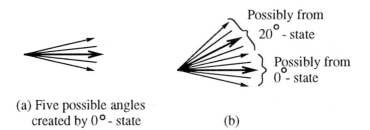

(a) Five possible angles
created by $0°$- state   (b)

Figure 7.5: In HMM, a desired horizontal line can have different appearances (features). As shown in (a), one state can be mapped to more than one feature. As a result, as shown in (b), different states can be mapped to the same feature. Thanks to multiple mappability, the total number of features representable by the HMM now increases to 72 features, that is, 4 times that of the Markov model.

is the probability of observing the feature v_k at time t under the condition that the state is q_i. (Here, "q_j at t" means that the *state* at time t is q_j; and "v_k at t" means that the *observation* at time t is v_k.)

$\mathbf{O}= \{O(1), \ldots, O(T)\}$, the observation sequence, and $O(t) \in V$.

Let us now consider an HMM, $\Lambda = \langle A, B, \pi \rangle$, with N possible states $\{q_j, \ j = 1, 2, \ldots, N\}$. At time $t = 1$, the *initial state-distribution probability* is given as π_j,

$$\pi_j = Pr(\ q_j \text{ at } t = 1)$$

Due to the Markovian property, the state entered at time $t + 1$ is governed by the *state-transition probability* a_{ij}, and the previous state at time t, that is,

$$a_{ij}(t) = Pr(\ q_i \text{ at } t + 1 \mid q_j \text{ at } t)$$

The main difference between the HMM and the simpler MM is that there are M possible features $\{v_i, \ i = 1, 2, \ldots, M\}$ that can be observed given any particular state. The observed feature is extracted stochastically based on an *emission distribution* function. Each feature, say, the k-th feature, at state q_i has an emission distribution denoted as $b_i(v_k)$:

$$b_i(v_k) = Pr(\ v_k \text{ at } t \mid q_i \text{ at } t)$$

(For notational convenience, from now on, $b_i(v_k)$ will be written as b_{ik}.) By this, an observation sequence $O = \{O(1), O(2), \ldots O(T)\}$ is generated.

Markov Model   The pure Markov model (singly stochastic model) is a special case of HMM. Here the emission-distribution matrix is identity, $B = I$. Namely, the emission stochastic process is deterministic with $b_i(O(t) = v_i) = 1$, and $b_i(O(t) = $ any others$) = 0$. For an OCR example, see Section 7.5.

7.3   Learning Phase of Hidden Markov Models

Learning Phase: The task of model training is to estimate the parameters of both the state-transition and emission distributions from the observed data. Given a sequence (or sequences) of observations and the number of states of an HMM (or MM), we want to determine the transition and emission-probability parameters so that the generative model is the most likely to have produced the sequence(s). Mathematically, given the training sequence O, we are to find $\langle A, B, \pi \rangle$, which gives

$$max_{A,B,\pi} Pr(O|\Lambda(A, B, \pi))$$

(In the case of the Markov model, $B \equiv I$.)

In this section, we discuss the learning algorithms for both MM and HMM networks given the observed data sequence. The learning rule for the former is considerably simpler than the latter. *The previous discussion set the stage for the much harder problem in MM training of estimating the state-transition matrix. This is discussed in Section 7.3.1. The task of HMM training involves estimation of both the state-transition matrix and the emission distributions from the observed data.* This is discussed in Section 7.3.2.

7.3.1   Learning Formulas for MM

Given an observation sequence $O = \{O(1), O(2), \ldots O(T)\}$ as the training data, derive a learning rule to estimate parameters π_j and a_{ij} for the pure Markov model.

Define *state counts* $\tilde{\gamma}_j$ and *state-transition counts* $\tilde{\xi}_{ij}$, respectively, as

$$\tilde{\gamma}_j(t) = \begin{cases} 1 & \text{if } q_j \text{ at } t \\ 0 & \text{otherwise} \end{cases}$$

$$\tilde{\xi}_{ij}(t) = \begin{cases} 1 & \text{if } q_j \text{ at } t \text{ and } q_i \text{ at } t+1 \\ 0 & \text{otherwise} \end{cases}$$

By this definition, it follows that

$$\sum_{t=1}^{T-1} \tilde{\gamma}_j(t) = \text{total number of transitions made from state } q_j$$

$$\sum_{t=1}^{T-1} \tilde{\xi}_{ij}(t) = \text{total number of transitions from state } q_j \text{ to state } q_i$$

This leads to a simple learning formula for a_{ij}:

$$a_{ij} = \frac{\sum_{t=1}^{T-1} \tilde{\xi}_{ij}(t)}{\sum_{t=1}^{T-1} \tilde{\gamma}_j(t)}$$

Example 7.2 (MM Learning Formula)

Derive a pure Markov process, that is, estimate π_j and a_{ij}, given that $N = 3$ and the observation sequence is $[2, 3, 2, 1, 2, 2, 3, 1]$.
Solution: *For the calculation of π_j,*

$$\pi_j = \begin{cases} 1 & \text{if } j = \text{ the initial state} \\ 0 & \text{otherwise} \end{cases}$$

and the initial condition is $\pi_1 = 0$, $\pi_2 = 1$, $\pi_3 = 0$.
Given the state sequence $[2, 3, 2, 1, 2, 2, 3, 1]$, the state counts are

$$\sum_{t=1}^{T-1} \tilde{\gamma}_1(t) = 1, \quad \sum_{t=1}^{T-1} \tilde{\gamma}_2(t) = 4, \quad \sum_{t=1}^{T-1} \tilde{\gamma}_3(t) = 2$$

and the state-transition counts are

$$\Xi = \left[\sum_{t=1}^{T-1} \tilde{\xi}_{ij}(t) \right] = \begin{bmatrix} 0 & 1 & 1 \\ 1 & 1 & 1 \\ 0 & 2 & 0 \end{bmatrix}$$

The state-transition matrix is estimated as

$$\mathbf{A} = \Xi \begin{bmatrix} \sum_{t=1}^{T-1} \tilde{\gamma}_1(t) & 0 & 0 \\ 0 & \sum_{t=1}^{T-1} \tilde{\gamma}_2(t) & 0 \\ 0 & 0 & \sum_{t=1}^{T-1} \tilde{\gamma}_3(t) \end{bmatrix}^{-1} = \begin{bmatrix} 0 & \frac{1}{4} & \frac{1}{2} \\ 1 & \frac{1}{4} & \frac{1}{2} \\ 0 & \frac{1}{2} & 0 \end{bmatrix}$$

7.3.2   BP-Type HMM Learning Rule

Given a sequence (or sequences) of observations, we can determine the HMM that is most likely to have produced the sequence(s). One HMM will be trained for each individual class (likewise for the MM models discussed previously). An important feature lies in its *independent training* strategy. More precisely, the training of an HMM subnet involves only the positive training patterns corresponding to that class. This distinguishes the HMM approach from other OCON approaches, which are based on the mutual or discriminant training strategy. In this section, we derive the HMM training rule by following the same procedure adopted for the BP learning [112, 113]. To facilitate the derivation of the HMM learning rule, the key notations are listed in Table 7.1, and the notational correspondence between the BP and HMM learning rules is displayed in Table 7.2.

7.3.2.1   Likelihood Energy Criterion and Forward Evaluation

The objective of learning is to find the model $\langle A, B, \pi \rangle$ that maximizes the *energy function* $E = Pr(O|\Lambda)$ for the given training sequence O [234]. The *forward likelihood function* $\alpha_i(t)$ is introduced as the probability of the partial observation sequence (until time t) and state q_i at time t, given model Λ,

$$\alpha_i(t) = Pr(O(1),\ O(2),\ \ldots O(t),\ q_i \text{ at } t \mid \Lambda)$$

The probability $\alpha_i(t)$ can be calculated inductively:

$$u_i(t+1) \quad = \quad \sum_{j=1}^{N} a_{ij}(t)\, \alpha_j(t) \qquad\qquad (7.1)$$

$$\alpha_i(t+1) \quad = \quad u_i(t+1)\, b_i(O(t+1)) \qquad\qquad (7.2)$$

where $1 \le t \le T - 1$ and $1 \le i \le N$, and the initial forward likelihood $\alpha_j(1) = \pi_j b_j(O(1))$, $1 \le j \le N$.

Given the observation sequence O, our approach is to iteratively update $\{a_{ij}^{(m)}(t)\}$ (where m denotes the iteration number) so as to gradually improve the likelihood function (or the energy function)

$$E = Pr(O|\Lambda) = \sum_{j=1}^{N} \alpha_j^{(m)}(T)$$

To maximize the energy function E, we propose a formulation resembling the gradient-type updating rule:

HMM Mathematical Notations		
Energy Function E	$=$	$Pr(O\|\Lambda)$
Forward Likelihood $\alpha_i(t)$	$=$	$Pr(O(1), O(2), \ldots O(t), q_i \text{ at } t \mid \Lambda)$
Backward Likelihood $\beta_i(t)$	$=$	$Pr(O(t+1), O(t+2), \ldots, O(T) \mid q_i \text{ at } t, \Lambda)$
$\xi_{ij}(t)$	$=$	$Pr(q_j \text{ at } t, q_i \text{ at } t+1, O\|\Lambda)$
$\gamma_j(t)$	$=$	$Pr(q_j \text{ at } t, O\|\Lambda)$

Table 7.1: Key notations for HMM.

HMM	$\Leftrightarrow$	BP (OCON)
maximize $E = Pr(O\|\Lambda) = \sum_j \alpha_j(T)$	$\Leftrightarrow$	minimize $E = \sum_j (t_j - a_j)^2$
$a_{ij}^{(m+1)} = a_{ij}^{(m)} \cdot \eta \frac{\partial E}{\partial a_{ij}^{(m)}}$	$\Leftrightarrow$	$w_{ij}^{(m+1)} = w_{ij}^{(m)} - \eta \frac{\partial E}{\partial w_{ij}^{(m)}}$
state	$\Leftrightarrow$	neuron
time (t)	$\Leftrightarrow$	layer (l)
a_{ij}	$\Leftrightarrow$	w_{ij}
$b_i(O(t))$	$\Leftrightarrow$	$f(net)$
$\alpha_j(t)$	$\Leftrightarrow$	a_j^l
$\beta_i(t) = \frac{\partial E}{\partial \alpha_i(t)}$	$\Leftrightarrow$	$\delta_i^l = \frac{\partial E}{\partial a_i^l}$

Table 7.2: Mathematical correspondence between the HMM and BP Models.

$$a_{ij}^{(m+1)}(t) = g\left(a_{ij}^{(m)}(t), \ \frac{\partial E}{\partial a_{ij}^{(m)}(t)}\right)$$

where the optimal updating function g is to be determined.

7.3.2.2   Baum-Welch Learning Rule

The weights $\{a_{ij}(t)\}$, representing the probability function, must satisfy the following constraints:

$$a_{ij}(t) \geq 0 \quad \text{and} \quad \sum_i a_{ij}(t) = 1 \tag{7.3}$$

This motivates a multiplicative recursive updating formulation:

$$a_{ij}^{(m+1)}(t) = \eta \, a_{ij}^{(m)}(t) \, \frac{\partial E}{\partial a_{ij}^{(m)}(t)} = \eta \, \xi_{ij}^{(m)}(t) \qquad (7.4)$$

where we define

$$\xi_{ij}^{(m)}(t) \equiv a_{ij}^{(m)}(t) \, \frac{\partial E}{\partial a_{ij}^{(m)}(t)}$$

Here we just use η to denote the positive updating step. (In rigorous notation, η should be written as $\eta^{(m)}$ because it changes with respect to m.) Note that the selection of η is unique since the new weights $\{a_{ij}^{(m+1)}(t)\}$ must satisfy the normalization constraint of Eq. 7.3. Furthermore, it can be shown that $\frac{\partial E}{\partial a_{ij}^{(m)}(t)}$, and thus $\xi_{ij}^{(m)}(t)$, is always nonnegative, (cf. Eq. 7.11). Most importantly, the multiplicative updating in Eq. 7.4 ensures that the energy function always increases by each updating. (See Problem 7.9.)

The HMM has the special property that all the T layers have homogeneous weights (i.e., $a_{ij}(t) = a_{ij}$). Therefore, they can be obtained by taking the average of $\xi_{ij}^{(m)}(t)$ over all layers. In other words,

$$a_{ij}^{(m+1)} = \eta' \sum_{t=1}^{T-1} \xi_{ij}^{(m)}(t)$$

The new weights $\{a_{ij}^{(m+1)}\}$ must meet the normalization constraint, $\sum_{i=1}^{N} a_{ij}^{(m+1)} = 1$, so η' can be uniquely determined

$$\eta' = \frac{1}{\sum_{t=1}^{T-1} \gamma_j^{(m)}(t)} \quad \text{where} \quad \gamma_j^{(m)}(t) \equiv \sum_{i=1}^{N} \xi_{ij}^{(m)}(t) \qquad (7.5)$$

In stating the following *Baum-Welch Learning Rule* for training the HMM [25], we denote the present model as $\Lambda^{(m)} = \langle A^{(m)}, B^{(m)}, \pi^{(m)} \rangle$ and the reestimated model as $\Lambda^{(m+1)} = \langle A^{(m+1)}, B^{(m+1)}, \pi^{(m+1)} \rangle$.

Algorithm 7.1 (Baum-Welch Learning Rule)

The Baum-Welch learning formulation is

$$a_{ij}^{(m+1)} = \frac{\sum_{t=1}^{T-1} \xi_{ij}^{(m)}(t)}{\sum_{t=1}^{T-1} \gamma_j^{(m)}(t)} \qquad (7.6)$$

$$b_i^{(m+1)}(v_k) \;=\; \frac{\sum_{t=1,\, O(t)=v_k}^{T} \gamma_i^{(m)}(t)}{\sum_{t=1}^{T} \gamma_i^{(m)}(t)} \tag{7.7}$$

$$\pi_j^{(m+1)} \;=\; \gamma_j^{(m)}(1)/Pr(O|\Lambda^{(m)}) \tag{7.8}$$

where

$$Pr(O|\Lambda^{(m)}) = \sum_{i=1}^{N} \alpha_i^{(m)}(T)$$

In the above,

1. *the probability measure $\xi_{ij}^{(m)}(t)$ is computed from*

$$\xi_{ij}^{(m)}(t) \;=\; a_{ij}^{(m)}(t)\beta_i^{(m)}(t+1)b_i^{(m)}(O(t+1))\alpha_j^{(m)}(t) \tag{7.9}$$

2. *the forward likelihood function $\alpha_j^{(m)}(t)$ is obtained from Eq. 7.1 and Eq. 7.2;*

3. *the backward likelihood function $\beta_i^{(m)}(t+1)$ is recursively computed from (with $\beta_i^{(m)}(T) = 1$):*

$$\beta_i^{(m)}(t) \;=\; \sum_{l=1}^{N} \beta_l^{(m)}(t+1)\, b_l^{(m)}(O(t+1))\, a_{li}^{(m)}(t) \tag{7.10}$$

4. *the probability measure $\gamma_j^{(m)}(t)$ is derived from Eq. 7.5.*

$\blacksquare$

Eq. 7.9 and Eq. 7.10 will be derived in Eq. 7.13 and Eq. 7.14.

7.3.2.3   Derivation of Baum-Welch Learning Rule

The justification of the learning rule hinges upon the proof of the following:

$$\xi_{ij}^{(m)}(t) \;=\; Pr(q_j \text{ at } t, q_i \text{ at } t+1,\; O|\,\Lambda^{(m)}) \tag{7.11}$$

$$\gamma_j^{(m)}(t) \;=\; Pr(q_j \text{ at } t, O|\Lambda^{(m)}) = \alpha_j(t)\beta_j(t) \tag{7.12}$$

In Eq. 7.16 we provide the final proof of Eq. 7.11 (and thus Eq. 7.12). It is extremely pivotal since it directly leads to the learning formula Eq. 7.6.

(Eq. 7.7 and Eq. 7.8 can be derived in a similar manner.) According to the chain rule,

$$
\begin{aligned}
\xi_{ij}^{(m)}(t) &\equiv a_{ij}^{(m)}(t) \frac{\partial E}{\partial a_{ij}^{(m)}(t)} \\
&= a_{ij}^{(m)}(t) \frac{\partial E}{\partial \alpha_i^{(m)}(t+1)} \frac{\partial \alpha_i^{(m)}(t+1)}{\partial a_{ij}^{(m)}(t)} \\
&= a_{ij}^{(m)}(t) \beta_i^{(m)}(t+1) \frac{\partial \alpha_i^{(m)}(t+1)}{\partial u_i^{(m)}(t+1)} \frac{\partial u_i^{(m)}(t+1)}{\partial a_{ij}^{(m)}(t)} \\
&= a_{ij}^{(m)}(t) \beta_i^{(m)}(t+1) b_i^{(m)}(O(t+1)) \alpha_j^{(m)}(t) \qquad (7.13)
\end{aligned}
$$

where the *backward likelihood function* is defined as

$$
\beta_i^{(m)}(t) = \frac{\partial E}{\partial \alpha_i^{(m)}(t)}
$$

This proves Eq. 7.9.

Backward Likelihood Function   Just as in the back-propagation learning, the backward likelihood function $\beta_i^{(m)}(t)$ can be computed recursively:

$$
\begin{aligned}
\beta_i^{(m)}(t) &= \frac{\partial E}{\partial \alpha_i^{(m)}(t)} \\
&= \sum_{l=1}^{N} \frac{\partial E}{\partial u_l^{(m)}(t+1)} \frac{\partial u_l^{(m)}(t+1)}{\partial \alpha_i^{(m)}(t)} \\
&= \sum_{l=1}^{N} \frac{\partial E}{\partial \alpha_l^{(m)}(t+1)} \frac{\partial \alpha_l^{(m)}(t+1)}{\partial u_l^{(m)}(t+1)} a_{li}^{(m)}(t) \\
&= \sum_{l=1}^{N} \beta_l^{(m)}(t+1) b_l^{(m)}(O(t+1)) a_{li}^{(m)}(t) \qquad (7.14)
\end{aligned}
$$

This proves Eq. 7.10. The initial value of the top layer is given as

$$
\beta_i^{(m)}(T) = 1
$$

therefore, for the layer $T - 1$, we have

$$
\begin{aligned}
\beta_i^{(m)}(T-1) &= \sum_l b_l^{(m)}(O(T)) a_{li}^{(m)}(T-1) \\
&= Pr(O(T) \mid q_i \text{ at } T-1, \Lambda)
\end{aligned}
$$

(See Problem 7.10.) For the layers $t = T\text{-}2, T\text{-}3, \ldots$, it follows by induction that:

$$\beta_i^{(m)}(t) = Prob(O(t+1), O(t+2), \ldots, O(T) \mid q_i \text{ at } t, \Lambda) \qquad (7.15)$$

Verification of Eq. 7.11:   Based on Eq. 7.15, Eq. 7.9 can be rewritten as

$$
\begin{aligned}
\xi_{ij}^{(m)}(t) &= \beta_i^{(m)}(t+1) b_i^{(m)}(O(t+1)) a_{ij}^{(m)}(t) \alpha_j^{(m)}(t) \\
&= \beta_i^{(m)}(t+1) b_i^{(m)}(O(t+1)) Pr(\, q_i \text{ at } t+1,\, q_j \text{ at } t \mid \Lambda) \times \\
&\quad\; Pr(\, q_j \text{ at } t, O(1),\, O(2),\, \ldots O(t) \mid \Lambda) \\
&= \beta_i^{(m)}(t+1) Pr(\, O(t+1) \mid q_i \text{ at } t+1,\, \Lambda) \times \\
&\quad\; Pr(\, q_i \text{ at } t+1,\, q_j \text{ at } t, O(1),\, O(2),\, \ldots O(t) \mid \Lambda) \\
&= Pr(O(t+2), O(t+3), \ldots, O(T) \mid q_i \text{ at } t+1,\, \Lambda) \times \\
&\quad\; Pr(\, q_i \text{ at } t+1,\, q_j \text{ at } t, O(1),\, O(2),\, \ldots O(t+1) \mid \Lambda) \\
&= Pr(q_j \text{ at } t, q_i \text{ at } t+1,\, O \mid \Lambda^{(m)}) \qquad (7.16)
\end{aligned}
$$

Thus Eq. 7.11 is verified. The proof of Eq. 7.12 is then straightforward.

7.3.2.4   Property of Baum-Welch Learning Rule

It can be proved that [25, 26, 234]

$$Pr(O|\Lambda^{(m+1)}) \geq Pr(O|\Lambda^{(m)}) \qquad (7.17)$$

In other words, the new model $\Lambda^{(m+1)}$ is more likely to produce the observation sequence O than the previous one. (See Problem 7.9.) as long as the likelihood function $Pr(O|\Lambda)$ continues to improve, the learning rule can be repeatedly applied. The training terminates when it reaches convergence, namely, when parameters $a_{ij}^{(m)}$, $b_{ik}^{(m)}$, and $\pi_j^{(m)}$ remain almost unchanged by additional training sweeps.

7.3.2.5   From Baum-Welch Reestimation to MM Learning

Let us now introduce a new set of notations:

$$\tilde{\xi}_{ij}(t) \equiv \frac{\xi_{ij}(t)}{Pr(O|\Lambda)} \quad \text{and} \quad \tilde{\gamma}_j(t) \equiv \frac{\gamma_j(t)}{Pr(O|\Lambda)}$$

Note that $\tilde{\xi}_{ij}(t)$ and $\tilde{\gamma}_j(t)$ may substitute for $\xi_{ij}(t)$ and $\gamma_j(t)$ in the Baum-Welch learning rule, and this leads to

$$a_{ij}^{(m+1)} = \frac{\sum_{t=1}^{T-1} \tilde{\xi}_{ij}^{(m)}(t)}{\sum_{t=1}^{T-1} \tilde{\gamma}_j^{(m)}(t)} \tag{7.18}$$

$$b_i^{(m+1)}(v_k) = \frac{\sum_{t=1,\ O(t)=v_k}^{T} \tilde{\gamma}_i^{(m)}(t)}{\sum_{t=1}^{T} \tilde{\gamma}_i^{(m)}(t)}$$

$$\pi_j^{(m+1)} = \tilde{\gamma}_j^{(m)}(1)$$

From Eq. 7.11 and Eq. 7.12, it follows that (cf. Problem 7.11)

$$\tilde{\xi}_{ij}(t) = Pr(q_j \text{ at } t, q_i \text{ at } t+1|O, \Lambda) \tag{7.19}$$

$$\tilde{\gamma}_i(t) = Pr(q_i \text{ at } t|O, \Lambda) \tag{7.20}$$

In other words, $\sum_{t=1}^{T-1} \tilde{\gamma}_i(t) =$ the expected number of transitions made from q_i, and $\sum_{t=1}^{T-1} \tilde{\xi}_{ij}(t) =$ the expected number of transitions made from state q_j to state q_i.

In the special case of a pure Markov model, that emission matrix B must be an identity matrix because the state is directly *observable*. In fact, in the HMM learning, if the matrix $B^{(0)}$ is initially set to be an identity matrix, then the matrix B will remain the same throughout the learning process. This can be verified by carefully checking Eq. 7.7. (See Problem 7.7.)

Recall the reestimation formula of $\{a_{ij}\}$ in Eq. 7.18. For the pure Markov model, the numerator $\sum_{t=1}^{T-1} \tilde{\gamma}_j(t)$ becomes the expected number of transitions made from state j. The denominator $\sum_{t=1}^{T-1} \tilde{\xi}_{ij}(t)$ is the expected number of transitions from state j to state i. Because the states are now directly observable, these two values can simply be counted. This simplification leads to the MM learning algorithm adopted in Example 7.2.

7.4 Retrieving Phase of Hidden Markov Models

A trained HMM can be used for the retrieving (or recognition) phase. In this phase, the model likely to generate the test sequence of (complete or incomplete) observations will be recognized. Two problems are often encountered:

1. *Model-Scoring Problem: Find the most likely model, given the complete observation sequence O.* To solve the problem, the likelihoods for all the HMM subnets are calculated and the most likely subnet is selected.

Mathematically, the objective is to determine the optimal subnet Λ_i (out of all the L subnets)

$$max_i Pr(O|\Lambda_i)$$

The Viterbi algorithm is known to be very effective for solving this problem. See Section 7.4.1.

2. *Pattern-Completion Problem: Find the most likely complete sequence given a partial observation of the sequence.* Let $O_{partial}$ denote the given incomplete observation sequence, the objective being to determine a most likely complete sequence $O_{complete}$, such that

$$max\, Pr(O_{complete}|O_{partial})$$

See Section 7.4.2. In short, the task is to complete a pattern given a key part of it as the cue. The model acts just like an auto-associative memory.

7.4.1   Viterbi Algorithm for Model-Scoring Problem

The model-scoring problem is to find the most likely model, given the complete observation data O. More precisely, given the L trained HMMs $\Lambda_i = \langle A, B, \pi \rangle_i, i = 1, \cdots, L$, and a test sequence $O = (\, O(1), \cdots, O(T)\,)$, the task is to calculate the scoring probability $Pr(O|\Lambda_i)$ for each subnet, and select the one that best matches the test sequence.

The Forward Evaluation Procedure   The objective is to determine the optimal model Λ_i according to the criterion $max_i Pr(O|\Lambda_i)$. If the HMM structure is properly utilized, the evaluation of the scoring probability

$$Pr(O|\Lambda) = \sum_{i=1}^{N} \alpha_i(T)$$

could involve a complex tree structure illustrated in Figure 7.6(a). The tree structure treats distinctive paths separately , as if the number of states were N^t at instance t. This leads to an exponential growth of complexity in T, as shown by the parenthesized indices in Figure 7.6(a). If all the tree nodes are traversed, $O(2T \cdot N^T)$ operations would be required to obtain the scoring probability $Pr(O|\Lambda)$. In contrast, the *forward evaluation procedure* utilizes the inherent trellis structure in the HMM, as shown in Figure 7.6(b), to replace the tree structure in Figure 7.6(a). The simplified structure is based on the observation that, at any instance t and any state q_i, *there are only N possible next states regardless of the past state-transition history.* That is, the branches in the tree structure merge into N states at every instance. This allows a drastic reduction of the computational complexity to only $O(N^2 T)$ operations [122, 234].

The Viterbi Algorithm   To determine the most probable state sequence Q^* generating the observation sequence O, dynamic programming techniques can be employed for finding the optimal single path in a trellis structure. A most prominent technique is the Viterbi algorithm [288]. More precisely, it searches the best state sequence $Q^* = (q_{k(1)}, q_{k(2)}, \ldots, q_{k(T)})$, such that

$$Pr(O, Q^*|\Lambda) = \max_{\text{all } Q} Pr(O, Q|\Lambda)$$

By utilizing the trellis structure, the Viterbi algorithm can be implemented in a fashion very similar to the forward evaluation procedure (without the path-backtracking steps). However, a maximization of the previous states is used in place of summing up the states in the evaluation procedure [234]. More precisely, the forward recursive formulation is

$$
\begin{aligned}
u_i(t+1) &= \max_{1 \leq j \leq N} a_{ij} \delta_j(t) \\
\delta_i(t+1) &= u_i(t+1) b_i(O(t+1))
\end{aligned}
\tag{7.21}
$$

for $1 \leq t \leq T - 1$ and $1 \leq i \leq N$. Here $\delta_j(t)$ denotes the probability of the most likely subsequence ending at candidate state j at stage t. The initial conditions are set to $\delta_i(1) = \pi_i b_i(O(1))$.

To facilitate the path backtracking, the indices $\{j_i^*(t)\}$ are introduced to keep track of the most probable incoming paths:

$$j_i^*(t) = \arg \max_{1 \leq j \leq N} a_{ij} \delta_j(t)$$

for $t = 1, \ldots, T - 1$, where arg max is the argument j corresponding to the maximum. Once the $\{j_i^*(t) \mid i = 1, \cdots, N, \ t = 1, \cdots, T - 1\}$ are obtained, the most probable path can be determined by path-backtracking (following the order of $t = T - 1, T - 2, \ldots, 1$)

$$k(t) = j_{k(t+1)}^*(t)$$

Path backtracking starts with the last layer of the trellis structure, with the initial index $k(T) = \arg \max_{1 \leq i \leq N} \delta_i(T)$.

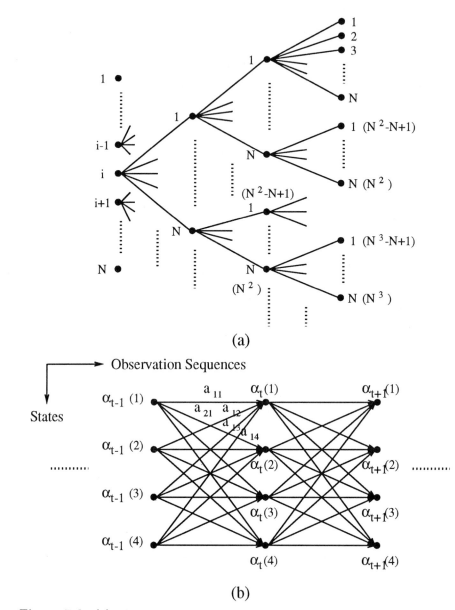

(a)

(b)

Figure 7.6: (a) The unnecessarily complex tree structure for evaluating the scoring probability $Pr(O|\Lambda)$. (b) In an HMM, the trellis structure can be utilized for effectively computing the scoring probability.

7.4.2   Pattern-Completion Problem

The pattern-completion problem determines the most likely complete sequence, given a partial observation. For example, in recognizing a word starting with the letters "foo" with the rest of the word unknown, the question is how to find the most probable letters to *complete* the word. Mathematically, the objective is to determine the best $O_{complete}$ that yields

$$max\, Pr(O_{complete}|O_{partial})$$

One approach is based on the modified Viterbi algorithm described below. Briefly, the algorithm substitutes each unknown feature with the most likely feature of each state. During path backtracking, the most likely sequence containing the known features is selected.

Modified Viterbi Algorithm: Denote the most likely feature for state i as $v_{\rho_i^*}$, where

$$\rho_i^* \equiv \arg \max_{1 \le \rho \le M} b_i(v_\rho)$$

Step 1 Initialization:
    If the feature $O(1)$ is known,

$$\delta_i(1) = \pi_i b_i(O(1)), \quad 1 \le i \le N$$

If the feature $O(1)$ is unknown,

$$\delta_i(1) = \pi_i b_i(v_{\rho_i^*}), \quad 1 \le i \le N$$

Step 2 Recursion ($t = 1, \cdots, T-1$):
    If the feature $O(t+1)$ is known:

$$\delta_i(t+1) = \max_{1 \le j \le N}[a_{ij}\delta_j(t)]b_i(O(t+1)), \quad 1 \le i \le N$$

If the feature $O(t+1)$ is unknown:

$$\delta_i(t+1) = \max_{1 \le j \le N}[a_{ij}\delta_j(t)]b_i(v_{\rho_i^*}), \quad 1 \le i \le N$$

Find the most likely state indices:

$$j_i^*(t) = \arg \max_{1 \le j \le N}[a_{ij}\delta_j(t)], \quad 1 \le i \le N$$

Step 3 Path Tracking:
    Set initially,

$$k(T) = \arg \max_{1 \le i \le N}[\delta_i(T)]$$

For $t = T-1, T-2, \ldots, 1$,

$$k(t) = j_{k(t+1)}^*(t)$$

7.5 Applications to Speech, ECG, and Character Recognition

The HMM models have been successfully applied to speech-recognition tasks [18, 119, 125, 234], English spelling checkers [109], enhancement of noisy speech [63], ECG signal classification, character recognition [289, 290], and phonetic typewriting [138]. In the following, some exemplary applications are discussed.

7.5.1 Application to Isolated Digit Recognition

Application of the HMM to isolated digit speech recognition was studied in [125]. For feature extraction, the sampling rate of the speech waveform was 6.67 kHz, and an eighth-order linear prediction method was adopted. In the training phase, 100 different waveforms for each digit (i.e., from 100 speakers) were grouped into two training sets. One HMM subnet was trained for each set, so there were in total 20 HMM models (10 digits $\times$ 2 models per digit). Each HMM has $N = 5$ states and $M = 5$ mixture features per state. In the recognition phase, each of the 20 models was scored by the Viterbi algorithm to determine the optimal alignment path corresponding to the test sequence. The most probable digit was then selected. The performance of the HMM recognizer was reported to be very close to the best performance of a DTW (dynamic-time-warping) recognizer [233].

7.5.2 Application to ECG Recognition

The original ECG data were composed of 10 classes, with 10 waveform patterns in each class. To test the tolerance of the HMM with respect to time-rescaling, the ECG waveforms were deliberately rescaled to be used as the test set, (cf. Figure 7.7). The different sampling rates adopted were $50/T$, $60/T$, and $70/T$, where T was the period of the ECG pulse. There were 100 sampled waveforms extracted for each sampling rate, which were further divided into two groups with 50 waveforms each. The first group of $60/T$ sampled waveforms was used as the training set. All 6 groups were used as testing sets. The original continuous (real) signal was quantized into 20 levels so that a HMM with $M = 20$ observation symbols could be applied. The number of states used was $N = 30$. The generalization accuracies are displayed in Table 7.3. The results indicate a high degree of tolerance of the HMM with respect to waveform time-rescaling.

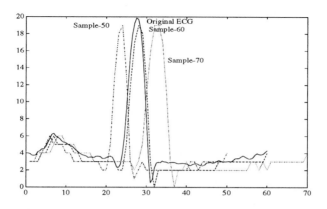

Figure 7.7: An original ECG pattern (solid line) and three time-rescaled waveforms of sampling rates $60/T$, $70/T$, and $50/T$, respectively.

Sampling Rate	First Group	Second Group
$50/T$	100%	88%
$60/T$	100%*	90%
$70/T$	98%	92%

Table 7.3: The test results with respect to different groups of resampled data. The training set is marked by *.

7.5.3   Application to Optical Character Recognition

In some recognition approaches, characters are individually recognized, with *linguistic context* information totally ignored. To improve recognition rate, errors made at the *letter level* may be corrected by utilizing the context information at the *word level*, as inspired by the HEARSAY system designed originally for speech recognition [21]. For this purpose, the HMM can facilitate the design of a hierarchical recognition system, proposed by Vlontzos and Kung [289, 290], that combines two levels of recognitions, (cf. Figure 7.8). At the *letter level*, a set of *candidate characters* can be selected for each particular letter position in a word. At the *word level*, the word most likely formed by the candidate characters will be recognized.

    The hierarchical system, consisting of an *HMM* at the letter level and an *MM* at the word level, has the potential for achieving an extremely high recognition rate. Recognition at the letter level is based on an OCON representation because the number of letters is small. An individual HMM is

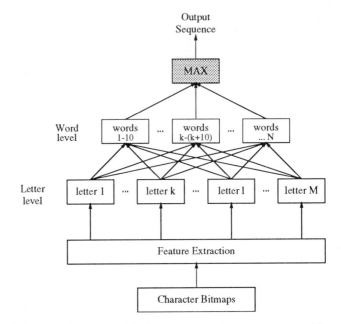

Figure 7.8: Hierarchical system for character recognition

trained for each letter. For the word level, it is more suitable to have *each MM subnet trained for a group of words.* The number of models can be reduced by taking advantage of the common subsequences shared by the words in the same group.

7.5.3.1 Recognition at the Letter Level

Consider any English character, say, "e" or "o"; each can be represented as a sequence of arcs and lines. The representations depend on how characters are traced. Therefore, at the letter level, it is important to take into account the variations in tracing the characters. The doubly stochastic generative model of the HMM is very suitable. The state sequence is modeled by a Markov process, with the actual features (e.g., an arc or a line) modeled by an emission-probability distribution. The key parameters for the *HMM* at the letter level are

Λ : The system contains 130 models for the letter level. Each character is associated with five models, one for each point size (8 pt to 48 pt), and each model has been trained with examples from twelve different fonts.

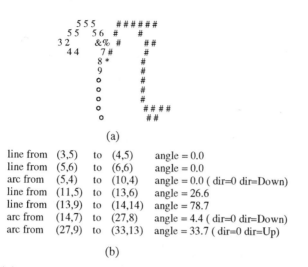

(a)

line from	(3,5)	to	(4,5)	angle = 0.0
line from	(5,6)	to	(6,6)	angle = 0.0
arc from	(5,4)	to	(10,4)	angle = 0.0 (dir=0 dir=Down)
line from	(11,5)	to	(13,6)	angle = 26.6
line from	(13,9)	to	(14,14)	angle = 78.7
arc from	(14,7)	to	(27,8)	angle = 4.4 (dir=0 dir=Down)
arc from	(27,9)	to	(33,13)	angle = 33.7 (dir=0 dir=Up)

(b)

Figure 7.9: (a) The character is segmented into sections separated by points with three neighbors. Each segment is denoted by its own symbol. (b) Final description in terms of structural primitives (arcs, lines) and their orientations.

Q : Each model consists of nine states: four for lines, four for arcs, and one separator state to mark the start or end of each character. Thus each state is associated with a *class* of lines or arcs. Each of the first eight states can produce three possible features, whereas the separator state can produce only one feature.

O : The input to the model is an observation sequence O consisting of codes of features obtained by the feature extractor. This input is used to calculate the probability $Pr(O|\Lambda)$ of all letter models, and the three highest-scoring models are selected for further processing at the word level.

A : It expresses the probabilities of one state (line or arc) following another state.

B : It expresses the probabilities of a state producing *one instance* (i.e., an angled line or an arc).

π : These initial values express the probabilities of a character, starting with a particular class of features (i.e., lines or arcs).

Feature Extraction The system deals with *isolated characters*. Each character is presented to the feature-extraction level as a bit map. The system obtains the character's skeleton by a thinning algorithm. The sequence of the features is determined by the way the character bit-map is scanned. Next, a segmentation of the character is performed by identifying the points of the skeleton that have more than two neighbors, cf. Figure 7.9. The last stage is a polygonal approximation of the segments to determine if they are lines or arcs and determine their orientations [221]. A new feature number is assigned for each 30-degree increment of the orientation, thus providing some rotation invariance.

Model Scoring To find which model is most likely for the observations, we need to calculate $Pr(O|\Lambda)$, that is, the probability of the observation sequence $O = \{O(1), O(2), \ldots, O(T)\}$ given the model Λ. This probability is the sum of probabilities of observing the sequence and ending up at any state at time T. For its computation, the forward evaluation procedure in Section 7.4.1 can be adopted. The three most likely characters, rank-ordered by their likelihoods, are selected as *candidate characters* for further processing at the word level.

7.5.3.2 Recognition at the Word Level

As mentioned earlier, the letter level produces three candidates for each letter position in a word. If T is the length of the word, there are 3^T possible character sequences that can be constructed using these candidates. The objective of the word level is to select one of these sequences according to some optimality criterion, subject to the constraints posed by the structure of the possible words. A common criterion is to maximize the likelihood of the selected sequence of characters.

Learning Phase At the word level, it is assumed that a group of words is produced by a stochastic automaton Λ, represented by a *pure* Markov model. The model is trained so that it is the most likely for the group of words (e.g., 10 words). The key parameters of the Markov model are

Λ : There are 1200 word-level models, each corresponding to 10 words out of a dictionary of 12,000 words based on the Unix `spell` utility.

Q : The model has 27 states. Each of the first 26 states corresponds to one character, and the final state stands for the separator feature.

O : The training sequence $O = \{O(1), O(2), \ldots, O(T)\}$ consists of the letters of the 10 words used to train the model.

A : The state-transition matrix expresses the probability of one letter following another.

B : Here $B = I$ because the (pure) Markov model is adopted.

π : The initial probabilities express the probability of a word starting with a particular character.

The transition probabilities of the model can be trained by the (simplified) Baum-Welch learning algorithm as discussed in Example 7.2. It determines the model most likely to produce the group of words. We used the dictionary of the Unix spell utility, containing 12,000 words to train 1200 models, each with 10 words. The training sequence $O = \{O(1), O(2), \ldots, O(T)\}$ consists of the characters of each word separated by the separator feature.

Recognition Phase In the recognition phase, the basic problem is to find the most likely sequence, given the model and the candidates from the lower (letter) level. To determine the most likely sequence of characters for a particular Markov model, we use a Viterbi-type dynamic programming technique [69]. The computation proceeds on a trellis diagram similar to the one depicted in Figure 7.6(b). We assume that, at each time t, the model makes a state transition according to transition probabilities a_{ij}. (The transition probabilities and their initial values are derived during the training phase.)

For word-level recognition, it is proposed that the state either produces its associated character with an assigned probability, or it simply produces no character. There are fixed probabilities $(w_i(t))$ for a state to produce its associated characters, as opposed to a hard rule: $b_i(O(t) = v_i) = 1$, $b_i(O(t) = \text{any others}) = 0$. More precisely, the probability $w_i(t)$ is predetermined according to its ranking in the letter-level classifier (as a likely candidate for the t-th position in a word). For example, 0.6 for the highest ranking candidate, 0.3 for the second highest, and 0.1 for the last. The most likely sequence ending with state i at time t should be the maximum of all probabilities of the sequences until $t-1$ ending at any state, multiplied by the transition probability to state i and the probability of producing the letter v_i. The algorithm is basically the same as the pattern-completion algorithm of Section 7.4.2, albeit that $b_i(O(t))$ being substituted by $w_i(t)$.

During training, the model is estimated in a way that each training sequence corresponds to a local maximum of the probability function of the

$$\text{a a \textbf{a} a \textit{a} a \textbf{a} \textit{a} a \textit{a} a \textbf{a}}$$

$$\text{g g \textbf{g} g \textit{g} g \textbf{g} \textbf{g} g \textit{g} g g}$$

Training set

$$\text{a a \textbf{a} a \textit{a} a \textit{a} \textbf{a} \textit{a} a \textit{a} a}$$

Testing set

Figure 7.10: Samples of training and testing characters.

model parameters. If too many words with common letter subsequences are used for the determination of the parameters of the Markov model, it might introduce false local maxima that would correspond to words not in the training set. For example, suppose that the words **carl** and **malt** are used for training the same model. The word **calt** becomes a possible selection if letters l and t are among the candidate characters in their corresponding positions. Depending on the context in the sentence, it may even score higher than any actual words used for training. In this case, the word **calt** will be erroneously selected. To alleviate the (false local maxima) problem, models should be conservatively trained. In the proposed hierarchical OCR system, there are only 10 words per model (group). Experiments suggested that satisfactory results could be achieved using as many as 190 words per model (cf. Figure 7.11). The best experimental results were obtained with 10 to 25 words per model.

The algorithm is used to generate a sequence of candidates for each model and its probability. Therefore, there are 1200 models (sequences) selected out of the 12,000 possible words. The model (sequence) with the highest probability is selected as the final output of our system. The general procedure requires the evaluation of the probabilities of a great number of sequences. In practice, to save model evaluations, the word database should be so structured that the models are trained only with words starting with a common letter. In this case, all models that have a starting letter not included in the three candidates produced by the letter level need not be considered.

The same algorithm can be used to complete sequences when the letter-level recognizer fails to produce any candidate character for some position, say, t_u. In this case we set $w_i(t_u)$ to be identical for all characters. At each

Two-Layer Example:
      Word Layer: 190 words (one model)
      Letter Layer: 12 fonts, five sizes (130 models)

Bitmap Input: `s y s t em   C h a r a c t e r`

Letter Candidates Ranked by Likelihood
      First: `sbsten charocter`
      Second: y   m   a
      Third: d

Result: system character

Figure 7.11: Example of the operation of the complete system.

stage where the observation is unknown, a set of paths is generated, one for each possible feature. If a path is obviously incompatible with the rest of the observations, it will be discarded. Among the remaining paths, the most likely one will be selected.

Simulation Results The training characters were taken from the Apple Macintosh screen fonts. In total, 12 fonts and five sizes ranging from 8 to 48 points were used. There were five models per character (one for each size) trained with examples from all fonts. The word-level models were trained using 12,000 words from the Unix `spell` dictionary. Each model was trained with 10 words to avoid creating too many local maxima of the probability function. For each character, all letter-level models were scored, and the top three were selected for the word level. At the letter level, the dynamic programming algorithm was used to select the letter sequence with the highest probability. This probability was used to score all word-level models for selection of the final sequence.

The system was tested with *italic* and **boldface** versions of the training set, as well as with handwritten characters (cf. Figure 7.10). (In some experiments, the training set contained only printed characters.) An example of the input and output of the system is shown in Figure 7.11. Note that the correct character was always one of the three top-scoring candidates. The recognition performance of the hierarchical OCR system is summarized in Table 7.4.

Training Set	Test Set	Single-Level	Two-Level
Printed	Printed	95%	97-99%
Printed	Boldface	95%	97-99%
Printed	Handwritten	70%	75-80%
Handwritten	Handwritten	93%	95-98%

Table 7.4: The performances of the HMM-based OCR system.

7.6   Concluding Remarks

This chapter presents the hidden Markov models for temporal pattern recognitions. One significant difficulty in dealing with temporal patterns lies in its inherent temporal variability and order-sensitivity. The HMM, with its doubly stochastic process, can effectively handle this problem. Therefore, the HMM is especially appealing for applications where the pattern generation process is uncontrollable and unpredictable. Examples are waveforms of speech signals or traces of handwritten characters.

As established in this chapter, there is a strong link between the learning algorithms of the HMM and BP models. From the numerical perspective, however, special attention should be paid to the scaling problem associated with the multiplicative HMM learning algorithm. For this, numerical solutions based on renormalization were proposed in [125, 171]. Theoretical relationships between the HMM and BP network, or Boltzmann machine, are studied in [34] and [230]. The HMM learning algorithm, as presented, utilizes no mutual information between two classes, since it is based on independent training. As a remedy, a mutual training scheme, such as the decision-based or fuzzy-decision learning rules, may be adopted. In fact, the reinforced/antireinforced decision-based learning rules are directly applicable to HMM, using the maximum likelihood function as the discriminant function.

7.7   Problems

Exercise 7.1 Compare the pros and cons of the HMM approach versus the dynamic time-warping approach when applied to speech-recognition applications. Discuss the requirements on the training phase and the retrieving phase separately.

Exercise 7.2 List the pros and cons of MM and HMM for speech or character recognitions.

Exercise 7.3 (Training a Pure Markov Model)
Consider a pure Markov stochastic process with the matrix $B = I$. Calculate π_j and a_{ij} when $N = 3$, $T = 8$, and the state sequence is $[A, B, A, C, B, B, A, C]$.

Exercise 7.4 (Baum-Welch Reestimation Algorithm for HMM)
Consider an HMM, with $N = 3$, $M = 3$, $T = 8$, and given the observation sequence as $[2, 3, 2, 1, 2, 2, 3, 1]$. Compute π_j, a_{ij}, and b_{ik} given initial conditions as

$$\pi_1^{(0)} = 0, \quad \pi_2^{(0)} = 1, \quad \pi_3^{(0)} = 0$$

the initial state-transition matrix as

$$A^{(0)} = \begin{bmatrix} 0 & \frac{1}{4} & \frac{1}{2} \\ 1 & \frac{1}{4} & \frac{1}{2} \\ 0 & \frac{1}{2} & 0 \end{bmatrix}$$

and $B^{(0)} = I$.

Exercise 7.5 (Apply Viterbi Algorithm to Trellis Diagram)
Given a test sequence $[2, 2, 1, 3, 2]$ for the HMM obtained in Problem 7.4, draw the trellis diagram and then apply the Viterbi algorithm to backtrack the optimal path.

Exercise 7.6 Repeat Exercise 7.4 with the initial state-transition matrix

$$A^{(0)} = \begin{bmatrix} \frac{1}{4} & \frac{1}{2} & \frac{1}{4} \\ \frac{1}{4} & \frac{1}{4} & \frac{1}{4} \\ \frac{1}{4} & \frac{1}{4} & \frac{1}{2} \end{bmatrix}$$

Show that matrix A will converge to the same value as Problem 7.4, and B will remain an identity matrix.

Exercise 7.7 From Exercise 7.6, verify that if the initial $B^{(0)}$ is set to the identity matrix; then B will remain an identity matrix throughout the learning phase. (Hint: Check Eq. 7.7.)

Exercise 7.8 Repeat Exercise 7.7 with the initial state transition matrix

$$A^{(0)} = \begin{bmatrix} 0 & 0 & \frac{1}{2} \\ 1 & 0 & \frac{1}{2} \\ 0 & 1 & 0 \end{bmatrix}$$

Show that there will be numerical difficulty involving division by 0.

Exercise 7.9 Verify that the multiplicative updating formulation in Eq. 7.4 always yields an increase in the energy function [24]. Show how this result leads to a proof for Eq. 7.17.

Exercise 7.10 Write down explicitly the back-propagation formula of Eq. 7.14 for the layer $t = T - 2$. Verify the induction proof.

Exercise 7.11 Review the the derivation of Eq. 7.11.
(a) Verify Eq. 7.12,

$$\gamma_j^{(m)}(t) = Pr(q_j \text{ at } t, O|\Lambda^{(m)}) = \alpha_j(t)\beta_j(t)$$

(b) Verify Eq. 7.20 and Eq. 7.19,

$$\tilde{\gamma}_i(t) = Pr(q_i \text{ at } t|O, \Lambda)$$
$$\tilde{\xi}_{ij}(t) = Pr(q_j \text{ at } t, q_i \text{ at } t+1|O, \Lambda)$$

Exercise 7.12 Derive the updating formulation for $\{b_i(k)\}$ and $\{\pi_j\}$ in Eq. 7.7 and Eq. 7.8. This should be similar to the derivation of $a_{ij}^{(m+1)}$ in Eq. 7.6.

Exercise 7.13 (Additive Weight Updating for HMM)
Additive weight updating, like the BP learning rule, can also be adopted in the training of HMM models. Develop an additive learning algorithm that takes into proper account that the weights must be positive and their sum must be equal to 1. (Hint: Redefine weights $a_{ij} \equiv w_{ij}^2$ to assure nonnegativeness.)

Exercise 7.14 Design mutual training networks based on HMM, e.g. decision-based or fuzzy-decision neural networks. (a) Define a proper loss function, and design the corresponding learning rule. (b) Identify the potential disadvantages or difficulties.

Exercise 7.15 (Incorporating the Scaling Scheme) Show that both $\alpha_i(t)$ and $\beta_i(t)$ tend to zero with geometric speed due to the consecutive multiplications of probability values that are less than 1.0. In order to avoid the *numerical underflow* problem frequently encountered in the learning phase, design a scaling scheme based on renormalization. (Hint: see [125, 171].)

PART V: ADVANCED TOPICS

Chapter 8

Principal Component Neural Networks

8.1 Introduction

Neural nets have been found very useful for extracting the most representative low-dimensional subspace from a high-dimensional vector space. In order to analyze multi-dimensional input vectors of, say, hundreds of different stock prices, it would be easier to work with the most critical and representative features of the data. The objective of feature-extraction is to search such effective representations for a given ensemble of data patterns. These features can, for example, be expressed by certain special linear combinations of all the prices. To retain the maximum relevant information, the representation should (1) extract the most significant features that can best manifest the original patterns, and (2) avoid duplication or redundancy between the neurons. Redundancy between the neurons tends to reduce the amount of total information. In statistics, a popular approach of extracting representation with maximum information is the *principal component analysis* (PCA).

269

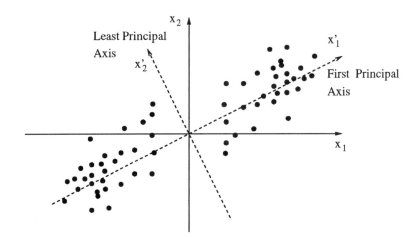

Figure 8.1: The x_1' axis represents the principal component for the pattern space.

Given an n-dimensional stationary stochastic (input) vector process $\mathbf{x} = [x_1, x_2, \cdots, x_n]^T$, if the probability distribution function of $\{\mathbf{x}\}$ is known a priori, then its autocorrelation matrix can be derived as

$$\mathbf{R}_x = E\{\mathbf{x}\mathbf{x}^T\}$$

The normalized eigenvectors of autocorrelation matrix $\mathbf{R}_x$ are $\{\mathbf{e}_i\}$, $\|\mathbf{e}_i\| = 1$, corresponding to the eigenvalues $\{\lambda_i\}$. An eigen-component of a stochastic process $\mathbf{x}(t)$, $\mathbf{e}_i^T \mathbf{x}(t)$, is its projection onto the one-dimensional subspace spanned by the eigenvector $\mathbf{e}_i$. The principal component of a signal is the first (and the largest) eigen-component

$$a(t) = \mathbf{e}_1^T \mathbf{x}(t)$$

(One simple example is illustrated in Figure 8.1.) Likewise, the first m principal components are the eigen-components corresponding to the largest m eigenvalues.

Statistical information on the autocorrelation matrix is often not directly available in practice. Instead, a large number of sample input vectors $\{\mathbf{x}(t),$ for $t = 1, \ldots, M\}$ are presented. In this case, an estimate of the autocorrelation matrix can be obtained by taking the time average over the sample vectors:

$$\tilde{R}_x = \frac{1}{M} \sum_{t=1}^{M} \mathbf{x}(t)\mathbf{x}^T(t)$$

In this chapter, it is assumed that $\mathbf{x}(t)$ is wide sense stationary and $\tilde{R}_x \to \mathbf{R}_x$ when $M \to \infty$. We also assume that the sample size M is always large enough so that there is no need to differentiate the actual autocorrelation matrix $\mathbf{R}_x$ and its estimate $\tilde{R}_x$. Such practice and assumption also applies to the estimation of the cross-correlation matrix $\mathbf{R}_{xy}$, where $\mathbf{y} = [y_1, y_2, \cdots, y_{n'}]^T$ is another n'-dimensional wide sense stationary stochastic vector.

Chapter Organization

Several neural models for PCA and their applications are explored. Section 8.2 provides the mathematical formulations for two PCA-type problems. In addition to the symmetric PCA, the *asymmetric* principal component analysis (APCA) is introduced. The APCA involves two different vector stochastic processes $\{\mathbf{x}\}$ and $\{\mathbf{y}\}$. In Section 8.3.1, adaptive learning models for extracting the first eigen-component for the PCA are presented. In Section 8.3.2, lateral orthogonalization networks for extracting multiple principal components for PCA are proposed. In Section 8.4, neural models for extracting asymmetric principal components are examined. Potential application examples are discussed in Section 8.5.

8.2   From Wiener Filtering to PCA

Wiener filtering is a very popular technique for the least-squares-error restoration of original signals. Under the context of neural models, we will now address two important cases: (1) full-rank Wiener filtering, and (2) rank-reduced Wiener filtering.

Full-Rank Wiener Filtering   The least-squares-error criterion for linear approximation is

$$\sum_{t=1}^{M} \|\mathbf{y}(t) - \mathbf{W}\mathbf{x}(t)\|^2 \equiv \|\mathbf{Y} - \mathbf{W}\mathbf{X}\|_F^2$$

where $\|\cdot\|_F$ denotes the Frobenius norm, and $\mathbf{Y} = [y_1 \ldots y_M]$, $\mathbf{X} = [x_1 \ldots x_M]$. If the network has a full hidden layer, then the full-rank optimal solution $\mathbf{W}^*$ can be achieved:

$$\mathbf{W}^* = \mathbf{Y}\mathbf{X}^T(\mathbf{X}\mathbf{X}^T)^{-1}$$

or, equivalently,

$$\mathbf{W}^* = \mathbf{R}_{xy}^T \mathbf{R}_x^{-1}$$

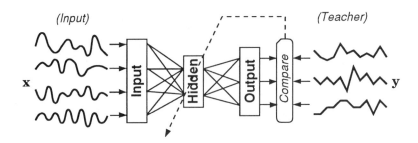

Figure 8.2: A linear, two-layer back-propagation network can be used for PCA and APCA. For the symmetric PCA problem, the network is self-supervised. That is, the teacher is the same as the input, $y \equiv x$. For the APCA problem, the teacher is different from the input.

The same solution can be obtained from a single-layer ADALINE network.

Rank-Reduced Wiener Filtering   Under the formulation of rank-reduced Wiener filtering, matrix $\mathbf{W}$ has a reduced rank. (The PCA can be regarded simply as a special case.) There are many applicational motivations for wanting the rank reduced, including data compression, noise removal, computational saving, and others. In data-compression, for example, a smaller rank implies a better compression rate. More precisely, a representation is sought that requires a minimum channel bandwidth and yet allows the best reconstruction of the original signal. To cover a broad application domain, two different formulations are proposed: symmetric principal component analysis (i.e., PCA) and *asymmetric* principal component analysis (i.e., APCA). [1]

1. **Symmetric PCA** The principal eigenvectors of $\mathbf{R}_x$ represent the directions where the signal has maximum energy. Projection of the signal onto the principal-component subspace is optimal in the sense that the reconstruction error is minimized, cf. Eq. 8.1 and Eq. 8.2. As shown in Figure 8.2, a linear, two-layer, self-supervised, back-propagation network can be used for PCA. The network has several distinctive features: (1) it is linear; (2) the hidden layer has a much smaller size than the dimension of the input; and (3) it is self-supervised (i.e., the teacher is the same as the input, $y \equiv x$). Mathematically, the PCA is, basically, the problem of finding the principal singular vectors in the singular value decomposition (SVD) of the autocorrelation matrix $\mathbf{R}_x$.

---

[1]In this chapter, the teacher values are denoted by the vector $\mathbf{y}$, instead of $\mathbf{t}$ used in the previous chapter.

2. **Asymmetric PCA** The APCA problem involves two different vector stochastic processes: $\{\mathbf{x}\}$ (input) and $\{\mathbf{y}\}$ (teacher). The objective is to find the most representative components of the input process $\mathbf{x}(t)$ so that they can be used to best recover the output process $\mathbf{y}(t)$. As shown in Figure 8.2, a linear two-layer back-propagation network (with relatively few hidden units) can be adopted to solve the APCA. However, unlike the PCA, the network is hetero-supervised since the teacher is different from the input. Mathematically, the APCA problem involves finding the principal left (right) singular vectors of matrix $\mathbf{R}_x^{-1/2}\mathbf{R}_{xy}$, (cf. Section 8.4).

8.2.1   Symmetric Principal Component Analysis (PCA)

Given an n-dimensional vector process $\mathbf{x}(t) = [x_1(t), x_2(t), \cdots, x_n(t)]^T$, then an m-dimensional representation vector $\mathbf{a}(t) = [a_1(t), a_2(t), \ldots, a_m(t)]^T$ can be obtained by the following linear mapping

$$\mathbf{a}(t) = \mathbf{W}^T\mathbf{x}(t)$$

where $\mathbf{W}$ is an $n \times m$ matrix. More specifically, the inputs are now connected to m outputs $\{a_1 \ldots a_m\}$ through the weights $\{w_{i,j}\}$, which form a matrix $\mathbf{W}$, with $\mathbf{w}_i^T$ as the i-th row.

The principal component analysis (PCA) problem is to find a matrix $\mathbf{W}$ such that an optimal (in the mean-square sense) estimate $\hat{\mathbf{x}}(t)$ of $\mathbf{x}(t)$ can be reconstructed from $\mathbf{a}(t)$. In Figure 8.1, the original pattern space is two-dimensional ($n = 2$) and the two principal axes for the pattern space are shown. Note that the first principal axis x_1' captures most of the distribution variance of the pattern space.

Errors in Optimal Reconstruction by PCA   The principal components can be used to optimally reconstruct the signal. In PCA, the optimality of an estimation is defined as an estimate $\hat{\mathbf{x}}(t)$ that minimizes the distance norm of $\mathbf{x}(t) - \hat{\mathbf{x}}(t)$. When the exact principal components are obtained, the optimal matrix $\mathbf{W}$ will be formed by the first m singular vectors of $\mathbf{R}_x$. The optimal estimate can then be obtained as

$$\hat{\mathbf{x}}(t) = \mathbf{W}\mathbf{a}(t)$$

The corresponding errors of the optimal estimate are [118]:

$$\text{matrix-2-norm error} = \lambda_{m+1} \tag{8.1}$$

$$\text{least-mean-square error} = \sum_{i=m+1}^{n} \lambda_i \tag{8.2}$$

8.2.2 Asymmetric Principal Component Analysis

Two different vector stochastic processes, the input process $\mathbf{x}(t)$ and the teacher process $\mathbf{y}(t)$, are involved in asymmetric principal component analysis (APCA). The APCA problem is a rank-reduced Wiener filtering problem. In many applications, a reduced rank is desirable. For example, in data-compression applications, a smaller rank implies a higher compression rate. In terms of a two-layer network, a small rank also means a small number of hidden units. So the APCA problem can be formulated as a BP network with reduced hidden units.

A two-layer network is adopted for the APCA. The input-output mapping matrix (denoted by $\mathbf{W}$) is factorized into two: $\mathbf{W} = \overline{\mathbf{W}}\,\underline{\mathbf{W}}^T$, where $\underline{\mathbf{W}}$ and $\overline{\mathbf{W}}$ are the lower and upper layer weights, respectively. Because the number of hidden units is fixed to small number (denoted by m), it imposes a limit on the rank of this mapping matrix $\mathbf{W}$.

The solution for the rank-deficient case is related to the SVD of matrix

$$\mathbf{R}_{xy}^T \mathbf{R}_x^{-1/2} = \mathbf{V}\boldsymbol{\Sigma}\mathbf{U}^T$$

Here $\mathbf{U}$ and $\mathbf{V}$ are orthonormal matrices:

$$\mathbf{V} = [\mathbf{v}_1 \ldots \mathbf{v}_{n'}], \quad \mathbf{U} = [\mathbf{u}_1 \ldots \mathbf{u}_n]$$

and

$$\boldsymbol{\Sigma} = \begin{bmatrix} \boldsymbol{\Lambda} \\ \mathbf{0} \end{bmatrix} \quad or \quad \boldsymbol{\Sigma} = [\boldsymbol{\Lambda} \mid \mathbf{0}]$$

where $\boldsymbol{\Lambda} = \text{diag}[\sigma_1 \ldots \sigma_p]$, with $\sigma_1, \ldots, \sigma_p$ being real non-negative values, and $p = \min\{n', n\}$. It can be shown that the weight solutions for the m-rank $(m \leq p)$ optimal filtering problems are

$$\begin{aligned} \underline{\mathbf{W}}_{opt} &= \mathbf{R}_x^{-1/2}\mathbf{U}_m\boldsymbol{\Sigma}_m \\ \overline{\mathbf{W}}_{opt} &= \mathbf{V}_m \end{aligned}$$

where $\mathbf{U}_m = [\mathbf{u}_1 \ldots \mathbf{u}_m]$, $\mathbf{V}_m = [\mathbf{v}_1 \ldots \mathbf{v}_m]$, and $\boldsymbol{\Sigma}_m = \text{diag}[\sigma_1 \ldots \sigma_m]$.

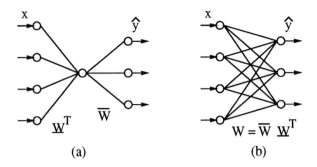

(a)   (b)

Figure 8.3: Equivalence between two linear networks: (a) a two-layer network with one hidden unit, and (b) a one-layer network with a rank-one weight matrix.

Single Hidden Unit   A single-rank $(m = 1)$ case is depicted in Figure 8.3. The objective is to find two vectors $\overline{w}$ and $\underline{w}$ to minimize the following:

$$J_1(\underline{w}, \overline{w}) = E\{\|y - \overline{w}\underline{w}^T x\|^2\} = E\{\|y\|^2\} - 2\underline{w}^T \mathbf{R}_{xy}\overline{w} + \|\overline{w}\|^2\underline{w}^T \mathbf{R}_x\underline{w} \quad (8.3)$$

The minimizing solution can be derived by taking the first-order derivative of J_1 with respect to $\underline{w}$ and $\overline{w}$ and making it equal to zero. This leads to the following:

$$\mathbf{R}_{xy}^T \underline{w} = \mu^2 \overline{w} \quad (8.4)$$

$$\mathbf{R}_{xy} \overline{w} = \rho^2 \mathbf{R}_x \underline{w} \quad (8.5)$$

where

$$\mu^2 = \underline{w}^T \mathbf{R}_x \underline{w}, \quad \rho^2 = \|\overline{w}\|^2$$

Equivalently,

$$[\mathbf{R}_{xy}^T \mathbf{R}_x^{-1/2}][\mathbf{R}_x^{1/2}\underline{w}] = \mu^2 \overline{w} \quad (8.6)$$

$$[\mathbf{R}_x^{-1/2}\mathbf{R}_{xy}]\overline{w} = \rho^2[\mathbf{R}_x^{1/2}\underline{w}] \quad (8.7)$$

Eq. 8.6 and Eq. 8.7 together imply that $[\mathbf{R}_x^{1/2}\underline{w}]$ and $\overline{w}$ are the left and right singular vectors of $\mathbf{R}_{xy}^T \mathbf{R}_x^{-1/2}$. If they are the i-th singular vectors, then $\rho\mu = \sigma_i$, where σ_i is the i-th singular value.

In fact, the global minimum of J_1 can be achieved when and only when the weight vectors are the principal singular vectors. (In other words, any other singular vectors cannot yield a true minimum.) So the minimizing solution is $[\mathbf{R}_x^{1/2}\underline{w}] = \mathbf{u}_1$ and $\overline{w} = \mathbf{v}_1$. The vectors $\mathbf{u}_1$ and $\mathbf{v}_1$ are the first (left and right) singular vectors, and $\rho\sigma = \sigma_1$ is the first singular value.

Multiple Hidden Units   When the rank $m > 1$, the objective is to find optimal vectors $\overline{\mathbf{w}}_i$ and $\underline{\mathbf{w}}_i$, $i = 1, \ldots, m$, to minimize the following criterion:

$$J_m(\underline{\mathbf{W}}, \overline{\mathbf{W}}) = E\{\|\mathbf{y} - \overline{\mathbf{W}}\underline{\mathbf{W}}^T\mathbf{x}\|^2\} \tag{8.8}$$

Without loss of generality, the following constraint can be imposed, for all $i \neq j$,

$$\overline{\mathbf{w}}_i^T\overline{\mathbf{w}}_j = 0 \tag{8.9}$$

$$\underline{\mathbf{w}}_i^T\mathbf{R}_x\underline{\mathbf{w}}_j = 0 \tag{8.10}$$

This orthogonality constraint does not affect the span of the subspace nor the least-squares error. The solution can be derived by induction. Suppose that the solution for rank m-1 is already obtained. The minimizing solution can be found by taking the derivatives of J_m with respect to $\overline{\mathbf{w}}_m$ and $\underline{\mathbf{w}}_m$ and making them equal to zero. The minimizing solution is (cf. Problem 8.4)

$$[\mathbf{R}_x^{1/2}\underline{\mathbf{w}}_m] = \mathbf{u}_m \quad \text{and} \quad \overline{\mathbf{w}}_m = \mathbf{v}_m \tag{8.11}$$

where $\mathbf{u}_m$ and $\mathbf{v}_m$ denote the m-th left and right singular vector of $\mathbf{R}_{xy}^T\mathbf{R}_x^{-1/2}$, and $\rho\sigma = \sigma_m$ equals the m-th singular value.

Subspace Spanned by Multiple Principal Components   The minimizing solution is obviously nonunique. For instance, if $\underline{\mathbf{W}}, \overline{\mathbf{W}}$ is a solution, then so is $\underline{\mathbf{W}}\mathbf{C}^T$ and $\overline{\mathbf{W}}\mathbf{C}^{-1}$, where $\mathbf{C}$ is any invertible matrix.

   In extending the method to extract multiple principal components (PCs), two approaches can be taken:

1. Determine the subspace spanned by the first m principal components when the constraints in Eq. 8.9 and Eq. 8.10 are not imposed.

2. Determine each of the first m principal components, and in proper order, when the constraints in Eq. 8.9 and Eq. 8.10 are imposed.

Errors in Optimal Reconstruction by APCA   The principal components

$$\mathbf{a} = \underline{\mathbf{W}}_{opt}^T\mathbf{x}$$

can be used to optimally reconstruct the signal. In the APCA, the optimality of an estimation is defined as an estimate $\hat{\mathbf{x}}$ that minimizes the distance norm of $\mathbf{y} - \hat{\mathbf{y}}$. The optimal estimate can be obtained as

$$\hat{y} = \overline{\mathbf{W}}_{opt}^T \mathbf{a}$$

The corresponding error of the optimal estimate for the APCA formulation is [253]:

$$\text{least-mean-square error} = \sum_{i=m+1}^{n} \lambda_i$$

8.3 Symmetric Principal Component Analysis

In this section, we will first treat the case of the single principal component, and then extend it to the extraction of multiple components. There are two important issues pertaining to adaptive networks for extracting principal components: *learning rules* and *network structures*. Section 8.3.1 focuses on the *learning rules* for extracting principal components. Section 8.3.2 treats *network structures* that ensure the "orthogonality" between multiple principal components. In order to extract multiple PCs, a new structure incorporating lateral connections into the network is proposed.

8.3.1 Extraction of the Single Principal Component

The learning rules involved are the Hebbian rule, the Oja rule, and the delta learning rule. The PCA problem can be viewed either as an unsupervised learning network or as a self-supervised learning network. The former, based on the unsupervised learning perspective, follows the traditional Hebbian-type learning. The latter follows the (self-)supervised learning formulation and is conceptually closer to the derivation of the delta learning rule, cf. Section 8.4. The PCA in this sense unifies the Hebbian rule and the delta learning rule. In the following, the relationships between these learning rules will be discussed. A numerical analysis on their learning rates and convergence properties will be provided.

8.3.1.1 Hebbian Learning Rule for PCA Networks

The basic network is shown in Figure 8.4 where the neuron is a simple linear unit with

$$a(t) = \mathbf{w}(t)^T \mathbf{x}(t) \tag{8.12}$$

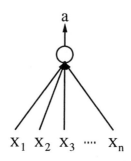

Figure 8.4: Neuron model based on the Oja rule or the normalized Hebbian rule).

To enhance the correlation between the input $\mathbf{x}(t)$ and the extracted component $a(t)$, it is natural to use a Hebbian-type rule:

$$\mathbf{w}(t+1) = \mathbf{w}(t) + \beta\mathbf{x}(t)a(t) \tag{8.13}$$

In the following analysis of system dynamics, we introduce two different time indices (t and t'): one corresponding to the substep (iteration), and the other the global step (block or sweep). This is explained in Figure 8.5.

To facilitate the analysis, we adopt a block-adaptive version of the Hebbian learning rule. The weights change according to the slower increment of t', not the faster increment of t. (The sweep number is indexed by t'.) This results in **piecewise constant** weights $\mathbf{w}(t)$ as shown in Figure 8.5. They remain constant within the same sweep, and the update occurs only at the end of a sweep.

Block-adaptive updating is motivated by the common assumption that the block period M is sufficiently long so that it permits a statistic averaging to effectively take place, and $\tilde{E}\{\mathbf{xx}^T\} \approx \mathbf{R}$, where $\tilde{E}\{\cdot\}$ denotes average over one sweep.

Substituting Eq. 8.12 into Eq. 8.13, we have

$$\mathbf{w}(t+1) = \mathbf{w}(t) + \beta\mathbf{x}(t)\mathbf{x}(t)^T\mathbf{w}(t)$$

By taking the average on the updating terms, Eq. 8.13 can be simplified to

$$\mathbf{w}(t'+1) = \mathbf{w}(t') + \beta'\mathbf{R}_x\mathbf{w}(t') \tag{8.14}$$

Note that the time index is changed to t', signifying that block-adaptive learning is being considered. Note also that if β is kept very small and $\beta = M^{-1}\beta'$, then the original Hebbian learning rule in Eq. 8.13 will behave

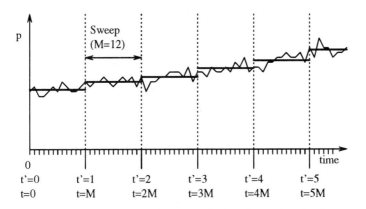

Figure 8.5: A block-adaptive updating rule is adopted only for purposes of analysis. The weights are assumed to be piecewise constant, as shown by the dotted lines. Here the index t indicates substeps during the iterations within the block, and the index t' denotes the block steps. Here block size M usually equals the number of training patterns. However, when the training patterns are presented in an indefinite basis, then M can be any number that is large enough from a statistical point of view.

approximately the same as the block-adaptive (i.e., piecewise-constant) rule in Eq. 8.14. [2]

Recall that $\{e_i\}$ denotes the eigenvectors of the autocorrelation matrix $\mathbf{R}_x$, corresponding to the eigenvalues $\{\lambda_i\}$. By using e_i as the new basis vectors, the weight vector can be rewritten as

$$\mathbf{w}(t') = \sum_{i=1}^{n} \theta_i(t')\mathbf{e}_i \qquad (8.15)$$

and Eq. 8.14 leads to

$$\theta_i(t'+1) = [1 + \beta'\lambda_i]\theta_i(t') \qquad (8.16)$$

During each block updating, the first eigen-component gets enhanced by a greater ratio than all other components, because it corresponds to the largest eigenvalue. It can be argued that if the updating process continues indefinitely (assuming for the time being that it is numerically feasible), the first component will eventually dominate. In contrast, all the other components will be relatively suppressed. This is why a Hebbian-type rule may be applied for extracting principal components.

---

[2] By a rigorous denotation, a new function $\mathbf{w}'(t')$ should have been introduced. However, for simplicity, we will use $\mathbf{w}(t')$ instead of $\mathbf{w}'(t')$ throughout this analysis.

8.3.1.2   Oja Learning Rule for PCA Networks

Unfortunately, the Hebbian rule is impractical for PCA, taking into account the finite-word-length effect. The training weights will eventually overflow (i.e., exceed the limit of dynamic range) before the first component totally dominates and the other components sufficiently diminish. An effective technique to overcome the overflow problem is to keep normalizing the weight vectors after each updating. This leads to the Oja learning rule or, simply, the Oja rule.

Equivalence with Normalized Hebbian Rule   *The Oja learning Rule is equivalent to a normalized Hebbian rule* [209]. It effectively solves the stability problem associated with the (unnormalized) Hebbian rule for PCA. In the following, we show why this is the case. The Hebbian rule can be normalized by using the following two steps:

$$\tilde{\mathbf{w}}(t+1) \;=\; \mathbf{w}(t) + \beta \mathbf{x}(t)a(t) \tag{8.17}$$

$$\mathbf{w}(t+1) \;=\; \|\tilde{\mathbf{w}}(t+1)\|^{-1}\tilde{\mathbf{w}}(t+1) \tag{8.18}$$

where $a(t) = \mathbf{w}(t)^T\mathbf{x}(t)$. The normalization at each step is a vital feature for numerical stability and is useful for other eigenvector-related algorithms as well. The equivalence of the Oja updating rule and the normalized Hebbian rule can be established through a *linearization* procedure. From Eq. 8.17 and Eq. 8.18, we obtain

$$\|\tilde{\mathbf{w}}(t+1)\|^2 = \|\mathbf{w}(t)\|^2 + 2\beta a(t)^2 + \mathcal{O}(\beta^2)$$

Approximating the inverse square root by the first-order Taylor expansion, and noting that $\|\mathbf{w}(t)\| = 1$, we obtain

$$\|\tilde{\mathbf{w}}(t+1)\|^{-1} = 1 - \beta a(t)^2 + \mathcal{O}(\beta^2) \tag{8.19}$$

Combining Eq. 8.18 and Eq. 8.19, we have

$$\mathbf{w}(t+1) = \mathbf{w}(t) + \beta[\mathbf{x}(t)a(t) - \mathbf{w}(t)a(t)^2] + \mathcal{O}(\beta^2)$$

The Oja rule can be derived by ignoring the $\mathcal{O}(\beta^2)$ term:

$$\mathbf{w}(t+1) = \mathbf{w}(t) + \beta[\mathbf{x}(t)a(t) - \mathbf{w}(t)a(t)^2] \tag{8.20}$$

In contrast to the Hebbian rule, the Oja rule is numerically stable.

Theorem 8.1 (Convergence of a Single Component) *For a PCA network with the learning rule in Eq. 8.20, $\mathbf{w}(t)$ converges asymptotically (with probability 1) to*

$$\mathbf{w} = \mathbf{w}(\infty) = \mathbf{e}_1 \qquad (8.21)$$

That is, the weight vector $\mathbf{w}(t)$ converges to the first principal component. ∎

This proof follows the same reasoning used previously by the Hebbian learning rule. The difference is that the weights are normalized so the numerical instability issue is resolved. For more detailed proof, see [209]. A similar analysis can be extended to derive the following convergence rate for the Oja learning rule. (More detailed derivation can be found in [158, 153].)

Theorem 8.2 (Convergence Rates) *By taking the "average" on the learning rule of Eq. 8.20 and an eigen-analysis similar to Eq. 8.15 and Eq. 8.16, it can be derived that each of the eigen-components is enhanced/dampened by the following rate.*

$$\theta_i(t'+1) = [1 + \beta'\lambda_i - \beta'\sigma(t')]\theta_i(t')$$

where $\sigma(t') = \tilde{E}\{a^2(t)\}$. (The time index t', instead of t, implies that the analysis is based on an "averaged" performance.) Therefore, the dominance of the principle component grows by the following rate:

$$\frac{1 + \beta'[\lambda_i - \sigma(t')]}{1 + \beta'[\lambda_1 - \sigma(t')]} \qquad (8.22)$$

∎

The simulation results shown in Figure 8.6 demonstrate that the PCA neural model converges according to the rates predicted by Theorem 8.2.

8.3.2 Multiple Principal Components: Lateral Orthogonalization Network

Two kinds of problems for extracting multiple principal components can be posted: (1) determine the subspace spanned by the first m principal components, and (2) determine exactly the m principal components. The task of determining the subspace spanned by the first m principal components is only a straightforward extension of the single-component case: We use $\mathbf{W}$ to denote the $n \times m$ weight matrix, and the network model becomes

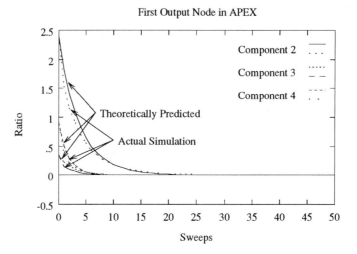

Figure 8.6: Simulation results indicate that the APEX network converges according to the rates predicted theoretically.

$$\Delta \mathbf{W}(t) = \beta \left[\mathbf{x}(t) - \mathbf{W}(t)\mathbf{a}(t) \right] \mathbf{a}(t)^T$$

This rule extracts a weight matrix $\mathbf{W}(t)$ whose columns span the same subspace as the m largest principal components.

For many applications, it is critical to extract the exact multiple principal components (PCs). It is not very straightforward. It cannot be accomplished, for example, by replicating the same network, because every neuron would simply duplicate independently the same first component. For a more effective approach, two basic techniques are available: (1) the deflation method, or (2) the lateral orthogonalization network (LON).

- **Deflation Method** The deflation method is a common numerical technique for eigenvalue and singular-value decomposition problems. Assume that the first component is already obtained; then the output value can be "deflated" by the following transformation:

$$\tilde{\mathbf{x}} = (I - \overline{\mathbf{w}}_1 \overline{\mathbf{w}}_1^T)\mathbf{x}$$

It can be shown that the deflation method will not affect any but the first singular value/vector [217]. The first principal component is nullified by the transformation, so the second principal component succeeds to be the new dominant mode. It can then be extracted by the same learning rule used for the first principal component. By a similar argument, the deflation method recursively applies to the other components ($m > 2$).

- **Lateral Orthogonalization Network (LON)** The basic idea is to allow the old hidden units to influence the new units so that the new ones do not duplicate information (in full or in part) already provided by the old units. By this approach, the deflation process is effectively implemented in an adaptive manner.

For the symmetric self-supervised case, a technique for extracting multiple components was proposed by Sanger [252], using the deflation technique. Another approach, proposed by Foldiak [68], adopts a notion of *anti-Hebbian* learning for extracting linearly independent components. In order to achieve the orthogonality between the hidden neurons, a lateral interaction between them can be incorporated. This leads to the *lateral orthogonalization networks* (LONs) proposed by Kung and Diamantaras [158].

8.3.2.1 Lateral Orthogonalization Networks

The learning rules used in *lateral orthogonalization networks* (LONs) to train the weights on lateral networks will be referred to as the *orthogonalization rules*. This assures that new components are "orthogonal" to the previous components. Two kinds of orthogonalization learning rules can be considered:

Local Orthogonalization Rule   Let $\{a_1\}$ and $\{a_2\}$ be two stochastic processes, where $\{a_1\}$ is the principal component of $\{x\}$, and let us define

$$a_2'(t) = a_2(t) - \alpha a_1(t) \tag{8.23}$$

As illustrated by Figure 8.7(a), in order to achieve the orthogonality between a_2' and a_1, the parameter α is set to

$$\alpha = \frac{\langle a_1, a_2 \rangle}{\|a_1\|^2} \tag{8.24}$$

where $\langle a_1, a_2 \rangle = \sum_t a_1(t) a_2(t)$ is the inner product of the two processes, and $\|a_1\| = \langle a_1, a_1 \rangle^{1/2}$. This means that the component removed from a_2 is equal to the projection of a_2 onto a_1, so that a_2' becomes orthogonal to a_1; cf. Figure 8.7(b). This follows the same principle as the Gram-Schmidt *orthogonalization* procedure [80]. Accordingly, the following adaptive *orthogonalization rule* can be derived for adaptively tracking parameter α:

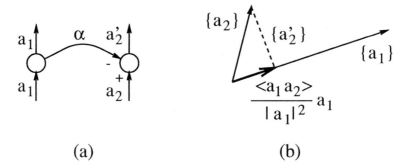

(a)   (b)

Figure 8.7: (a) The lateral orthogonalization network is based on the principle of removing any duplication of old components from a new component. (b) In the *local orthogonalization rule*, the parameter α can be adaptively trained, as shown in Eq. 8.25. The part to be removed in order to achieve orthogonality can be depicted as the projection from the new component to the old. As shown, the residue is orthogonal to the old component. The alternative *dynamic orthogonalization rule* is, unfortunately, not easy to illustrate by a figure.

$$\Delta\alpha(t) = \beta \left[a_1(t)a_2(t) - \alpha(t)a_1(t)^2 \right] \tag{8.25}$$

(As a justification of Eq. 8.25, note that $\Delta\alpha(t) = 0$ in convergence. Thus, by an averaging process, $\alpha(t) \to \alpha$, where as α is given in Eq. 8.24.)

Dynamic Orthogonalization Rule   In contrast to the local orthogonalization rule, the dynamic orthogonalization rule adopts the approach of tracking existing dynamic equations. Its derivation depends on the learning rules used in the forward network. An example is given in Eq. 8.28.

8.3.2.2   Lateral Networks for Symmetric PCA

The LON network for multiple components is depicted in Figure 8.8. Because the LON is arranged in a cascaded manner, it can function in an inductive manner. For example, given the first m-1 principal components, it can produce the m-th component.

Recall that $\mathbf{w}_i^T$ is the row vector denoting the weights connecting the input to the i-th output. If $j < i$, we introduce a lateral link α_{ij} from the j-th output node to the i-th output node:

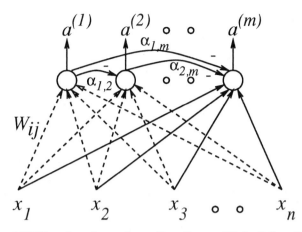

Figure 8.8: APEX network configuration for multiple PCs. The solid arcs indicate the Hebbian and anti-Hebbian weights for the extraction of the m-th component.

$$a_i(t) = \mathbf{w}_i(t)^T \mathbf{x}(t) - \sum_{j=1}^{i-1} \alpha_{ij}(t) a_j(t), \quad i = 1, 2, \ldots, m$$

The corresponding network configuration is shown in Figure 8.8. Several neural networks have been proposed [153, 158], based on applications of these orthogonalization learning rules, and their convergence properties have also been studied.

This leads to the so-called **APEX** (Adaptive Principal-component Extractor), which consists of two training rules:

1. **The Oja Rule:** For training the i-th component

$$\Delta \mathbf{w}_i(t) = \beta[\mathbf{x}(t)a_i(t) - \mathbf{w}_i(t)a_i(t)^2] \tag{8.26}$$

2. **Orthogonalization Rule:** One of the following is adopted.

   - *Local Orthogonalization Rule*

$$\Delta \alpha_{ij}(t) = \beta \left[a_i(t)a_j(t) - \alpha_{ij}(t)a_j(t)^2 \right] \tag{8.27}$$

   - *Dynamic Orthogonalization Rule* (cf. Figure 8.7)

$$\Delta \alpha_{ij}(t) = \beta \left[a_i(t)a_j(t) - \alpha_{ij}(t)a_i(t)^2 \right] \tag{8.28}$$

for all j, $1 \leq j < i$. The justification of Eq. 8.28 is provided below.

Theorem 8.3 (Convergence - Multiple Component Case)
Based on the learning rules Eq. 8.26 and Eq. 8.27 (or Eq. 8.26 and Eq. 8.28), the Hebbian weight matrix $\mathbf{W}(t)$ *in the* **APEX** *network converges asymptotically to the matrix formed by the m largest principal components. More precisely, weight matrix* $\mathbf{W}(t)$ *converges to* $\mathbf{W}(\infty) = \mathbf{W}$ *(with probability 1), where* $\mathbf{W}$ *is the matrix formed by m row vectors* $\{\mathbf{w}_i^T\}$ *, where* $\mathbf{w}_i = \mathbf{w}_i(\infty) = \mathbf{e}_i$. ∎

Proof: Our proof is by induction. Assuming that all the first m-1 principal components are already extracted, it suffices to show that the m-th component a_m can be properly extracted according to the learning rule. Referring to Figure 8.8, we denote $z(t) = [\alpha_{1m}(t), \alpha_{2m}(t), \cdots, \alpha_{m-1,m}(t)]$ and $w(t) = [w_{1m}(t), w_{2m}(t), \cdots, w_{m-1,m}(t)]$.

$$a_m(t) = \mathbf{x}(t)^T \mathbf{w}(t) - \nu(t)^T \mathbf{z}(t) \tag{8.29}$$

where

$$\nu(t) = \mathbf{V}^T \mathbf{x}(t)$$

and

$$\mathbf{V} = [\mathbf{e}_1, \mathbf{e}_2, \cdots, \mathbf{e}_{m-1}]$$

Namely, it is formed from the column vectors $\{\mathbf{e}_i\}$.

The training rules Eq. 8.26 and Eq. 8.28 for the m-th component can be rewritten as

$$\mathbf{w}(t+1) = \mathbf{w}(t) + \beta[\mathbf{x}(t)a_m(t) - \mathbf{w}(t)a_m^2(t)] \tag{8.30}$$

$$\mathbf{z}(t+1) = \mathbf{z}(t) + \beta[\nu(t)a_m(t) - \mathbf{z}(t)a_m^2(t)] \tag{8.31}$$

where β is a positive learning rate. Substituting Eq. 8.29 into Eq. 8.30 and Eq. 8.31, and taking the "average", we obtain

$$\mathbf{w}(t'+1) = [I + \beta'\mathbf{R}_x - \beta'\sigma(t')I]\mathbf{w}(t') - \beta'\mathbf{R}_x\mathbf{V}\mathbf{z}(t') \tag{8.32}$$

$$\mathbf{z}(t'+1) = \beta'\mathbf{V}^T\mathbf{R}_x\mathbf{w}(t') + [I - \beta'\sigma(t')I - \beta'\mathbf{V}^T\mathbf{R}_x\mathbf{V}]\mathbf{z}(t') \tag{8.33}$$

where $\sigma(t') = \tilde{E}\{a^2(t)\}$. As a result of adopting the block-adaptive variant, the "nonlinear" form of Eq. 8.30 and Eq. 8.31 is now simplified into a "linearized" form in Eq. 8.32 and Eq. 8.33.

Premultiplying Eq. 8.32 by $\mathbf{V}^T$ and then subtracting the result from Eq. 8.33, we obtain

$$\mathbf{z}(t'+1) - \mathbf{V}^T\mathbf{w}(t'+1) = [1 - \beta'\sigma(t')][\mathbf{z}(t') - \mathbf{V}^T\mathbf{w}(t')] \qquad (8.34)$$

Because $1 - \beta'\sigma(t') < 1$, in the steady state

$$\mathbf{z}(t') - \mathbf{V}^T\mathbf{w}(t') \to 0 \qquad (8.35)$$

as $t' \to \infty$. Substitute Eq. 8.35 into Eq. 8.32, we have, in the steady state,

$$\mathbf{w}(t'+1) = \{I + \beta'[\mathbf{R}_x(I - \mathbf{V}\mathbf{V}^T) - \sigma(t')I]\}\mathbf{w}(t') \qquad (8.36)$$

Now an analysis very similar to that used previously in the Hebbian learning rule can be adopted. In the steady state, the largest eigenvector in $\mathbf{R}_x(I - \mathbf{V}\mathbf{V}^T)$ dominates all the other eigen-components. Note that $\mathbf{V} = [\mathbf{e}_1, \mathbf{e}_2, \cdots, \mathbf{e}_{m-1}]$, therefore, it effectively rules out the first m-1 largest eigenvectors of $\mathbf{R}_x$ as possible candidates for the new dominant mode. Among the remaining contenders, the largest eigenvector is $\mathbf{e}_m$, the m-th eigenvector of the autocorrelation matrix $\mathbf{R}_x$, corresponding to the eigenvalue $\{\lambda_m\}$. Note that this derivation strongly resembles the deflation process.

∎

Convergence Rates   Based on the learning rules in Eq. 8.26 and Eq. 8.28, the components are enhanced/dampened by the following rate (here $i \geq m$):

$$\theta_i(t'+1) = [1 + \beta'\lambda_i - \beta'\sigma(t')]\theta_i(t')$$

Therefore, the m-th component will becoming increasingly dominant by a rate

$$\frac{1 + \beta'[\lambda_i - \sigma(t')]}{1 + \beta'[\lambda_m - \sigma(t')]}$$

Most important, it can be shown that *the dynamic system is stable*.

It is worth noting that *all the lateral connections have zero weights in the steady state*. This is because $\mathbf{w}(t') \to \mathbf{e}_m$, so $\mathbf{z}(t') = \mathbf{V}^T\mathbf{w}(t') \to 0$. (Note that all the eigenvectors are orthogonal.) This, however, does not mean that the lateral connections will become unnecessary. The presence of such connections not only directs the network to converge to the m-th principal component, but also helps maintain the required "orthogonality" between the components under any changing environments.

Learning Rates   Summing up the learning procedure, the weights $\mathbf{w}_i$ and α_{ij} for neurons $i = 1$ to m are initialized by random values; then they are updated according to Eq. 8.26 and Eq. 8.27. The training procedure is considered to have converged when both $\Delta\mathbf{w}_i$ and $\Delta\alpha_{ij}$ become sufficiently small. One important factor in the learning rule is the estimation of the (optimal) learning rate, which can significantly affect the convergence properties.

Based on Eq. 8.34, the fastest convergence rate can be achieved by making the decay factors very close to zero, namely,

$$1 - \beta'\sigma(t') \approx 0 \qquad (8.37)$$

This leads to an estimate of the optimal learning rate:

$$\beta_i = \frac{1}{\sum_t a_i(t)^2} \qquad (8.38)$$

where the time index t runs over a block of M (most recent) data. Assuming there is no forgetting factor, the above rate can also be directly derived via the *recursive least square* algorithm derived in [179].

To cope with changing environments, a forgetting factor, say $0 < \gamma < 1$, is commonly incorporated into the learning rate. The modified learning rate becomes

$$\beta_i = \frac{1}{\sum_t \gamma^t a_i(t)^2} \qquad (8.39)$$

The use of a a forgetting factor allows us to track (or simulate) a moving window. It also effectively prevents overflow from happening. All these numerical properties are critical for digital implementation. Therefore, further analysis is needed on the learning rates and convergence properties of PCA and APCA.

Constraint PCA Problem   The constraint PCA problem is similar to the PCA problem, except for the added condition that the representation vector must be extracted from a given subspace [153]. Similar to the PC problem, the CPC problem involves the extraction of representative components, which contain the most essential information wanted. Unlike the PC problem, however, the CPC representations must be selected from a predefined subspace. Detailed discussion on an adaptive network for extracting CPC representations can be found in [153]. (See Problem 8.15.)

This constraint subspace is often characterized as the vector space orthogonal to a given constraint vector or matrix $\mathbf{V}$. In one type of application, the

CPC formulation extracts innovative components (as opposed to redundant information). In such applications, $\mathbf{V}$ stands for the redundant subspace that is known *a priori*. In the noise/interference-cancellation applications, the formulation is useful for recovering a "clean" signal while avoiding or suppressing undesirable noisy components. Therefore, the components wanted should be "orthogonal to" the noise subspace spanned by matrix $\mathbf{V}$.

8.4   BP Network for Asymmetric PCA Problems

In this section, we extend the symmetric PCA problem to the more general asymmetric formulation, in which the input and the output are different, cf. Figure 8.2. In terms of extracting the first principal component, a linear two-layer network with one hidden unit is sufficient. In using the BP algorithm to the APCA problems, it can be proven that there is no local minimum if the linear network is used to minimize least-squares errors [19]. Theoretically speaking, the nonlinearity in the hidden unit(s) does not offer any additional advantage [33]. Another theoretical observation is that the deflation technique originally proposed for the symmetric PCA can also be applied to the APCA for extracting multiple principal components. (Again, lateral orthogonalization networks can be used to achieve the effect of deflation in an adaptive manner.)

8.4.1   Extraction of the Single Principal Component

The linear two-layer network with one hidden unit is depicted in Figure 8.9. The model for extracting the largest component, which minimizes J_1 in Eq. 8.3, has the following learning rule:

$$\Delta\overline{\mathbf{w}}(t) \;=\; \beta\left[\mathbf{y}(t) - \overline{\mathbf{w}}(t)a(t)\right]a(t) \tag{8.40}$$

$$\Delta\underline{\mathbf{w}}(t) \;=\; \beta\,\mathbf{x}(t)\left[\mathbf{y}(t) - \overline{\mathbf{w}}(t)a(t)\right]^{T}\overline{\mathbf{w}}(t) \tag{8.41}$$

where

$$a(t) = \underline{\mathbf{w}}(t)^{T}\mathbf{x}(t)$$

This rule converges to, at least theoretically, the unique (global) minimum when $[\mathbf{R}_{x}^{1/2}\underline{\mathbf{w}}]$ and $\overline{\mathbf{w}}$ are principal singular vectors. (See Problem 8.3)

Special Case: Self-Supervised BP Network   A special case of this result is the self-supervised BP network, where $\mathbf{x} = \mathbf{y}$. This leads to a symmetric PCA solution.   Note that the BP learning rule for the upper layer,

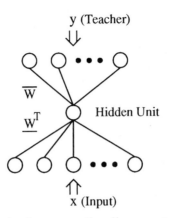

y (Teacher)

$\overline{W}$

$\underline{W}^T$

Hidden Unit

x (Input)

Figure 8.9: A two-layer back-propagation linear network for extracting the single principal component in the APCA problem.

Eq. 8.40, is just the *delta learning rule*. In the self-supervised case, teacher y(t) is substituted by x(t) and we have

$$\Delta \overline{w}(t) = \beta \left[x(t) - \overline{w}(t) a(t) \right] a(t) \tag{8.42}$$

This is similar to the *normalized Hebbian*, or the *Oja* rule [209]. A noticeable difference, however, is that $a(t) = \underline{w}^T x(t)$ instead of $a(t) = \overline{w}^T x(t)$. Due to symmetry, $\underline{w}$ and $\overline{w}$ are expected to converge to the same solution.[3] Therefore, it is plausible to change the BP rule by imposing $\underline{w} \equiv \overline{w} \equiv w$ for all times t. Accordingly, Eq. 8.42 now becomes the same as the Oja rule in Eq. 8.20, namely

$$\Delta w(t) = \beta \left[x(t) - w(t) a(t) \right] a(t)$$

where $a(t) = w^T x$. This demonstrates that the Oja rule can be derived by either the Hebbian learning rule or the delta learning rule. (Note that both the upper-layer and lower-layer weights are now governed by the same learning rule.)

8.4.2 Lateral Networks for Multiple Components

Determine the Subspace of m Principal Components For the *asymmetric PCA problem*, the traditional BP model is directly applicable [19].

---

[3]This can be verified by substituting $\mathbf{R}_{xy} = \mathbf{R}_x$ into Eq.8.5 and setting $\rho = 1$. (Here $\mathbf{R}_x$ is assumed to be invertible.)

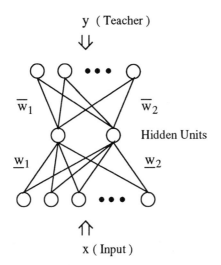

Figure 8.10: Neuron model based on the traditional two-layer back-propagation network which does not have lateral connections. This network can yield the subspace spanned by the principal components; however, it cannot extract the exact components.

This is depicted in Figure 8.10. Here we use $\overline{\mathbf{W}}$ and $\underline{\mathbf{W}}$ to denote $n' \times m$ and $n \times m$ weight matrices, respectively, where m is the number of hidden units.

$$\Delta\overline{\mathbf{W}}(t) = \beta \left[\mathbf{y}(t) - \overline{\mathbf{W}}(t)\mathbf{a}(t)\right] \mathbf{a}(t)^T \qquad (8.43)$$
$$\Delta\underline{\mathbf{W}}(t) = \beta \, \mathbf{x}(t) \left[\mathbf{y}(t) - \overline{\mathbf{W}}(t)\mathbf{a}(t)\right]^T \overline{\mathbf{W}}(t) \qquad (8.44)$$

where $\mathbf{a}(t) = \underline{\mathbf{W}}(t)^T\mathbf{x}(t)$. This is the standard linear BP procedure for a two-layer net with m hidden units, and it extracts the same subspace as that of the m principal components [33].

Deflation Method for the BP Network   The lateral orthogonalization network also can be incorporated into the back-propagation model for the extraction of multiple principal components. In the subsequent discussion, the basic idea follows closely that of the deflation method. Assume that the first component is already obtained; then the teacher value can be properly deflated by the following transformation:

$$\tilde{\mathbf{y}} = (I - \overline{\mathbf{w}}_1\overline{\mathbf{w}}_1^T)\mathbf{y}$$

We first focus on the rule for extracting the **second** eigen-component. This rule can be derived by using a modified teacher value: $\tilde{\mathbf{y}}(t) = \mathbf{y}(t) - \overline{\mathbf{w}}_1\underline{\mathbf{w}}_1^T\mathbf{x}(t)$.

This change leads to a learning rule for the second component:

$$\Delta\overline{\mathbf{w}}_2(t) = \beta[\mathbf{y}(t) - \overline{\mathbf{w}}_1 a_1(t) - \overline{\mathbf{w}}_2(t)a_2(t)]a_2(t) \qquad (8.45)$$

$$\Delta\underline{\mathbf{w}}_2(t) = \beta\mathbf{x}(t)[\mathbf{y}(t) - \overline{\mathbf{w}}_1 a_1(t) - \overline{\mathbf{w}}_2(t)a_2(t)]^T\overline{\mathbf{w}}_2(t) \qquad (8.46)$$

where $a_1(t) = \underline{\mathbf{w}}_1^T\mathbf{x}(t)$, $a_2(t) = \underline{\mathbf{w}}_2(t)^T\mathbf{x}(t)$. This transformation is equivalent to the deflation on matrix $\mathbf{R}_{xy}^T\mathbf{R}_x^{-1/2}$. We have

$$\mathbf{R}_{x\tilde{y}} = \mathbf{R}_{xy} - \mathbf{R}_x\underline{\mathbf{w}}_1\overline{\mathbf{w}}_1^T$$

Therefore,

$$\mathbf{R}_{x\tilde{y}}^T\mathbf{R}_x^{-1/2} = \mathbf{R}_{xy}^T\mathbf{R}_x^{-1/2} - \overline{\mathbf{w}}_1\underline{\mathbf{w}}_1^T\mathbf{R}_x^{1/2}$$

As before, let $\mathbf{V}\boldsymbol{\Sigma}\mathbf{U}^T$ be the SVD of $\mathbf{R}_{xy}^T\mathbf{R}_x^{-1/2}$. The single hidden unit analysis of BP indicates that $\mathbf{R}_x^{1/2}\underline{\mathbf{w}}_1 = \mu_1\mathbf{u}_1$ and $\overline{\mathbf{w}}_1 = \rho_1\mathbf{v}_1$ with $\mu_1\rho_1 = \sigma_1$ = the largest singular value. Hence,

$$\mathbf{R}_{x\tilde{y}}^T\mathbf{R}_x^{-1/2} = \mathbf{V}\boldsymbol{\Sigma}\mathbf{U}^T - \sigma_1\mathbf{v}_1\mathbf{u}_1^T = \mathbf{V}\hat{\boldsymbol{\Sigma}}\mathbf{U}^T$$

where

$$\hat{\boldsymbol{\Sigma}} = \begin{bmatrix} 0 & & & & \\ & \sigma_2 & & & \\ & & \ddots & & \\ & & & \sigma_p & \end{bmatrix} \; 0 \quad \text{if} \quad \boldsymbol{\Sigma} = \begin{bmatrix} \sigma_1 & & & & \\ & \sigma_2 & & & \\ & & \ddots & & \\ & & & \sigma_p & \end{bmatrix} \; 0$$

or

$$\hat{\boldsymbol{\Sigma}} = \begin{bmatrix} 0 & & & \\ & \sigma_2 & & \\ & & \ddots & \\ & & & \sigma_p \\ \hline & & 0 & \end{bmatrix} \quad \text{if} \quad \boldsymbol{\Sigma} = \begin{bmatrix} \sigma_1 & & & \\ & \sigma_2 & & \\ & & \ddots & \\ & & & \sigma_p \\ \hline & & 0 & \end{bmatrix}$$

Therefore, $\mathbf{R}_{x\tilde{y}}^T\mathbf{R}_x^{-1/2}$ has the same singular vectors as $\mathbf{R}_{xy}^T\mathbf{R}_x^{-1/2}$ except that now the pair $\mathbf{u}_1$, $\mathbf{v}_1$ is associated with a zero singular value; thus, the pair $\mathbf{u}_2$, $\mathbf{v}_2$ becomes the new dominant eigen-component. It follows that $\mathbf{R}_x^{1/2}\underline{\mathbf{w}}_2$ and $\overline{\mathbf{w}}_2$ converge to $\mu_2\mathbf{u}_2$ and $\rho_2\mathbf{v}_2$ with $\mu_2\rho_2 = \sigma_2$.

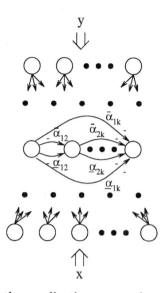

Figure 8.11: Lateral orthogonalization connections for networks with three (or more) hidden neurons. The LON parameters of the lower connections α are applied to the forward neuron values in Eq. 8.51. The LON parameters of the upper connections $\bar{\alpha}$ are applied to the backward neuron values in Eq. 8.52.

Incorporation of Lateral Orthogonalization Network The lateral orthogonalization network (LON) can be utilized to extract the exact asymmetric principal components, just as in the deflation method. For the APCA, we propose an asymmetric linear model. More precisely, *for each hidden node, two different neuron values, one forward and one backward, are introduced* [313]:

$$a_m(t) = \underline{\mathbf{w}}_m(t)^T \mathbf{x}(t) \qquad (8.47)$$

$$b_m(t) = \overline{\mathbf{w}}_m(t)^T \mathbf{y}(t) \qquad (8.48)$$

Extraction of the Second Neuron With reference to Figure 8.11, the proposed model for the second neuron is defined:

$$\Delta\overline{\mathbf{w}}_2(t) = \beta\left[\mathbf{y}(t)a_2'(t) - \overline{\mathbf{w}}_2(t)a_2^2(t)\right] \qquad (8.49)$$

$$\Delta\underline{\mathbf{w}}_2(t) = \beta\mathbf{x}(t)\left[b_2'(t) - \|\overline{\mathbf{w}}_2(t)\|^2 a_2(t)\right] \qquad (8.50)$$

Here lower (forward) and upper (backward) inhibition parameters are used for the forward and backward neuron values, respectively. The lateral connections in the hidden layer prove to be the critical key for extracting multiple principal components. More precisely,

$$a'_2(t) = a_2(t) - \underline{\alpha} a_1(t) \tag{8.51}$$

$$b'_2(t) = b_2(t) - \overline{\alpha} b_1(t) \tag{8.52}$$

Due to the asymmetry of the network, two sets of lateral connections must be introduced (cf. Figure 8.11).

$$\Delta \underline{\alpha}(t) = \beta \left[a_1(t) a_2(t) - \underline{\alpha}(t) a_1(t)^2 \right] \tag{8.53}$$

$$\Delta \overline{\alpha}(t) = \beta \left[b_1(t) a'_2(t) - \overline{\alpha}(t) a_2(t)^2 \right] \tag{8.54}$$

Note that the local orthogonalization rule is used in the first equation, and the dynamic orthogonalization rule, in the second equation. It is important to note that, (1) the dynamic equations in effect carry out the deflation process, and (2) the key strategy is used to avoid "vector-product-free updating" in the computations. We divide our proof into two parts: **Part I** of the proof establishes the equivalence between Eq. 8.46 and Eq. 8.50 for the lower-layer weights. **Part II** of the proof establishes the equivalence between Eq. 8.45 and Eq. 8.49 for the upper-layer weights.

    Part I: In order to employ the dynamic orthogonalization rule, we first multiply Eq. 8.49 by $\overline{w}_1^T$ (from the left) and subtract Eq. 8.54 from it. This leads to the proof of the steady state in the following:

$$\overline{\alpha} = \overline{w}_1^T \overline{w}_2(t') \tag{8.55}$$

Eq. 8.55 should now suffice to establish the equivalence between the two lower-weight equations, Eq. 8.46 and Eq. 8.50.

    Part II: To show the equivalence of the upper-weight equation, we first note that if we are allowed to substitute $y'(t)a_2(t)$ in Eq. 8.49 by $[y(t) - \underline{\alpha}\overline{w}_1 a_1(t)]a_2(t)$, then Eq. 8.49 becomes the same as Eq. 8.45. Then we show that such substitution is valid. More precisely, in the steady state and on an average, the two sides of Eq. 8.56 are the same:

$$E[\mathbf{y}(t)a'_2(t)] = E[(\mathbf{y}(t) - \underline{\alpha}\overline{w}_1 a_1(t))a_2(t)] \tag{8.56}$$

To show Eq. 8.56, we note that

$$\mathbf{y}(t)a'_2(t) = \mathbf{y}(t)a_2(t) - \underline{\alpha}\mathbf{y}(t)a_1(t)$$

It can be verified that, on an average,

$$
\begin{aligned}
E[\mathbf{y}(t)a_2'(t)] &= E[\mathbf{y}(t)a_2(t)] - \underline{\alpha}E[\mathbf{y}(t)a_1(t)] \\
&= E[\mathbf{y}(t)a_2(t)] - \underline{\alpha}\overline{\mathbf{w}}_1\mathbf{w}_1^T\mathbf{R}_x\underline{\mathbf{w}}_2(t) \\
&= E[\mathbf{y}(t)a_2(t)] - \underline{\alpha}\overline{\mathbf{w}}_1 E[a_1(t)a_2(t)] \\
&= E[(\mathbf{y}(t) - \underline{\alpha}\overline{\mathbf{w}}_1 a_1(t))a_2(t)]
\end{aligned}
$$

Thus, the proof of Eq. 8.56. From Eq. 8.56, it follows that Eq. 8.45 and Eq. 8.49 are equivalent. In this derivation we use the fact that, in the steady state,

$$
\overline{\mathbf{w}}_1 E[a_1(t)a_2(t')] = \overline{\mathbf{w}}_1\mathbf{w}_1^T\mathbf{R}_x\underline{\mathbf{w}}_2(t') \tag{8.57}
$$

$$
E[\mathbf{y}(t)a_1(t)] = \mathbf{R}_{xy}^T\underline{\mathbf{w}}_1 = \overline{\mathbf{w}}_1\mathbf{w}_1^T\mathbf{R}_x\underline{\mathbf{w}}_1 \tag{8.58}
$$

$$
\underline{\alpha} = \frac{\mathbf{w}_1^T\mathbf{R}_x\underline{\mathbf{w}}_2(t')}{\underline{\mathbf{w}}_1^T\mathbf{R}_x\underline{\mathbf{w}}_1} \tag{8.59}
$$

Combining Eq. 8.57 through Eq. 8.59, Eq. 8.56 can be established. In order to avoid the vector-product computation of $\|\overline{\mathbf{w}}_2(t)\|^2$ (for computational saving), we further substitute into Eq. 8.50 the following two equations:

$$
\begin{aligned}
\Delta\underline{\mathbf{w}}_2(t) &= \beta\mathbf{x}(t)\left[b_2'(t) - \rho_2(t)a_2(t)\right] \\
\Delta\rho_2(t) &= 2\beta\left[b_2(t)a_2'(t) - \rho_2(t)a_2^2(t)\right]
\end{aligned}
$$

In the steady state,

$$
\rho_2(t') = \|\mathbf{w}_2(t')\|^2 \tag{8.60}
$$

The proof of Eq. 8.60 follows a similar argument for the proof of Eq. 8.55. For the extraction of $m > 2$ **components**, a similar argument works.

Simulation Results   The estimation of the general convergence rate for the asymmetric problem is complicated. It remains an open question. Thus far, the convergence speed can be predicted only for the symmetric case. In terms of simulation results, the first neuron (not shown here) can be accurately trained by the BP method. Figure 8.12 shows the convergence of the second neuron to the second component by the combined BP and LON learning rule. The training data consists of a block of 200 (x, y) pairs, repeated by multiple sweeps. (Thus, each sweep contains 200 iterations.) The speed and the smoothness of the learning convergence is affected (somewhat sensitively) by the selection of the learning rate. The convergence speed obtained is about the same rate as the deflation method (conducted in a separate simulation).

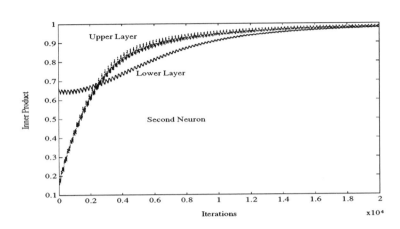

Figure 8.12: Convergence rate of the combined BP and LON learning rule. The linear net has 2 hidden units laterally connected by LON, cf. Figure 8.11. The y-axis in the plot corresponds to the inner product of the normalized vector $\overline{\mathbf{w}}_i$ or $\mathbf{R}_x^{1/2}\underline{\mathbf{w}}_i$ with the corresponding principal singular vector $\mathbf{v}_i$ or $\mathbf{u}_i$.

8.5   Applications to Signal/Image Processing

The PCA shares many common applications with the well-known SVD (singular value decomposition) techniques. The potential application domain of PCA and SVD techniques is very broad. They have many useful applications in signal/image filtering, restoration, pattern classification, and recognition. Specific application examples include biomedical signal processing, speech and image processing, antenna applications, seismic signal processing, geophysical exploration, data compression, high-resolution beamforming, separation of a desired signal from interfering waveforms (e.g., fetal ECGs from maternal ECGs), and noise cancellation.[60, 83, 118, 155, 157, 173, 201, 209, 211, 251, 280, 283, 312]. For example, in noise-cancellation or signal-separation applications, the SVD of the measurement matrix can be used to effectively estimate the subspace with a maximal signal-to-signal ratio. It is worth mentioning that there are already widely available batch-processing methods (with very mature software developments, e.g., LINPACK and EISPACK) for SVD computations. For sequential processing at least, these existing softwares are numerically more effective then the new neural models.

8.5.1 Rotational Compensation Applications

Compensation of misalignment of an image due to rotations and/or translations is important to many image-analysis applications. The first principal component of an object in a picture can be used to identify the major axis of the object because it indicates the direction of maximum variance of the data [83, p. 107]. The coordinates of each pixel in the object can be interpreted as two-dimensional random variables with mean

$$m_x = \frac{1}{P} \sum_{i=1}^{P} x_i$$

and covariance matrix

$$C_x = \frac{1}{P} \left[\sum_{i=1}^{P} x_i x_i^T \right] - m_x m_x^T$$

where P is the number of pixels in the object, and x_i is the two-dimensional vector composed of the two coordinates of the i-th pixel. Because the principal eigenvector of C_x points in the direction of maximum variance, a new coordinate system should be selected so that it aligns with the eigenvector. The realigned images make it easier for the pattern classifier to recognize.

8.5.2 Data-Compression Applications: Extraction of Innovative Components

The PCA and CPC techniques can be applied to image data compression. To motivate the use of the CPC technique, note that between the principal components and the conventional DCT there exists a trade-off between performance and compression rate. For the same number of components, the principal components approach, in general, yields a better performance, but it also requires a greater channel bandwidth. The CPC offers a compromise: first k DCT components are used as the original representation $\nu = [\nu_1 \ldots \nu_k]^T$, then, in addition, m CPCs $a = [a_1 \ldots a_m]^T$ are extracted. The final image is reconstructed by the CPC estimation formula discussed in Problem 8.15.

Illustrated in Figure 8.13(a) is one example, where the original picture of Walter Cronkite is given in 48 × 48 pixels and 8 bits/pixel. For the PC example, Figure 8.13(e) shows the image reconstructed from only 8 principal components, the signal-to-noise ratio (SNR) is about 18.8. The image of Figure 8.13(d), using a very small number of CPCs, has an SNR (17.8) far better than those of Figure 8.13(b), with 8 DCT (SNR = 11.6), or Figure 8.13(c), with 16 DCT components (SNR = 12.8). By comparing Figures 8.13(e) and 8.13(f), we conclude that using 8 CPCs, in addition to the 8 DCT components of Figure 8.13(b), yields a far better image than the one using only 8 principal components. (The SNRs are 22.5 vs. 18.8.)

8.5.3　Signal-Separation Applications:　Separate Signal from Noise

The PCA/APCA adaptive techniques can be employed for Many applications, such as FECG/MECG separation, noise cancellation, mobile telephone, cockpit conversations, and other speech/image processing. An application example on the FECG/MECG separation is now presented. The ECG measurements are obtained from cutaneous electrodes placed on the chest and the abdomen of the mother. The objective is to suppress the maternal ECG (MECG), while optimally enhancing the fetal ECG (FECG). In other words, there are two facets of the separation problem. One is to suppress the influence of the much stronger MECG. The other is to best extract the weaker FECG signal. For example, if there are p measurement channels (typically, 6 to 8), the sampled data are stored in a $p \times q$ matrix C, where q denotes the number of consecutive samples extracted. The p observed signals $m_i(t)$ (the rows of C) are modeled as unknown linear combinations (modeled by a static $p \times r$ matrix $\mathbf{H}$) of r source signals $S_i(t)$. The source signals are corrupted by additive noise signals $n_i(t)$ with known (or experimentally verified) second-order statistics. The problem is mathematically described by

$$\mathbf{X} = \mathbf{HS} + \mathbf{N} \tag{8.61}$$

where the rows of $\mathbf{S}$ are the source signals [282]. Let the singular-value decomposition of matrix $\mathbf{X}$ be $\mathbf{X} = \mathbf{U\Sigma V}^T$, where $\mathbf{U}, \mathbf{\Sigma}$, and $\mathbf{V}^T$ are $p \times p, p \times p$, and $p \times q$ matrices, respectively. More explicitly, the singular value decomposition of $\mathbf{X}$ is given by

$$\mathbf{X} = [\mathbf{U_1 U_2}] \begin{bmatrix} \mathbf{\Sigma_1} & 0 \\ 0 & \mathbf{\Sigma_2} \end{bmatrix} \begin{bmatrix} \mathbf{V}_1^T \\ \mathbf{V}_2^T \end{bmatrix}$$

where $\mathbf{U}_1$ and $\mathbf{\Sigma_1}$ are $p \times r$ and $r \times r$ matrices, respectively. Here some practical assumptions are made on the uncorrelatedness between signal and noise. One assumption is that the location of external sensors is chosen so that the columns of $\mathbf{H}$ are orthogonal to each other. It can then be shown [39] that $\mathbf{U}_1^T \mathbf{X} \approx \mathbf{DS}$, $\mathbf{D}$ being a diagonal matrix, and the vector $\mathbf{S}$ can

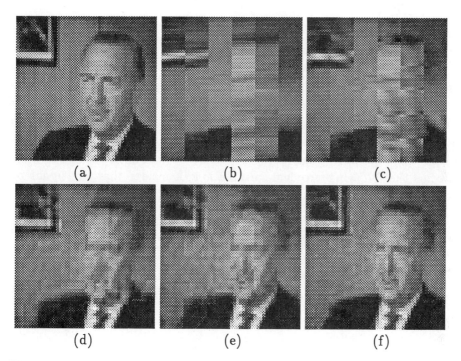

Figure 8.13: APEX network can be applied to a CPC problem where hybrid DCT and KL transform codes are computed for image compression. The hybrid uses k DCT components and m (constrained) KL components (i.e., CPCs). Shown here are (a) the original image; and the compressed/decoded images using (b) only $k = 8$ DCT components (SNR = 11.6), (c) only $k = 16$ DCT components (SNR = 12.8), (d) combined DCT/CPC, with $k = 4$, $m = 4$ (SNR = 17.8), (e) KL transform (i.e., conventional PCA), using $m = 8$ principal components (SNR = 18.8), and (f) combined DCT/CPC, with $k = 8$, $m = 8$ (SNR = 22.5).

be estimated from $\hat{\mathbf{S}} = \mathbf{U}_1^T \mathbf{X}$. The PCA neural network can be applied for on-line extraction of $\mathbf{U}_1 = \mathbf{W} = [\mathbf{w}_1, \ldots, \mathbf{w}_r]$ as the weight matrix.

8.5.4 Sinusoidal Retrieval Applications: Harmonic Spectrum Analysis

The SVD techniques are very efficient for the high-resolution spectrum analysis. The objective is to achieve maximal resolution of closely spaced frequencies using as small a sample size as possible. The same method applies to the problem of direction-of-arrival estimation by an antenna array. There are critical factors, for example, the sample size, signal-to-noise ratio, model order, and minimal frequency spacing, that could limit the resolution powers of any method [189].

The harmonic retrieval of very closely spaced frequencies in presence of noise has the following problem formulation: Consider that the signal x_k is embedded in an additive stationary white noise ν_k with variance σ^2:

$$x_k = \sum_{i=1}^{m} a_i \exp(j(kw_i + \phi_i)) + \nu_k$$

Let $r(l) = E\{x_k x_{k+l}^*\}$ be the autocorrelation sequence of x_k, where x_{k+l}^* denotes the complex conjugate of x_{k+l}. Let $\mathbf{R}$ be the infinite Toeplitz correlation matrix constructed with $r(l)$

$$\mathbf{R} = \tilde{\mathbf{R}} + \sigma^2 \mathbf{I}$$

where $\mathbf{I}$ is the identity matrix, and $\tilde{\mathbf{R}}$ is the correlation matrix for the noise-free sinusoidal signals. The matrix $\mathbf{R}$ is now full-rank because its eigenvalues are shifted by $+\sigma^2$. It is important to note that its eigenvectors, however, remain the same as those of $\tilde{\mathbf{R}}$.

The SVD technique by Kung [150, 155] extends the classical Pisarenko method [226] and provides a numerically stable solution for the harmonic retrieval problem. It is based on the SVD of $\mathbf{R}$:

$$\mathbf{R} = \mathbf{U}\mathbf{\Sigma}\mathbf{U}^*$$

where the asterisk denotes the complex conjugate transposition. Based on the distribution of singular values, one can estimate the number of sources ($\hat{m}$) because a gap is expected to exist between the m largest eigenvalues and the rest. The former provides the nonzero eigenvalues of $\mathbf{R}$ and the latter represents an estimate of σ^2. Because the true correlation matrix $\tilde{\mathbf{R}}$ should be of rank m, a rank-$\hat{m}$ approximation is sought. Such an approximation is given by $\mathbf{U}_s \Sigma_s \mathbf{U}_s^*$, where $\mathbf{U}_s$ is approximately the matrix formed by the eigenvectors corresponding to the $\hat{m}$ largest eigenvalues of R, and Σ_s is the diagonal matrix of these eigenvalues. The sinusoidal frequencies can be obtained from the eigenvalues of the following matrix [155]

$$\mathbf{A} = \mathbf{U}_s^T \mathbf{U}_s^\uparrow$$

where $\mathbf{U}_s^\uparrow$ is the shifted-up version (by one row) of $\mathbf{U}_s$. Some numerical improvements and simulation studies were performed in [189]. In an experiment resolving two frequency components, 100 different pseudo-random simulations were performed. In 16 out of 100 cases, only a single frequency was found. (No outside frequencies were observed.) In all the remaining cases, the two frequency components (i.e., two targets) were successfully resolved.

8.5.5   Signal-Restoration Applications: Remove or Cancel Unwanted Noises

Noise-Cancellation Filtering   As shown in Figure 8.14, the APCA problem is suitable for noise-cancellation filtering when the additive noise is generated from a small number of interference sources. Under this circumstance, the noise waveforms may be assumed to have some underlying low-rank property. Then a reduced-rank Wiener filtering structure may be adopted. Figure 8.14 can be viewed as a generalization of Widrow's adaptive filter [303]. If $n'(t)$ and $n(t)$ are correlated, then it can be shown that the output of the adaptive filter $\hat{n}(t)$ will asymptotically approach a good estimate of $n(t)$. The reduced hidden units are used to properly control the rank of the filter, thereby suppress the unwanted noise.

8.5.6   Subspace Classification Applications

PCA is closely related to the so-called *subspace methods* for pattern classification [210]. Different classes of patterns have different statistics, hence different principal component vectors. Furthermore, the patterns of a class tend to have larger projections on their own class components than any other vector. Therefore, (weighted) projection-length discriminating rules are adopted in several prominent approaches such as CLAss-Featuring Information Compression (CLAFIC) [298], *Adaptive Learning Subspace Method* (ALSM) [211], and other subspace separation techniques, for example, OLSM and the Fisher

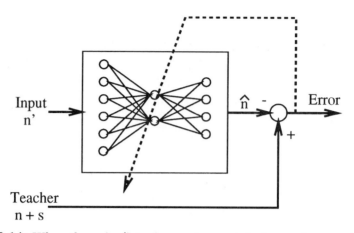

Figure 8.14: When the noise/interference has certain low-rank properties, the APCA problem can be useful for designing a noise-cancellation filter.

classifier [157]. In the following, these *principal component subspace methods* and their simulation performances on *texture-classification* are discussed.

In the subspace classification methods, a pattern $\mathbf{x}$ is represented by a point in an n-dimensional vector space. We define the (unnormalized) correlation matrices $\mathbf{R}^{(1)}, \ldots, \mathbf{R}^{(K)}$ for the classes $\Omega_1, \ldots, \Omega_K$ as $\mathbf{R}^{(i)} = \sum_{\mathbf{x} \in \Omega_i} \mathbf{x}\mathbf{x}^T$. Denote $\mathbf{u}_1, \ldots, \mathbf{u}_{p_i}$ as the first p_i principal component (normalized) vectors of the matrix $\mathbf{R}^{(i)}$. The distance between pattern $\mathbf{x}$ and its projection to the i-th subspace (spanned by $\mathbf{u}_1, \ldots, \mathbf{u}_{p_i}$) is

$$d^{(i)}(\mathbf{x}) = \sqrt{\|\mathbf{x}\|^2 - \sum_{j=1}^{p_i}(\mathbf{x}^T\mathbf{u}_j)}$$

The CLAFIC method is based on a minimum-distance criterion. That is, the class with the minimal distance is recognized as the winner.

In the ALSM Algorithm, the (unnormalized) conditional correlation matrices representing the misclassified vectors of class Ω_i are added to matrix $\mathbf{R}^{(i)}$ (i.e., reinforced learning), and the matrices corresponding to the other classes, misclassified into Ω_i, are subtracted from matrix $\mathbf{R}^{(i)}$ (i.e., anti-reinforced learning). The subspace classifiers compute the representation vectors of the individual classes independently and ignore the mutual discrepancy between classes. This hampers the discriminating capability. There are several methods that exploit the relative distances between classes. For example, the orthogonal subspace (OS) method was originally proposed by Fukunaga and Koontz [72], and later generalized by Kittler [133]. An or-

Error Percentage	Training Accuracy	Generalization Accuracy
CLAFIC	90.8%	89.4%
OLSM	100%	92.4%

Table 8.1: Texture classification comparison between the CLAFIC and OLSM.

thogonal learning subspace method (OLSM) [271] combines the OS method and subspace learning. Yet another approach is based on the Fisher's linear discriminant function.

In the experiment of the OLSM texture classification, based on the co-occurrence matrices [271], 11 Brodatz textures were classified. The texture numbers were 84, 57, 77, 33, 28, 49, 68, 16, 103, 3, and 34; cf. Figure 4.14. For each texture, 100 64×64 blocks were randomly chosen. The co-occurrence matrices were computed and averaged into 4×4 matrices. The rows were then stacked into a column vector that was used as sample vector. Among the 100 samples (blocks), 70 were used as the training set, and 30 as the testing set. Table 8.1 compares the performances of CLAFIC and OLSM.

The Fisher Classifier [61] stresses the relative differences between the statistics of the two classes. The goal is to maximize Fisher's linear discriminant function

$$J(\mathbf{w}) = \frac{\mathbf{w} S \mathbf{w}^T}{\mathbf{w} R \mathbf{w}^T}$$

by choosing an appropriate orientation $\mathbf{w}$. The matrices S and R are the between-cluster and within-cluster spread matrices of the data. (These matrices are of the form $S = M M^T$ and $R = U U^T$ for specific matrices M and U, respectively.) The formulation is very compatible with that of the oriented principal component (OPC) [312, 311]. Its criterion is

$$\text{maximizing } J = \frac{\|\mathbf{w}^T(\mathbf{m}_1 - \mathbf{m}_2)\|^2}{\sum_{class_1} \|\mathbf{w}^T(\mathbf{x} - \mathbf{m}_1)\|^2 + \sum_{class_2} \|\mathbf{w}^T(\mathbf{x} - \mathbf{m}_2)\|^2}$$

The Fisher's classifier was applied to classify 12 Brodatz textures (with the same texture numbers as before, except No. 93 was added). In this experiment, the network was trained by a $240(= 20 \times 12)$ blocks of textures and tested by $420(= 35 \times 12)$ different testing texture blocks. The generalization accuracy was 97%, which compared very favorably with the 90% accuracy by the ALSM algorithm [211]. The rate was also considerably higher than the CLAFIC and OLSM; cf. Table 8.1.

8.6 Concluding Remarks

This chapter presents several adaptive networks for principal component extraction and numerical and convergence properties of the networks. The promising features of the networks include its *on-line adaptive processing* (for nonstationary processes), a *novel filter* structure, and its potential on *nonlinear and parallel processing*.

One of the main strengths of the neural model is its adaptiveness to any time-varying environment. It offers a simple structure with an on-line adaptive processing capability. The neural model, in a sense, offers a novel filter structure, inviting a combined use of lateral orthogonalization network (LON) and nonlinearity. In the LON, the new hidden nodes are directed along a direction "orthogonal" to the subspace spanned by the old hidden nodes. In other words, a lateral orthogonalization network can avoid redundant representation.

The lateral orthogonalization network can be used to identify the most "innovative" representative hidden nodes. The LON may be applied to the laterally growing techniques, which select the hidden nodes with an ordered importance. The power of neural information processing lies partially in its nonlinear processing. Conceivably, the lateral networks can be applied to find the orthogonal neuron nodes, which can be used as a good initial condition for the conventional (nonlinear) BP algorithm. It offers one approach to overcome the problem of indecisive learning due to the presence of nonunique solutions and local minima. A closely related technique is the *cascaded correlation networks* [64]. To better understand nonlinear behaviors of the PCA-type and cascaded correlation networks, further theoretical and simulational studies are needed.

The concept of PCA is very closely related to that of singular-value decomposition (SVD) or eigenvalue decomposition. In addition, PCA and the conventional least-squares Wiener filtering have a very close relationship. They are all popular tools for signal/image processing applications. It is important to compare the neural models with the conventional methods, including gradient-ascent, conjugate gradient, quasi-Newton, power, Householder-QR, and Jacobi methods. Many batch-processing techniques have been developed for the eigenvalue decomposition and SVD, including the inverse iteration method [85], the subspace iteration method [217], Lanczos algorithm [218], Golub's SVD algorithm [82], and the adaptive SVD algorithm [283].

An appealing feature of a neural network is its potential ability to cope with changing environments. Thus, on-line techniques are most closely related

to neural processing technique. Most of the previously mentioned batch methods can also be reformulated for on-line processing. In particular, an on-line
Jacobi-type algorithm is proposed in [200]. It is a fast, adaptive, and parallel
updating method, based on a combination of the Jacobi-type SVD and QR
updating procedure. The method is computationally very cost-effective with
$\mathcal{O}(n^2)$ operations per updating. It can reportedly obtain a fairly accurate
approximation of SVD. Furthermore, it is also very amenable to systolic or
wavefront parallel architectures [151].

In conclusion, in the future research, it is beneficiary to study a unified
perspective between neural approaches and conventional on-line numerical
methods for PCA and SVD.

8.7   Problems [4]

Exercise 8.1 Show that when the exact principal components are obtained, the
optimal matrix $\mathbf{W}$ is formed by the first m singular vectors of $\mathbf{R}_x$. Verify that the
errors of the optimal estimate are as given in Eq. 8.1 and Eq. 8.2.

Exercise 8.2 Suppose that a vector stochastic process has the following correlation
matrix

$$\mathbf{R} = \begin{bmatrix} 5 & 3 & 0 \\ 3 & 5 & 3 \\ 0 & 3 & 5 \end{bmatrix}$$

Find the eigenvector corresponding to the first principal component of $\mathbf{R}$.

Exercise 8.3 Prove that the problem in Eq. 8.3 has a unique (global) minimum
when $[\mathbf{R}_x^{1/2}\underline{\mathbf{w}}]$ and $\overline{\mathbf{w}}$ are principal (left/right) singular vectors. (Hint: Show that all
other singular vectors correspond only to saddle points on the error surface.)

Exercise 8.4 Find the minimizing solution for the criterion function Eq. 8.8

$$J_m(\underline{\mathbf{W}}, \overline{\mathbf{W}}) = E\{\|\mathbf{y} - \sum_{i=1}^{m} \overline{\mathbf{w}}_i \underline{\mathbf{w}}_i^T \mathbf{x}\|^2\}$$

---

[4]The basic problems in this chapter are Problems 8.1 to 8.9. The remaining problems
are more advanced.

by taking the derivatives of J_m with respect to $\overline{\mathbf{w}}_i$ and $\underline{\mathbf{w}}_i$ and equating to zero:

$$\mathbf{R}_{xy}^T \underline{\mathbf{w}}_i = \mu_i^2 \overline{\mathbf{w}}_i + \sum_{j<i} \overline{\mathbf{w}}_j \underline{\mathbf{w}}_i^T \mathbf{R}_x \underline{\mathbf{w}}_j$$

$$\mathbf{R}_{xy} \overline{\mathbf{w}}_i = \rho_i^2 \mathbf{R}_x \underline{\mathbf{w}}_i + \sum_{j<i} (\overline{\mathbf{w}}_i^T \overline{\mathbf{w}}_j) \mathbf{R}_x \underline{\mathbf{w}}_j$$

for $i = 1, \ldots, m$, where

$$\mu_i^2 = \underline{\mathbf{w}}_i^T \mathbf{R}_x \underline{\mathbf{w}}_i \qquad \rho_i^2 = \|\overline{\mathbf{w}}_i\|^2$$

Simplify the solution by imposing the constraints Eq. 8.9 and Eq. 8.10 and verify Eq. 8.11.

Exercise 8.5 Suppose that two vector stochastic processes have the following cross-correlation matrix:

$$\mathbf{R}_{xy} = \begin{bmatrix} 5 & 3 & 0 & 0 \\ 2 & 4 & 2 & 0 \\ 0 & 2 & 5 & 1 \end{bmatrix}$$

Find the left and right eigenvectors corresponding to the first asymmetric principal component.

Exercise 8.6 Suppose that a vector stochastic process has the following correlation matrix

$$\mathbf{R} = \begin{bmatrix} 4 & 2 & 0 \\ 2 & 4 & 2 \\ 0 & 2 & 4 \end{bmatrix}$$

(a) Find the first, second, and third principal components of $\mathbf{R}$.
(b) Find the first and second CPCs (constrained principal components) with the constraint $\mathbf{q}\mathbf{V}^T = 0$, where

$$\mathbf{V} = \frac{1}{\sqrt{2}}[1, -1, 0]$$

Exercise 8.7 (Gradient-Ascent Batch Technique)
Assume that the correlation matrix $\mathbf{R}_x$ of a stochastic vector process $\{\mathbf{x}\}$ is known a priori. The principal component is a row vector $\tilde{\mathbf{w}}$ that maximizes the energy function

$$E = \frac{\tilde{\mathbf{w}} \mathbf{R}_x \tilde{\mathbf{w}}^T}{\tilde{\mathbf{w}} \tilde{\mathbf{w}}^T}$$

By a gradient-ascent method, we have

$$\Delta \tilde{\mathbf{w}} = \beta \bigtriangledown E = \beta \left(\frac{2\tilde{\mathbf{w}} \mathbf{R}_x}{\|\tilde{\mathbf{w}}\|^2} - \frac{2\tilde{\mathbf{w}} \mathbf{R}_x \tilde{\mathbf{w}}^T \tilde{\mathbf{w}}}{\|\tilde{\mathbf{w}}\|^4} \right)$$

(a) Define the normalized vector

$$\mathbf{w} = \frac{\tilde{\mathbf{w}}}{\|\tilde{\mathbf{w}}\|}$$

Show that

$$\Delta \mathbf{w} = \beta_1 (\mathbf{w} \mathbf{R}_x - \mathbf{w} \mathbf{R}_x \mathbf{w}^T \mathbf{w})$$

for some scalar β_1.

(b) Show that this is basically equivalent to the Oja rule averaged over one sweep, when $\mathbf{w}$ is assumed to be approximately constant in the sweep.

Exercise 8.8 Review the definition of eigenvalue decomposition and SVD, as well as that of generalized eigenvalue decomposition and generalized singular-value decomposition.

(a) Show that the optimal solution $\underline{\mathbf{W}}_{opt}$ and $\overline{\mathbf{W}}_{opt}$ of the APCA problem may also be obtained in terms of a generalized singular-value decomposition of $\{\mathbf{Y}\mathbf{X}^T, \mathbf{X}\}$.

(b) Show the validity of the above analysis when $\mathbf{R}_x$ is singular.

Exercise 8.9 (Power Method)
The Power method [85] is a batch method. The formula for extracting the first component is:

$$\tilde{\mathbf{w}}_{m+1} = \mathbf{w}_m \mathbf{R}_x, \qquad \mathbf{w}_{m+1} = \frac{\tilde{\mathbf{w}}_{m+1}}{\|\tilde{\mathbf{w}}_{m+1}\|}$$

(a) Show that $\mathbf{w}$ converges to the normalized principal eigenvector of $\mathbf{R}_x$.

(b) Show that the following *deflation* technique

$$\mathbf{x}_m^{(2)} = (I - \mathbf{e}_1^T \mathbf{e}_1) \mathbf{x}_m$$

$$\mathbf{R}_x^{(2)} = (I - \mathbf{e}_1^T \mathbf{e}_1) \mathbf{R}_x (I - \mathbf{e}_1^T \mathbf{e}_1)$$

can be used to transform the input data such that the second component becomes the new principal component.

(c) Derive the formula for extracting the third and fourth principal eigenvectors $\mathbf{e}_3$ and $\mathbf{e}_4$.

Exercise 8.10 (Application of Dynamic Orthogonalization Rule)
For the PCA problem:

(a) Verify again the convergence analysis on APEX networks using the dynamic orthogonalization rule.

(b) Derive the relative decay rates for the non-dominant components.

Exercise 8.11 (Application of Local Orthogonalization Rule)
For the PCA problem:

(a) Prove the convergence of APEX networks using the local orthogonalization rule.

(b) Derive the relative decay rates for the non-dominant components.

Exercise 8.12 (Parallel Processing of APEX Networks)
For the APEX network in Figure 8.8(a), prove the convergence property even when
learning rules for each of the m components are executed in parallel. (A useful
reference is [46].)

Exercise 8.13 (Conjugate-Gradient Batch Technique)
Assume that the correlation matrix $\mathbf{R}_x$ of a stochastic vector process $\{\mathbf{x}\}$ is known
a priori. The PCA problem is a constrained minimization problem:

$$\text{minimize } -\frac{1}{2}\mathbf{w}\mathbf{R}_x\mathbf{w}^T$$

$$\text{subject to } \mathbf{w}\mathbf{w}^T = 1$$

(a) Show that the problem can be approximated by the following unconstrained
formulation:
$$\text{minimize } f(\mathbf{w}) = -\frac{1}{2}\mathbf{w}\mathbf{R}_x\mathbf{w}^T + \mu(\mathbf{w}\mathbf{w}^T - 1)^2$$

where μ is a large positive constant. The problem is now given in a quadratic
formulation.
  (b) Derive an iterative updating algorithm by applying the conjugate-gradient
method.

Exercise 8.14 In designing the lateral orthogonalization network in the BP network for APCA, it is possible to avoid computing the inner products by adaptively
estimating (i.e., tracking) the values of $\overline{\alpha}_{12}(t)$ and $\underline{\alpha}_{12}(t)$. The adaptive formulas are

$$\Delta\overline{\alpha}_{12}(t) = \beta \left[\overline{a}_1(t) - \overline{\alpha}_{12}(t)\overline{a}_2(t)\right] \underline{a}_2'(t) \tag{8.62}$$

$$\Delta\underline{\alpha}_{12}(t) = \beta \left[\underline{a}_1(t) - \underline{\alpha}_{12}(t)\underline{a}_2(t)\right] \overline{a}_2'(t) \tag{8.63}$$

  (a) Show that under certain initial conditions, the inhibition parameters will
converge in the steady state to

$$\overline{\alpha}_{12}(t) \rightarrow \overline{\mathbf{w}}_1^T \overline{\mathbf{w}}_2(t) \qquad \underline{\alpha}_{12}(t) \rightarrow \overline{\mathbf{w}}_1^T \underline{\mathbf{w}}_2(t)$$

  (b) Why is this version more appealing computationally?
  (c) Show that the algorithm converges to the second normalized component of
$\mathbf{R}_{xy}$, namely,

$$\underline{\mathbf{w}}_2(t) \rightarrow \mathbf{u}_2$$

$$\overline{\mathbf{w}}_2(t) \rightarrow \mathbf{v}_2$$

as $t \rightarrow \infty$.

Exercise 8.15 (Property of the CPC Network)
The mathematical formulation of CPC is the following: Given an n-dimensional stationary stochastic input vector $\mathbf{x}(t) = [x_1(t), x_2(t), \cdots, x_n(t)]^T$, and a k-dimensional

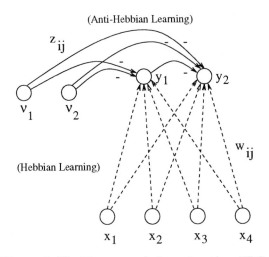

(Anti-Hebbian Learning)

(Hebbian Learning)

Figure 8.15: The network for extracting CPCs.

known (redundant) vector $\nu(t) = [\nu_1(t), \cdots, \nu_k(t)]^T$, $\nu(t) = V^T x(t)$. With reference to Figure 8.15, the output is denoted by $a(t)$, $a(t) = q^T x(t)$, where q is a column vector. The CPC problem is to find a vector q, subject to the constraint that $V^T q = 0$, such that an optimal estimate $\hat{x}(t)$ of vector $x(t)$ can be reconstructed from output vector $a(t)$.

Assume that, without loss of generality, the matrix V is orthonormal. That is, $V^T V = I$. We denote the (non-negative) eigenvalues of $R[I - VV^T]$ as $\{ \tilde{\lambda}_i \}$ $(\tilde{\lambda}_1 \geq \tilde{\lambda}_2 \geq \ldots \geq \tilde{\lambda}_n)$ and the corresponding eigenvectors as $\{ \tilde{e}_i \}$. Also, let $\theta_i = \{1 - \|\tilde{e}_i V\|^2\}^{-1/2}$.

(a) With reference to Figure 8.15, prove that in the steady state (i.e., as $t \to \infty$,)

$$w = w(\infty) = \theta_1 \tilde{e}_1 \qquad (8.64)$$

(b) Verify that

$$V^T q = 0$$

where $q = w - Vz$, and z denotes the vector of the weights for the lateral inhibitory connection.

(c) Show that the optimal estimate $\hat{x}(t)$ of vector $x(t)$ can be reconstructed (from $\nu(t)$ and $a(t)$) as

$$\hat{x}(t) = V\nu(t) + qa(t)$$

(d) Show that the above convergence analyses apply to both single and multiple CPC cases.

Hint: *The proof for the PCA problem is largely valid for the CPC problem.*

Exercise 8.16 Show that the CPC problem is the generalized eigenvalue decomposition of $\{(I - VV^T)R_x(I - VV^T), (I - VV^T)\}$.

Exercise 8.17 Ljung's convergence theorem [176] can be applied to establish the convergence of the CPC neural model given in Eq. 8.30 and Eq. 8.31 $y(t)$. Denote $\sigma(t) = \tilde{E}\{y^2(t)\}$. Show that the convergence of the algorithm holds if the solution of the following differential equation is uniformly asymptotically stable.

$$\frac{dw(t)}{dt} = w(t)[R - \sigma(t)I] - z(t)[\mathbf{V}R] \qquad (8.65)$$

$$\frac{dz(t)}{dt} = w(t)[RV^T] + z(t)[-\sigma(t)I - \mathbf{V}RV^T] \qquad (8.66)$$

Show that these equations are the continuous-time counterparts of Eq. 8.30.

Chapter 9

Stochastic Annealing
Networks for Optimization

9.1 Introduction

This chapter discusses the basic formulation of stochastic optimization networks for searching the global optimum an energy function. The energy function (or cost function) for the optimization problem falls into several categories. For example, combinatorial optimization, Bayesian likelihood function, or some other entropy measure. The stochastic optimization neural models can be applied to constrained optimization [182], combinatorial optimization [106, 267], linear programming [269], computational vision [134], parameter estimation [238], and many others.

Two major classes of optimization techniques are the deterministic gradient methods and the stochastic annealing methods. The former is subject to a fundamental limitation of being easily trapped in local minima. In this chapter, therefore, we explore the other alternative by the stochastic techniques.

For stochastic optimization networks, two phases are involved: (1) the weight determination phase and (2) the search phase. (They correspond to the training and retrieving phases respectively.) The former is to determine an energy function appropriate for a given application. In the non-constraint optimization applications, the energy function can be directly obtained as the cost function (e.g., regularized least-squares applications). In constraint optimization, the energy function must be derived indirectly from the original cost function *and* the required constraints (e.g., traveling salesman problem).

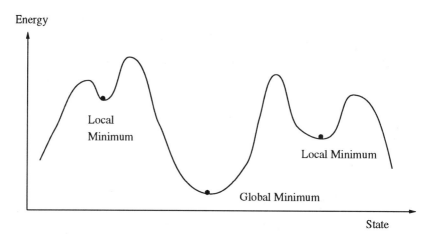

Figure 9.1: In the optimization (minimization) problem, the solution can be trapped by a local optimum (minimum). The global optimum (minimum) is the desired target.

If a second-order energy function like Eq. 9.8 (cf. Eq. 2.6) can be formed, then the synaptic weights $\{w_{ij}\}$ and the external inputs $\{\theta_i\}$ of a Hopfield-type model are derived. Indeed, in Chapter 2, the deterministic Hopfield model was adopted for associative memory applications, where the optimization formulation requires only the convergence to a local optimum, cf. Figure 9.1. The Hopfield model, or any deterministic gradient-descent method, is not suitable for solving the global optimization problem.

To study the stochastic neural networks, we use the assumption that the states of the network obey a Boltzmann-Gibb distribution. The statistical equilibrium condition leads to a *Boltzmann state-transition rule*. It is the basis for both the stochastic simulated annealing (SSA) and the mean-field annealing (MFA) formulations. The stochastic neural models, based on the annealing techniques, provide a solution to counter the local minimum problem. A stochastic network has non-zero probability to go from one state to another. It has the ability to move (temporarily) toward a *worse* state so as to escape from local traps. The probability function depends on the temperature and the energy difference between the two states. At a higher temperature, a stochastic network has a better probability to go to a higher energy state (i.e., hill climbing). The global minimum has lower energy than the local minima, therefore, it may attract a higher-energy local optimal state out of the local trap.

In the special case of a second-order energy function, the SSA and MFA techniques lead to a Hopfield-type network structure that can be applied to the combinatorial optimization problems. There is no learning for the Hopfield associative memory (i.e., the weights are precomputed as correlations of the original patterns). In contrast, in the Boltzmann machine, a stochastic learning technique can be adopted to train the weights of a Boltzmann-type associative memory.

Chapter Organization

This chapter presents several stochastic techniques for solving optimization problems. Section 9.2 introduces stochastic networks based on the annealing techniques. The actual network implementation may depend significantly on the intended applications. Section 9.3 provides application examples on image processing and combinatorial optimization problems. In Section 9.4, the Boltzmann machine for associative memory is explored.

9.2   Stochastic Neural Networks

Statistical mechanics techniques offer a viable approach to global optimization. The equilibrium condition leads to a *Boltzmann state-transition rule* for state update, which is the basis for the stochastic simulated annealing (SSA) and the mean-field annealing (MFA) formulations.

9.2.1   Equilibrium in Stochastic Networks

For a stochastic network, let $P(a)$ denote the state-distribution function and $Prob(a \rightarrow a')$ denote the state-transition function from a state a to another state a'. In equilibrium, the *state-distribution function* and the *state-transition rule* reach a balance:

$$P(a)Prob(a \rightarrow a') = Prob(a' \rightarrow a)P(a') \qquad (9.1)$$

Equivalently,

$$\frac{P(a')}{P(a)} = \frac{Prob(a \rightarrow a')}{Prob(a' \rightarrow a)} \qquad (9.2)$$

This and the *Boltzmann-Gibb distribution* (Eq. 9.6) lead to the following *Boltzmann state-transition rule*

$$Prob(a \rightarrow a') = \frac{1}{1 + exp(\Delta E/T)} \equiv f(-\Delta E/T) \qquad (9.3)$$

where $f(\cdot)$ is the sigmoid function, T is the temperature, and E denotes the energy function with $\Delta E = E(a') - E(a)$. It is important to note that the *Boltzmann state-transition rule*, used throughout the subsequent discussion, directs the stochastic model (with Boltzmann-Gibb distribution) to move towards its thermal equilibrium. This is verified below. Based on Eq. 9.3, it follows that

$$\frac{Prob(a \to a')}{Prob(a' \to a)} = \frac{1 + exp(-\Delta E/T)}{1 + exp(\Delta E/T)} = exp(-\Delta E/T) \tag{9.4}$$

Therefore, by Eq. 9.2,

$$\frac{P(a')}{P(a)} = exp(-\Delta E/T) \tag{9.5}$$

By inspection of Eq. 9.5, the *state-distribution function* is verified to be a Boltzmann-Gibb distribution (as previously assumed):

$$P_T(a) = \frac{1}{Z} exp(-E(a)/T) \tag{9.6}$$

where Z is a normalizing factor. Thus, it is indeed a Boltzmann-Gibb distribution, justifying the adoption of Eq. 9.3 in the first place. The *Boltzmann state-transition rule* ensures that, in thermal equilibrium, "the relative probability of the two global states is determined solely by their energy difference and temperature, and the probability of being in a state follows a Boltzmann distribution" [98].

Minimization of the Energy Function   Note that if $P_T(a) \geq P_T(a')$, then $E(a) \leq E(a')$, and vice versa. *So maximizing the probability function is equivalent to minimizing the energy function.* With reference to the two curves in Figure 9.2 corresponding to two distinct temperatures T and T', we note also that $P_T(a) \geq P_T(a')$ when and only when $P_{T'}(a) \geq P_{T'}(a)$.

Thus the temperature parameter T provides a new free parameter to help steer the search direction (and step-size) toward the global optimum. With a high temperature, the equilibrium can be reached more rapidly. When the temperature is too high, however, all the states will have a similar level of probability. So it is necessary to gradually lower the temperature to eventually $T \to 0$. Correspondingly, the probable state will then gradually concentrate around the globally minimum. This is illustrated by the dashed curve in Figure 9.2. Furthermore, when $T \to 0$, the average state should be very close to the global optimal solution. This idea, though very attractive at the first glance, is not necessarily directly implementable in practice. In fact, with a low temperature, it will take a very long time to reach equilibrium and, more seriously, the state is more easily trapped by local minima.

A plausible compromise is to apply the updating rule, Eq. 9.3, starting with a high temperature and gradually decreasing it. This approach leads to several popular statistical mechanics annealing techniques, for example, the stochastic simulated annealing (SSA) and the mean-field annealing (MFA) techniques. As will be elaborated on momentarily, these techniques are key to the stochastic computational models for optimization. These models have the following characteristics:

1. Both annealing techniques are based on the *Boltzmann state-transition rule* described in Eq. 9.3.

2. They start with a high temperature and decrease it according to a pre-specified schedule. A proper temperature schedule is instrumental to the success of reaching the global minimum.

3. They both resort to some kind of averaging of neuron values in equilibrium, although they differ in the stages to execute the averaging process.

9.2.2   Stochastic Simulated Annealing(SSA)

Stochastic simulated annealing creates a non-zero probability to move a state (temporarily) toward a higher-energy state (i.e., hill climbing) [132] so it may escape a local trap. The simulated annealing technique has been applied to many different problems, for example, Geman-Geman for image restoration [79]. Another important application domain is vision processing, where large constraint-satisfaction problems are solved to interpret a two-dimensional image [20, 98].

The SSA scheme is based on a Monte-Carlo simulation following the *Boltzmann state-transition rule*, that is, the probability of changing a bit (in a sequential manner) is

$$Prob(a_i \rightarrow -a_i) = f(-\Delta E_i/T) \tag{9.7}$$

In this case, $\mathbf{a} = [a_1, a_2, \cdots, a_i, \cdots, a_N]$, $\mathbf{a}' = [a_1, a_2, \cdots, -a_i, \cdots, a_N]$, and $\Delta E_i = E(a) - E(a')$. The updating neuron can be randomly selected.

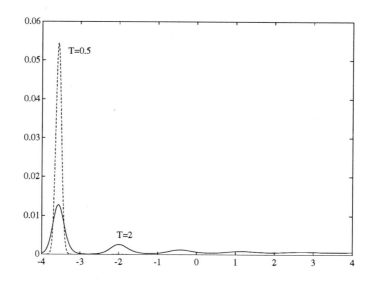

Figure 9.2: Relation between temperature and probability of the state.

Now the hill climbing (i.e., the bit change resulting in $\Delta E_i > 0$) is probable, although the probability is always less than 50%. (Show this!) When the temperature is very high, such a probability approaches 50%. When the temperature is lower, then the probability is much lower than 50%. Thus, in the initial phase, a higher temperature should be used so that it is easier for the states to escape from a local minimum. (See Figure 9.3.) The temperature will be gradually decreased according to a pre-specified schedule. After the state is (hopefully) placed near the neighborhood of the global minimum, a lower temperature will more likely make the state move closer to the exact global minimum. (See Figure 9.3.) *Having a proper temperature schedule is critical for both convergence speed and final performance of the SSA*. At each temperature, the SSA searches for an equilibrium point. For a new temperature, the iteration always restarts with the final equilibrium state reached by the previous temperature. This process continues until the final convergence is reached.

An important special case is when the energy function is second order:

$$E(A) = -\frac{1}{2} \sum_{ij} w_{ij} a_i a_j - \sum_i \theta_i a_i \qquad (9.8)$$

where a_i is the output of the i-th neuron, and w_{ij} is the symmetric weight

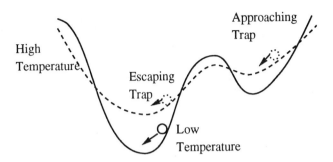

Figure 9.3: The adjusted energy levels for a high and a low temperature. In the initial phase, a higher temperature allows a state to escape from a local trap, as shown by the dashed line. At the final stage, it may be more preferable to lower the temperature so that the state converges faster to the global minimum, as shown by the solid line.

matrix. Then
$$\Delta E_i = 2u_i a_i$$

By Eq. 9.7,
$$Prob(a_i \to -a_i) = f(-2u_i a_i/T) \tag{9.9}$$

where
$$u_i = \sum_j w_{ij} a_j + \theta_i \tag{9.10}$$

Note that the Hopfield-like network reduces into the original Hopfield model when $T \to 0$. More exactly, the state-transition function approximates the sequential (bit-by-bit) updating rule in the Hopfield model. (See Problem 9.1.) The SSA technique, theoretically speaking, must update each bit sequentially. It is, however, very desirable to perform parallel bit update.

9.2.3 Mean-Field Annealing and the Continuous-Valued Hopfield Model

The state transitions of different neurons are likely to influence each other, making the theoretical analysis extremely intractable. The analysis can be much simplified by replacing the actual values (of u and a) by the average values. It can be shown that when a network reaches equilibrium, the average output values become time-independent [95]. Therefore, it is justifiable to adopt time-averaging, leading to the *mean-field approximation*.

Continuous-Valued Hopfield Model   Suppose that there is only one bit to update at one time, say, a_i. By Eq. 9.5,

$$\frac{Prob(a_i = +1)}{Prob(a_i = -1)} = e^{-\Delta E/T} = e^{-2u_i/T}$$

Note that $Prob(a_i = +1) + Prob(a_i = -1) = 1$, that is

$$\begin{array}{ll} Prob(a_i = +1) = & f(2u_i/T) \\ Prob(a_i = -1) = & 1 - f(2u_i/T) \end{array} \tag{9.11}$$

where u_i is defined in Eq. 9.10 and $f(\cdot)$ denotes the sigmoid function. The average value $\mathbf{E}[a_i|u_i]$ given a constant u_i is

$$\mathbf{E}[a_i|u_i] = Prob(a_i + 1) - Prob(a_i - 1) = tanh(u_i/T) \tag{9.12}$$

where

$$tanh(u_i/T) \equiv \frac{e^{u_i/T} - e^{-u_i/T}}{e^{u_i/T} + e^{-u_i/T}}$$

Based on Eq. 9.12, we have for unit i

$$\mathbf{E}[a_i] \approx tanh(\mathbf{E}[u_i]/T) \tag{9.13}$$

Note that the average output has a continuous (real) value, while the actual individual outputs are bipolar-valued (± 1).

Second-Order Case   In case of a second-order energy function, the mean-field annealing technique leads to a Hopfield-like continuous-valued model. This is explained in what follows. Combining Eq. 9.10 and Eq. 9.13, we obtain the following MFA model:

$$\begin{array}{rl} u_i(k+1) = & \displaystyle\sum_j w_{ij}a_j(k) + \theta_i \end{array} \tag{9.14}$$

$$a_i(k+1) = tanh(u_i(k+1)/T) \tag{9.15}$$

(At a low temperature, the $tanh(u_i/T)$ function yields an average neuron value very close to either $+1$ or -1. Therefore, the final solution in MFA is approximately in a bipolar or binary state.)

   Compared with the continuous-state Hopfield model in Chapter 2, the only key distinction is that the activation function is a *tanh* function, instead of a sigmoid function, (The *tanh* function is more naturally associated with

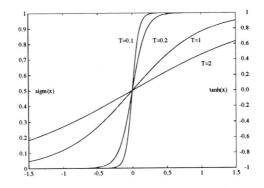

Figure 9.4: Comparison between a sigmoid function (left coordinate) and a *tanh* function (right coordinate). Note that $tanh(x) = 2f(x)-1$, where function $f(u_i/T)$ is a sigmoid function, and $tanh(u_i/T)$ is a tanh function. When T becomes lower, $tanh(u_i/T)$ reduces to a sign function.

the bipolar representation (1/-1), while the sigmoid function is with the binary (1/0) representation.) As shown in Figure 9.4, the *tanh* function and the sigmoid function are basically equivalent, albeit an additive constant and a scaling factor.

In summary, the MFA algorithm consists of the following steps:

1. *Initialization:* Start with a high temperature and set the initial average value to a random number.

2. *Iterations:* Select a neuron randomly and update its neuron value according to Eq. 9.14 and Eq. 9.15. Repeat the iteration with another randomly selected neuron until convergence.

3. *Annealing Schedule:* Decrease T according to a prescribed schedule and repeat step 2 until a desired low temperature is reached.

General Case   When the cost function is of higher-order, the basic principle of the MFA is still valid. Apply Eq. 9.5 to a single-bit update,

$$a_i = \begin{cases} +1 & \text{with probability } f(\Delta E_i/T) \\ -1 & \text{with probability } 1 - f(\Delta E_i/T) \end{cases}$$

By the mean-field approximation, the average neuron value for the unit i is

(provided that ΔE_i is given)

$$\mathbf{E}[a_i|\Delta E_i] = tanh(\Delta E_i/2T)$$

It then follows that

$$\mathbf{E}[a_i] \approx tanh(\mathbf{E}[\Delta E_i]/2T) \qquad (9.16)$$

In summary, the MFA gives a simple approximation of the state in thermal equilibrium. In the MFA, the state values are replaced with their means. In contrast, the SSA employs the computationally costly Monte-Carlo simulations and then extracts the average as the final result. Therefore, a major computational savings can be obtained by directly calculating steady-state average values (Eq. 9.13 or Eq. 9.16) in the MFA technique. Indeed, a lot of simulation results support that the MFA reaches the equilibrium faster than the SSA.

Parallel Processing with MFA Techniques   The derivation of the MFA is, theoretically speaking, based on sequential bit updating. Further study is required in order to better support parallel bit updating. Fortunately, for image-processing applications, MFA annealing techniques can be incorporated into a Markov random-field model, (cf. Section 9.3.2.) It provides a natural basis for massively parallel processing by updating many pixels simultaneously. Therefore, a technique combining MFA and MRF, as discussed in the next section, is potentially very appealing.

9.3   Applications to Combinatorial Optimization and Image Restoration

This section discusses the applications of stochastic annealing techniques to several optimization problems, including *combinatorial optimization* and *image-restoration*. In a general constrained optimization problem, the objective is to find $\mathbf{x}$ which

minimizes $\phi(\mathbf{x})$, under the constraints $P_j(\mathbf{x}) = 0$

where ϕ is a continuous function of n-dimensional vector $\mathbf{x}$ (continuous or discrete) and $\{P_j(\mathbf{x}), j = 1, 2, \cdots, p\}$ are continuous and nonnegative constraint functions. The constrained optimization problem can be approximated by an unconstrained optimization problem, which involves minimizing a new energy function

$$E' = \phi(\mathbf{x}) + \sum_{j=1}^{p} \kappa_j P_j(\mathbf{x}) \tag{9.17}$$

where $\{\kappa_j\}$ are large positive constants.

9.3.1 Combinatorial Optimization

A combinatorial optimization problem in a discrete system involves searching for the state which minimizes the energy function. The number of possible solutions, for combinatorial optimization based on a discrete-valued model, is an exponential function of the size of the network [214]. For example, if there are N independent variables, then there are 2^N possible states. The exhaustive search is impractical when N is large. The neural model approach offers a different alternative, though its effectiveness is yet to be thoroughly examined.

We discuss two examples: the *perfect matching problem* and the *traveling salesman problem* (TSP). The binary state representation (1/0), adopted in this section, is more popular for combinatorial optimization problems.

Perfect Matching Problem

In the perfect matching problem, there are two sets of nodes of equal number, S_1 and S_2. Each node in S_1 is mapped onto one (and only one) node of S_2, and vice versa. The matching can be represented by a connection matrix $[x_{ij}]$, which is restricted to a permutation matrix (defined in Eq. 9.19 and Eq. 9.20). Also if $x_{ij} = 1$, it means that node i of S_1 is matched to node j of S_2. For every connection, an associated cost c_{ij} is assigned.

The perfect matching problem can be formally stated as follows: Given a cost matrix $\{c_{ij}\}$, find a connection matrix $\{a_{ij}\}$ ($a_{ij} = 0$ or 1) that

1. minimizes the cost function:

$$\sum_i \sum_j c_{ij} a_{ij} \tag{9.18}$$

2. satisfies the constraint that matrix $\{a_{ij}\}$ is a permutation matrix, or, equivalently,

$$\sum_{j}^{n} a_{ij} = 1 \quad i = 1, 2, \ldots, n \tag{9.19}$$

and

$$\sum_{i}^{n} a_{ij} = 1 \quad j = 1, 2, \ldots, n \tag{9.20}$$

Note that the neuron state a_{ij} has double indices; correspondingly, the energy function takes the following form (cf. Eq. 9.17):

$$
\begin{aligned}
E \;=\; & A/2 \sum_{i,j} c_{i,j} a_{i,j} \\
& + B/2 \sum_{i} \sum_{j} \sum_{j' \neq j} a_{i,j} a_{i,j'} \\
& + C/2 \sum_{j} \sum_{i} \sum_{i' \neq i} a_{i,j} a_{i',j} \\
& + D/2 \Big(\sum_{i} \sum_{j} a_{i,j} - n \Big)^2
\end{aligned}
\tag{9.21}
$$

where A, B, C, and D are proper (positive) weighting constants to be determined. This lowest energy state corresponds to the best match. To show this, note that the first term in Eq. 9.21 corresponds to the minimized cost function given in Eq. 9.18. The last three terms help assure that matrix $\{a_{ij}\}$ is approximately a permutation matrix.[1] To help enforce a valid solution state (i.e., discrete $[a_{ij}]$ is a permutation matrix), B, C, and D should be chosen to be sufficiently large compared to A. One possible approach is to use small B, C, and D at the beginning, and then increase their values gradually.

In terms of weight parameters, the energy function for double-indexed states has the following expression (cf. Eq. 2.6):

$$E = -(1/2) \sum_{i=1}^{n} \sum_{j=1}^{n} \sum_{i'=1}^{n} \sum_{j'=1}^{n} w_{i,j,i',j'} \, a_{i,j} a_{i',j'} - \sum_{i=1}^{n} \sum_{j=1}^{n} \theta_{i,j} a_{i,j} \tag{9.22}$$

By comparing Eq. 9.21 and Eq. 9.22, the synaptic weights $w_{i,j,i',j'}$ and the threshold values $\theta_{i,j}$ can be obtained as

---

[1] The second (third) term in Eq. 9.21 enforces that no more than one entry in each row (column) of matrix $\{a_{ij}\}$ is 1. The fourth term enforces that there are exactly n entries in matrix $\{a_{ij}\}$ equal to 1. The second and fourth terms together enforce the constraint specified in Eq. 9.19, while the third and fourth terms together enforce Eq. 9.20.

$$w_{i,j,i',j'} = -B\delta_{i,i'}(1 - \delta_{j,j'})$$
$$-C\delta_{j,j'}(1 - \delta_{i,i'})$$
$$-D$$

$$\theta_{i,j} = nD - \frac{A}{2}c_{i,j} \qquad (9.23)$$

where $\delta_{ij} = 1$, if $i = j$ and 0 otherwise.

Once the synaptic weights are so determined and stored in the neural network, then the annealing techniques discussed in Section 9.2 can be adopted for the search phase. If the SSA is chosen, then the dynamic system follows Eq. 9.9 and Eq. 9.10. If the MFA is adopted, then Eq. 9.14 and Eq. 9.15 apply instead.

Traveling Salesman Problem

The constraint optimization problem formulation can be easily extended to other graph-matching problems, for example, bipartite graph matching, and finding the best match between two sets of nodes of different size [214]. Its extension to the traveling salesman problem (TSP) is somewhat involved.

The objective of solving the (N cities) TSP problem is to find the shortest route of visiting all N cities and returning to the starting city. Referring to Figure 9.5, the 5-city TSP is defined by the distance matrix:

$$\{d_{ij}\} = \begin{bmatrix} 0 & \infty & 20 & 7 & 35 \\ \infty & 0 & \infty & 10 & 23 \\ 20 & \infty & 0 & 15 & 12 \\ 7 & 10 & 15 & 0 & 29 \\ 35 & 23 & 12 & 29 & 0 \end{bmatrix} \qquad (9.24)$$

where d_{ij} is the distance between city i and city j.

Because there are N cities and N stops, a total of $N \times N$ neurons is used to solve the TSP in the Hopfield net formulation. A high neuron value $a_{ij} = 1$ indicates that the ith city is the jth stop. Therefore, the solution is valid only if the matrix $\{a_{ij}\}$ is a permutation matrix.

Similar to the perfect match problem, the TSP problem can be formulated in terms of minimizing a second-order energy function:

$$E = A/2 \sum_{i,j} \sum_{i',j'} c_{i,j,i',j'} a_{i,j} a_{i',j'}$$

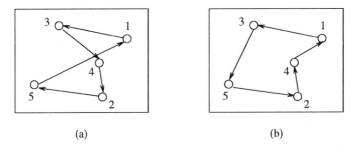

(a)   (b)

Figure 9.5: Different solutions for a traveling salesman problem: (a) a non-optimal solution, and (b) an optimal solution. Note that, in practice, the number of cities N is very large, and the number of neurons in Hopfield-like model (N^2) may represent a major difficulty.

$$+B/2 \sum_i \sum_j \sum_{j' \neq j} a_{i,j} a_{i,j'}$$

$$+C/2 \sum_j \sum_i \sum_{i' \neq i} a_{i,j} a_{i',j}$$

$$+D/2 (\sum_i \sum_j a_{i,j} - n)^2 \qquad (9.25)$$

where A, B, C, and D are positive weighting constants to be chosen properly. The second-order energy function leads naturally to a Hopfield model; cf. Eq. 9.22.

Just like the perfect match problem, the first term in Eq. 9.25 is used to ensure that the total traveling length is minimized. Again the last three terms help enforce $\{a_{ij}\}$ to be approximately a permutation matrix. Unlike the perfect match problem, the coefficients $c_{i,j,i',j'}$ for the TSP have to be specially derived:

$$c_{i,j,i',j'} = \begin{cases} 0 & |j - j'|_{\text{mod } N} \neq 1 \\ d_{i,i'} & |j - j'|_{\text{mod } N} = 1 \end{cases}$$

where $d_{i,i'}$ is the distance between city i and city i'.

One of the major hurdles in the TSP application is the undesirably large size of the neural model. More precisely, there are N^2 neurons for an N-city TSP. The performance on TSP, unfortunately, is reported to degrade rapidly with the increase of network size. Furthermore, according to empirical experiments, the local minimum problem remains a serious concern despite the use of annealing techniques.

9.3.2 Image-Restoration Model: Markov Random Field(MRF)

The *Markov Random Field* (MRF) image model allows a maximum exploitation of the image's locally dependent characteristics [29], making it very amenable to parallel MFA algorithms. In this section, we study an optimization formulation for image restoration, based on incorporation of an adaptive regularization into the MRF model. Thereafter, the mean-field technique becomes a natural iterative technique to find the optimal image model.

For many image-processing applications, it is practical to assume that the image field is modeled after a Markov random field. An MRF is a two-dimensional locally dependent random process, whose probability distribution depends on the pixels in the immediate neighborhood. The image restoration problem is to restore an original image f from a degraded observed image g. There are various kinds of degradations, for example, blurring, nonlinear deformation, and multiplicative/additive noise. Let us assume that, for simplicity, the original image f is degraded only by an additive noise n:

$$g = f + n$$

It is popular to use the Bayesian likelihood approach for image restoration and vision processing. Let F denote the set of all possible solutions of f and assume that the probability function $P(f) > 0$ for all $f \in F$. Based on the Bayesian theorem, the maximum a posteriori (MAP) estimate $\hat{f} \in F$ is the one that maximizes the a posteriori probability:

$$P(\hat{f}|g) \propto P(g|\hat{f})P(\hat{f}) \tag{9.26}$$

Furthermore, let the pixels of an image be represented by a set D and any possible solution be represented by $f = \{f_{ij}, \forall \text{ pixels } s_{ij} \in D\}$. The observed image g is now represented by $g = \{g_{ij}, s_{ij} \in D\}$. Based on the local dependence property of the MRF model, characteristics:

$$P(f_{ij}|f_{D-s_{ij}}) = P_{ij}(f_{ij}|f_{\mathcal{N}_{ij}})$$

where the $\mathcal{N}_{ij}$ denotes the immediate neighborhood of the pixel site s_{ij}. Similarly, the following conditional probability function is dependent only on the local neighborhood [28]:

$$P(f_{ij}|g_{ij}, \hat{f}_{D-s_{ij}}) \propto P(g_{ij}|f_{ij})P_{ij}(f_{ij}|\hat{f}_{\mathcal{N}_{ij}}) \tag{9.27}$$

The best estimate of f_{ij}, given g_{ij}, and all the current estimates $\hat{f}_{D-s_{ij}}$, can be obtained as the one that maximizes $P(f_{ij}|g_{ij}, \hat{f}_{D-s_{ij}})$ for all $s_{ij} \in D$ in Eq. 9.27.

For finding a feasible Bayesian estimator of Eq. 9.27, there exist direct methods, for example, the *iterated conditional modes* proposed by Besag [29]. In this section, however, we focus on the applications of the annealing techniques to the MRF image model. Eq. 9.26 and Eq. 9.27 together lead to an energy function formulation, from which the corresponding stochastic neural networks can be constructed. Geman and Geman [79] proposed a stochastic simulated annealing (SSA) approach for computing the conditional probability of any state f, given g, as in Eq. 9.27. It is essentially a stochastic relaxation algorithm that generates a sequence of images that converges to the MAP estimate. The mean-field annealing techniques are equally applicable and are in fact computationally more effective. In several known experiments, the MFA is faster than the SSA. Under the MRF model, both annealing techniques permit massively parallel processing.

Restoration of Smooth Images

In image modeling, it is popular is to combine the Markov random field (MRF) with the Boltzmann-Gibb distribution. Suppose first that the original image is smooth and it has negligible edge structure. Now the two terms in the product of Eq. 9.27 (1) $P(g_{ij}|f_{ij})$ and (2) $P_{ij}(f_{ij}|\hat{f}_{N_{ij}})$ are separately treated. If the noise is an additive independent Gaussian process, then the first term becomes

$$P(g_{ij}|f_{ij}) \propto e^{-(\sum_{ij}(f_{ij}-g_{ij})^2)/T} \qquad (9.28)$$

Because it is MRF, by the Clifford-Hammersley theorem, the distribution function must be of the Boltzmann-Gibb type. Therefore, the second term becomes

$$P_{ij}(f_{ij}|\hat{f}_{N_{ij}}) \propto e^{-\alpha(\delta_j^2 f + \delta_i^2 f)/T} \qquad (9.29)$$

where $\delta_j^2 f$ denote the square of the derivative of f, with δ_i and δ_j obtained as follows:

$$
\begin{aligned}
\delta_i &= K_{ij} + M_{ij} \\
\delta_j &= K_{ij} - M_{ij} \\
M_{ij} &= (f_{ij-1} - f_{i-1j})/2 \\
K_{ij} &= (f_{ij} - f_{i-1j-1})/2
\end{aligned}
$$

Substituting Eq. 9.28 and Eq. 9.29 into Eq. 9.27, we have

$$P(f_{ij}|g_{ij}, \hat{f}_{D-s_{ij}}) \propto exp(-E(f)/T)$$

where

$$E(f) = \sum_{ij}(f_{ij} - g_{ij})^2 + \alpha(\delta_j^2 f + \delta_i^2 f)$$

Restoration of Images with Edges

When the image contains important edge features, then the objective of image restoration must take into account the preservation or enhancement of the edge features. Now the problem involves not only smoothing the field, but also simultaneously detecting/preserving physical discontinuities. To cope with the new situation, a new energy function $E(f,l)$ is introduced that depends not only on f (the image field), but also on l (the discontinuities due to the line process) [77]. More precisely, Eq. 9.29 is modified to

$$P_{ij}(f_{ij}|\hat{f}_{\mathcal{N}_{ij}}) \propto e^{-\alpha(\delta_j^2 f + \delta_i^2 f)(1-l_{ij}) - \gamma l_{ij}/T}$$

where γ is the parameter to moderate the role of the line process. The new Boltzmann-Gibb's distribution becomes

$$P(f,l) = \frac{1}{Z}e^{-E(f,l)/T} \tag{9.30}$$

where the energy function is obtained by combining the two terms in Eq. 9.28 and Eq. 9.29.

$$E(f,l) = \sum_{ij}(f_{ij} - g_{ij})^2 + \alpha(\delta_j^2 f + \delta_i^2 f)(1 - l_{ij}) + \gamma l_{ij}$$

The use of a single line process instead of a pair of horizontal and vertical lines helps reduce the anisotropy and the bias toward preferring horizontal and vertical lines [77]. The line process leads to another combinatorial optimization formulation.

Either the SSA or the MFA techniques can be adopted to search the optimal solution. In [77], a parallel and iterative MFA algorithm is proposed for the image analysis problem. The experimental results indicate that the MFA technique is computationally more effective than the SSA technique.

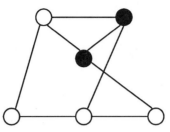

Figure 9.6: The network of a Boltzmann machine can be irregularly or partially connected. There are two types of neurons: the black and white neurons denote respectively the hidden and visible units. The neurons are binary-valued.

9.4 Boltzmann Machine

Hinton and Ackley [98] applied simulated annealing to the Hopfield model, which led to the development of the Boltzmann machine. The units in a Boltzmann machine are divided into *visible units* and *hidden units*; cf. Figure 9.6. The hidden units are uncontrollable. More precisely, in the training phase, the hidden units cannot be clamped to any fixed values, while the visible units can. The values of the hidden units are not directly observed in the learning phase. Only the values of the visible units (or their probability distributions) are of concern in training the networks.

Relative Entropy H The objective of Boltzmann learning is to match as closely as possible the state distribution in the *free phase* with the distribution in the *clamped phase*. The energy criterion used is the so-called *relative entropy H*, which is based on the Kullback's information criterion [147]. (Basically, the same measure is used as the harmony criterion proposed in [263].)

- **Without Hidden Units** The Boltzmann training algorithm is based on minimizing the following relative entropy energy function H:

$$H = \sum_a D(a) \log \frac{D(a)}{P(a)} \tag{9.31}$$

  where $D(a)$ and $P(a)$ are the desired and actual probability distributions of state a, respectively.

- **With Hidden Units** Additional hidden units often offer extra flexibility, facilitating a better match. For example, the stochastic networks in Figure 9.6 have both the visible and hidden units. A state vector a is then divided into two subcomponents: the visible units (denoted by α) and the hidden units (denoted by γ). Let us denote $Prob(a) = Prob(\alpha, \gamma)$; then the probability distribution function of the visible state becomes

$$P_\alpha = \sum_\gamma P_{\alpha\gamma} = \sum_\gamma \frac{1}{Z} e^{-E(\alpha\gamma)/T}$$

The *relative entropy* has the following expression:

$$H = \sum_{\alpha \in visible\ units} D_\alpha \log \frac{D_\alpha}{P_\alpha}$$

Here D_α is determined with the visible units clamped to the desired values, and P_α is determined with all the units in the network running freely with no units clamped.

9.4.1 Training Phase

Note that under no circumstance can the relative entropy become negative; cf. Problem 9.9. If the distributions of $P(a)$ and $D(a)$ happen to match each other, the entropy H will be exactly zero. In general, it is not possible to make entropy H exactly zero. A practical strategy is thus to search for a distribution that minimizes the relative entropy. For this, the gradient-descent approach can be adopted:

$$w_{ij}^{new} = w_{ij}^{old} + \Delta w_{ij}$$

where

$$\Delta w_{ij} = -\eta \frac{\partial H}{\partial w_{ij}} \tag{9.32}$$

This leads to the Boltzmann updating algorithm:

$$\Delta w_{ij} = \frac{\eta}{T} \{ \langle a_i a_j \rangle_{clamped} - \langle a_i a_j \rangle_{free} \} \tag{9.33}$$

where η is a small positive learning rate. (The complete derivation can be found in [3, 98, 246].) The two correlation terms, $\langle a_i a_j \rangle_{clamped}$ and $\langle a_i a_j \rangle_{free}$, are proportional to the average probability that both neurons are on (i.e., $a_i^{(m+1)} = a_j^{(m+1)} = 1$) over the patterns sampled under two separately controlled environments.

Therefore, the training of the Boltzmann machine comprises two separate phases of the correlations in Eq. 9.33. Basically, the objective is to find the best weights such that the state probability distribution during the *free* phase matches as closely as possible with the *clamped* phase. Eq. 9.33 is also consistent with the Hebbian learning rule. Namely, if $\langle a_i a_j \rangle_{clamped} = \langle a_i a_j \rangle_{free}$, then there is no need of further update. Otherwise, the weights are adjusted by an amount proportional to the discrepancy between $\langle a_i a_j \rangle_{clamped}$ and $\langle a_i a_j \rangle_{free}$.

The actual computation for both phases will be carried out by a Monte-Carlo simulation based on the *Boltzmann state-transition rule* in Eq. 9.34. The weights are updated only after enough training patterns are taken. The two phases on the computation of the clamped and free correlations are now explained separately:

1. Compute the correlation with clamped states: $\langle a_i a_j \rangle_{clamped}$

   In the computation of $\langle a_i a_j \rangle_{clamped}$, the states of the visible units are *clamped* so that their values are the same as the given training patterns. (In the Monte-Carlo simulation, the training patterns are randomly drawn from a pool of the training set according to a given probability distribution.) The states of the hidden units (if there are any) are computed by the iterative retrieving rule based on Eq. 9.34. Just like the annealing techniques, it follows a prespecified temperature schedule until convergence.

2. Compute the correlation with free states: $\langle a_i a_j \rangle_{free}$.

   In this phase, none of the neural units is clamped. Again, the network iterates (following the same annealing schedule) until it reaches a new convergent state. (The computation of $\langle a_i a_j \rangle_{free}$ follows the same procedure, with or without hidden units.)

Training Procedure of the Boltzmann Machine Given any initial weights, the *Boltzmann machine training algorithm* repeats the following loops until convergence (i.e., $\triangle w_{ij} \approx 0$):

- **When enough samples are collected:**

  Calculate $\langle a_i a_j \rangle_{clamped}$ in the clamped phase (i.e., the visible units are clamped to the desired patterns), and calculate $\langle a_i a_j \rangle_{free}$ in the free (unclamped) phase.

Update the weights (Eq. 9.33):

$$\triangle w_{ij} = \eta\{\langle a_i a_j\rangle_{clamped} - \langle a_i a_j\rangle_{free}\}$$

- **The state a is computed via the following iterations:**

  - *For any individual temperature T, repeat until equilibrium is established. At each temperature, a_i is calculated via the Boltzmann state-transition rule in Eq. 9.34:*

  $$Prob(a \rightarrow a') = \frac{1}{1 + exp(\Delta E/T)}$$

  - *Repeat the process for each temperature according to a prescribed decreasing temperature schedule until a final temperature T_f is reached.*

The global minimum relative entropy can be reached only with a carefully selected temperature schedule.

Example 9.1 (Exclusive-OR Problem)

The exclusive-OR (XOR) classification problem provides an example for the use of the hidden units in the Boltzmann machine [1]. The basic network for the XOR problem has two input units, u_1 and u_2, and one output unit, u_3, as shown in Figure 9.7(a). The XOR function cannot be implemented with this simple configuration. It can be solved if an extra hidden unit, u_4, is added to the network, as shown in Figure 9.7(b). Now we have four states a_1, a_2, a_3, and a_4, corresponding to the three visible units and one hidden unit. Therefore, there are a total of 16 possible state combinations, shown in Table 9.1. It can be shown that 10 out of these 16 combinations are feasible. A solution is called feasible if a 4×4 weight matrix W exists for the Boltzmann machine such that its global minima of the energy function match the four states. (The four states correspond to the four rows of a_1, a_2, a_3, and the chosen a_4 in Table 9.1.) For example, the column of a_4 (0 1 0 1) is not a feasible internal representation for the hidden unit (see Table 9.1) because there exist no weight solution that satisfies the global minima constraints. (See Problem 9.8.) A simulation study [256] showed that, using hundreds of random initial conditions, the Boltzmann machine training algorithm successfully found 8 of the 10 feasible internal representations.

Input	Output	Hidden Unit	
a_1 a_2	a_3	Feasible a_4	Infeasible a_4
0 0	0	0 0 0 0 0 1 1 1 1 1	0 0 0 1 1 1
0 1	1	0 0 1 1 1 0 0 0 1 1	0 0 1 0 1 1
1 0	1	0 1 0 1 1 0 0 1 0 1	0 1 0 1 0 1
1 1	0	1 0 0 0 1 0 1 1 1 0	0 1 1 0 0 1

Table 9.1: The 16 possible states for the Boltzmann machine in Figure 9.7(b).

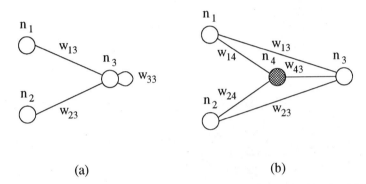

(a)   (b)

Figure 9.7: Network structures of the Boltzmann machine for the XOR problem. (a) A configuration without any hidden neuron is invalid. (b) A valid model needs only one hidden neuron.

9.4.2   Retrieving Phases

The retrieving mechanism of the Boltzmann machine is for the static pattern completion problem (PCP). The known patterns are clamped and the missing patterns left unclamped. (In the retrieving phase, the missing patterns are the patterns to be completed). Given a temperature, the Boltzmann machine executes the state transition according to the weights derived in the training phase. The same is repeated with the temperature gradually lowered. By an optimal temperature schedule, the global minimum can hopefully be reached and the final pattern retrieved.

The retrieving rule of the Boltzmann machine uses the following state transition probability of changing from one state a to another a':

$$Prob(a \rightarrow a') = \frac{1}{1 + exp(\Delta E/T)} \tag{9.34}$$

	OCON/ ACON	Training Methods	Static PCP/ Temporal PCP
Hopfield Model	ACON	No training Hebbian rule	Static PCP Partial pattern as initial state
Boltzmann Machine	ACON	Mutually trained Clamped vs. fixed correlations SSA used for computing correlations	Static PCP Partial pattern as clamped state
HMM	OCON	Independently trained BP type learning Weights averaged	Temporal PCP Viterbi algorithm

Table 9.2: Comparison of different types of recurrent models. Here PCP stands for pattern-completion problem.

where

$$E(a) = -\frac{1}{2} \sum_{ij} w_{ij} a_i a_j$$

The actual probability distribution of the state follows the Boltzmann-Gibb distribution:

$$P(a) = \frac{1}{Z} e^{-E(a)/T}$$

where $Z = \sum_a e^{-E(a)/T}$. Since the retrieving rule is the same as the *Boltzmann state-transition rule* in Eq. 9.3, the model is called *Boltzmann machine* [3, 98].

Comparison with Hopfield Model and HMM   The comparison of the three recurrent structures, Hopfield model, Boltzmann Machine, and HMM, is summarized in Table 9.2. Both the *Hopfield model* and the *Boltzmann machine* are recurrent associative memory networks suitable for static pattern recognition/completion. Unlike the Hopfield model, the weights of the Boltzmann machine need to be trained via a stochastic technique. As to the comparison between the *hidden Markov model* (HMM) and the *Boltzmann machine*. Both of them are stochastic networks with their system dynamics governed by a recurrent state-transition function. In the training phase, the (common) objective is to find the generative models (i.e., the state-transition functions) that are most likely to have produced the ensemble of the training patterns. The Boltzmann machine and HMM differ significantly, however, in their training algorithms, network structures, and application domains. As to network structures, the Boltzmann machine uses an ACON structure, while the HMM is based on an OCON approach. In term of applications, the Boltzmann machine is useful for static pattern recognition. In contrast, the HMM is suitable for temporal pattern recognition.

9.5 Concluding Remarks

Stochastic computational models provide a possible answer to the very challenging local optimum problem. They are largely based on the assumption that the state follows a Boltzmann-Gibb distribution. The statistical equilibrium condition leads to the *Boltzmann state-transition rule* for state update. The rule is the basis for the stochastic simulated annealing (SSA) and the mean-field annealing (MFA) techniques. For a second-order energy function, both the SSA and MFA lead to a Hopfield-type network structure. In particular, the MFA leads to a continuous-valued Hopfield model. Applying the SSA techniques to fully connected or partially connected Hopfield-type recurrent networks further evolves into the Boltzmann machine.

Although stochastic neural networks have a very profound theoretical footing from based on statistical mechanics, many practical aspects remain to be solved before they can be applied to real-world optimization problems. For example, so far there is no conclusive study on how to determine a proper temperature schedule, which is extremely critical in order to attain good speed and/or performance. In terms of parallel processing implementation, a very urgent open research issue is to establish a theoretical or practical basis for parallel annealing techniques. For image processing applications, for example, the combination of MFA and the locally dependent MRF model naturally invites (massively) parallel processing.

9.6 Problems

Exercise 9.1 Show that the Hopfield-like model in Eq. 9.9 and Eq. 9.10 reduces into a Hopfield network when $T \to 0$, barring a minor exception when $u_i = 0$.

Exercise 9.2 Verify that the dynamic rule in Eq. 9.11 can be written as

$$Prob(a = \pm 1) = f(\pm u_i)$$

Exercise 9.3 Show that when the coefficient u_0 approaches zero, the activation function of the Hopfield neural net becomes a *step function* as given in Eq. 9.35:

$$a_i(k+1) = \begin{cases} 1 & u_i(k+1) > 0 \\ 0 & u_i(k+1) \le 0 \end{cases} \qquad (9.35)$$

In the special case, with $\kappa_1 = 0$ and $\kappa_2 = 1$, the model further reduces into a discrete-state neural net, where only two-state (0 and 1) neurons are allowed.

Exercise 9.4 (Graph Coloring Problem) The graph coloring problem is that, given a graph, color all the nodes with a minimum number of different colors such that no adjacent nodes have the same color. Design a Hopfield model for the problem.

Exercise 9.5 (Traveling Salesman Problem)
For the 5-city TSP, defined in Eq. 9.24, derive the weights and thresholds of the Hopfield model. Show that there are 25 neurons. Perform simulation study for the TSP based on (a) the deterministic Hopfield model, (b) the SSA technique, and (c) the MFA technique. Compare the solutions with the global optimum?

Exercise 9.6 (Bipartite Graph Matching) Bipartite graph matching is finding the best match between two sets of nodes of different size [214]. Develop a neural net approach to this problem.

Exercise 9.7 Assume that the degradation transformation is a linear operator denoted by H. A straightforward method is to find an estimate f that minimizes the total estimation error:

$$min(g - H\hat{f})^T(g - H\hat{f})$$

Show that, if a priori information about the image properties (e.g., smoothness and intensity distribution) is known, then the following modified least-squares formulation can be adopted:

$$min(g - H\hat{f})^T(g - H\hat{f}) + \gamma(W\hat{f})^T(W\hat{f})$$

where the W matrix represents the intensity weighting for the overall smoothness measure of the image, and γ is a proper regularization parameter. Can the regularization formulation of image restoration be solved by a neural model?

Exercise 9.8 This problem concerns the Boltzmann machine for the XOR problem with reference to Table 9.1 and Figure 9.7.
    (a) Show that the column $(0,1,1,0)$ for a_4 is a feasible internal representation for the hidden unit a_4 by finding the qualifying weight solution.
    (b) Show that $(0,1,0,1)$ is *not* a feasible internal representation for the hidden unit. *Hint:* Proof by contradiction. If $(0,1,0,1)$ were feasible values for a_4, then all the four states $[0\ 0\ 0\ 0]$, $[0\ 1\ 1\ 1]$, $[1\ 0\ 1\ 0]$, and $[1\ 1\ 0\ 1]$ would be the global minima of the energy function. In particular, the state $[0\ 0\ 0\ 0]$ would have lower energy than $[1\ 0\ 0\ 0]$, leading to the constraint that $w_{11} < 0$. Similarly, other constraints could be derived to yield contradiction.

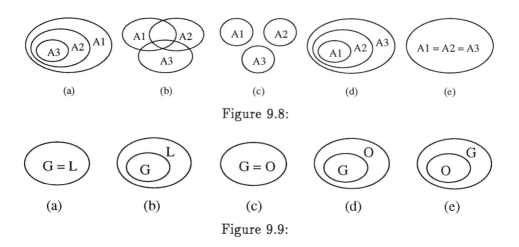

Figure 9.8:

Figure 9.9:

Exercise 9.9 Prove that the relative entropy in Eq. 9.31 cannot be negative.

Exercise 9.10 Show that, when there is no hidden unit, the Boltzmann machine converges to a solution with zero relative entropy. In other words, it converges to a set of weights such that the probability distribution of visible states is the same as the desired distribution. *Hint:* Use the convexity property of the relative entropy function [1].

Exercise 9.11 Suppose that the MFA technique is applied to an optimization problem. Let A1 denote the set of attractors when the diagonal terms of the synaptic weight matrix are set to 0. Let A2 and A3 denote the set of attractors when the diagonal values are $w_{ii}/2$ and w_{ii}, respectively. (Assume that $w_{ii} > 0$.) Under the most ideal situation, which (one or more) of the set relationships in Figure 9.8 is valid? Will the answer remain the same under practical situations? Justify your answer by either simulation or a plausible explanation.

Exercise 9.12 Let O denote the set of original patterns (plus their complementary patterns) to be memorized by a Boltzmann machine for associative memory, L the set of local minima, G the set of global minima, and A the set of attractors. Suppose all the original patterns are orthogonal. Under the best possible temperature schedule, which (one or more) of the set relationships in Figure 9.9 is generically valid?

PART VI: IMPLEMENTATION

Chapter 10

Architecture and Implementation

10.1   Introduction

Most neural models are extremely demanding in both computation and storage requirements. An enormous amount of computation has to be spent on training the networks. In the retrieving phase, extremely high throughputs are required for real-time recognition. The attractiveness of the digital approach to real-time processing hinges upon its massively parallel processing capability. In this regard, there are two fundamental issues:

- Parallelism of Neural Algorithms

  A thorough theoretical understanding of explicit and inherent parallelism in neural models can help design cost-effective real-time processing hardware. We have shown that most neural models, such as the back-propagation network, are very parallelizable. Some models are inherently suitable to parallel processing, for example, *hierarchical per-*

ceptron and *HMM*. Yet some other neural models, for example, the original Hopfield model, Boltzmann machine, and annealing techniques can become parallelizable after proper modification of the original models.

- Parallelism of Neural Architectures

  Most neural algorithms involve primarily those operations that are repetitive and regular. They can be efficiently mapped to parallel architectures. For these classes of algorithms, an attractive and cost-effective architectural choice is an array processor, which uses mostly local interconnection network. This paves the way for massively parallel processing, which represents the most viable future solution to real-time neural information processing. This point is further illuminated in this chapter.

The first focal point of our discussion is on systolic/wavefront designs that exploit the potential of parallel processing offered by VLSI/ULSI technologies. One very desirable architecture is based on pipelined processing on primarily locally interconnected processor elements. To achieve such a design, dependence-graph-based mapping methodology is the most effective tool for neural information-processing applications. This tool can accommodate several key neural models. In a broader sense, it is also suitable to other closely related applications including image recognition, signal classification, and digital filtering. Of course, array processors alone can hardly cover the architectural requirements for all neural processing systems. Other architectural innovations, such as hierarchical and distributed processing, also play important roles for system-level designs.

The second focal point of this chapter is digital implementation for neural nets. Implementation of information-processing can become much more practical and attractive when high-speed and cost-effective neural computing hardware is made available. Based on the applications intended, the digital neural implementations can be divided into two categories: (1) dedicated neural processor, for which the structure of a neural model is directly mapped onto hardware for optimal efficacy; and (2) ideal digital neurocomputer that provides an adaptive and flexible platform for neural network algorithms. The inherent neural algorithmic properties can be harnessed to reduce hardware burden. For both dedicated and general-purpose implementations, speed is naturally of primary concern. Other important hardware factors include learning and weight-updating capabilities, system size, linear/nonlinear functionality and control circuits, I/O data links and interfaces, memory size, word length, clock rate, and power consumption.

Dedicated Design In a dedicated design, the hardware architecture directly imitates the structure of neural networks. This means a very direct mapping from the structure of the model to that of the computing hardware. Unfortunately, all the connectionist neural models rely on extensive (and global) communication. (This is reflected by the name *connectionist models*.) Thus, a direct mapping of communication onto hard wires also implies very high communication costs. This is a very severe price to pay, because it would limit the size of realizable neural networks. The implementation depends very much on the application domain. In addition, dedicated neural processing circuits are also influenced by their implementation technology, such as *electronic processors* (including *analog CMOS*, *digital CMOS*, and *CCD*) and *optical processors*. Examples of dedicated electronic implementation are found in [5, 11, 48, 86, 100, 102, 106, 249, 261]. Examples of dedicated optical implementation are found in [65, 66, 167, 294].

Neurocomputers The development of general-purpose neurocomputers can be viewed as an application-driven approach to massively parallel supercomputers. The intent is to design supercomputing systems that will outperform the conventional supercomputers in intelligent system applications. General-purpose neurocomputers are mostly digital, as evidenced by many examples [10, 36, 115, 161, 163, 164, 275]. They often comprise a large number of processing elements enhanced with extensive and/or structured interconnectivity. From a system-design perspective, it is important to place major emphasis on the issues related to total system integration. A neurocomputer must be more general-purpose and embrace a broad set of connectionist networks, as exemplified by the unified formulation in Table 1.4.

Chapter Organization

This chapter demonstrates how to systematically design and implement (parallel processing) neural architectures that optimize performance for one or several neural models. Section 10.2 discusses systematic (and automatic) mapping of neural algorithms onto systolic/wavefront designs. Section 10.3 presents several dedicated neural networks implemented by a variety of hardware technologies (e.g., CMOS and CCD). Section 10.4 discusses the architectural and implementation requirements for general-purpose and system-oriented designs. Examples of major existing digital neurocomputers are surveyed.

10.2   Mapping Neural Nets to Array Architectures

By employing a mapping methodology, the original neural network can be converted into a practical computing structure. It is vital to develop a systematic design methodology that maps neural algorithms to cost-effective parallel processors. First, we observe that most neural processing algorithms are computationally iterative and intensive, and demand very high throughput. Multiprocessors, array processors, and massively parallel processors provide a natural solution. Furthermore, various connectionist models can be presented by a unified mathematical framework, as depicted in Table 1.4. Based on this, the neural algorithms can be expressed in basic matrix operations (such as inner-product, outer-product, and matrix multiplications), which, in turn, can be mapped to basic processor arrays.

This approach matches very well the design principle of a VLSI system, which exploits modular, pipelined, and parallel architectures, and reduces the communication hardware to mostly local interconnections. A typical example of VLSI parallel/pipelined architectures is pipelined arrays, for example, *systolic* or *wavefront* arrays. They have the following key advantages:

1. The exploitation of pipelining is very natural in regular and locally connected networks. They yield high throughput and simultaneously save the cost associated with *communication*.

2. They provide a good balance between computation and communication, which is critical to the effectiveness of array computing.

3. VLSI array architectures appear to be the most viable to support all the models listed in Table 1.4.

10.2.1   Mapping Design Methodology

In this section, we review a systematic mapping methodology for deriving systolic arrays. We stress that similar methods can be used to map algorithms onto wavefront architectures or other SIMD/MIMD architectures [152].

Deriving DGs from Given Algorithms Our design begins with a (data) dependence graph (DG) to express recurrence and parallelism. A DG is a directed graph that specifies the data dependencies of an algorithm. In a DG, *nodes* represent computations and *arcs* specify the data dependencies between computations. For regular and recursive algorithms, the DGs are also regular and can be represented by a grid model; therefore, the nodes can be specified by simple indices, such as (i, j, k). *Design of a locally linked DG is a critical step in the design of systolic arrays.*

Mapping DGs onto Array Structures This phase of mapping consists of two key tasks: *processor assignment* and *schedule assignment* [152].

- **Processor Assignment via Linear Projection**

  Mathematically, a linear projection is often represented by a *projection vector* $\vec{d}$. Because the DG of a locally recursive algorithm is very regular, the linear projection maps an n-dimensional DG onto an $(n-1)$-dimensional lattice of points, known as *processor space*. It is common to use a *linear projection* for processor assignment, in which nodes of the DG along a straight line are projected (assigned) to a PE in the processor array; see Figure 10.1(a).

- **Schedule Assignment via Linear Scheduling**

  A *scheduling* scheme specifies the sequence of the operations in *all* PEs. More precisely, a schedule function represents a mapping from the n-dimensional index space of the DG onto a 1-D schedule (time) space. *Linear scheduling* is very common for schedule assignment, cf. Figure 10.1(b). A linear schedule is based on a set of parallel and uniformly spaced hyperplanes in the DG. These hyperplanes are called *equitemporal hyperplanes* — all the nodes on the same hyperplane are scheduled to be processed at the same time. A linear schedule can also be represented by a *schedule vector* $\vec{s}$, which points in the direction normal to the hyperplanes. For any computation node indexed by a vector n in the DG, its scheduled processing time is $\vec{s}^T n$. A set of (linear schedule) hyperplanes and their associated schedule vector is illustrated in Figure 10.1(b).

Systolic Schedules Given a DG and a projection direction $\vec{d}$, not all schedule vectors $\{\vec{s}\}$ are valid for the DG. Some may violate the precedence rela-

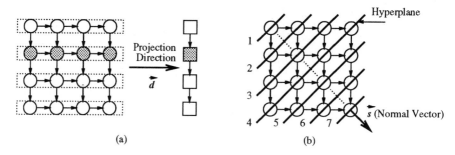

Figure 10.1: (a) A linear projection with projection vector $\vec{d}$. (b) A linear schedule $\vec{s}$ and its hyperplanes.

tions specified by the dependence arcs. For systolic design, the schedule vector $\vec{s}$ in the projection procedure must satisfy the following two conditions:

- *Causality Condition* Let the vector $\vec{e}$ represents any of the dependence arcs in the DG, then

$$\vec{s}^T \vec{e} > 0$$

  It means that every edge of the resulting systolic array will have one or more delay elements. This satisfies the *causality* condition required for a systolic array [152]. The condition must hold for *all* dependence arcs.

- *Positive Pipeline Period* In order to make sure the nodes on an equitemporal hyperplane are *not* projected to the same PE, we must have

$$\vec{s}^T \vec{d} \neq 0$$

  Without loss of generality, it can be replaced by a somewhat more restrictive condition:

$$\vec{s}^T \vec{d} > 0$$

  Without loss of generality, both vectors $\vec{s}$ and $\vec{d}$ can be assumed to be *irreducible*.[1] Then the pipeline period is equal to $\vec{s}^T \vec{d}$ [152].

The mapping methodology has been adopted to derive systolic/wavefront array architectures for various numerical, signal/image-processing, and neural net algorithms. In the following, we illustrate the methodology with a simple example.

---

[1] Vector $\vec{s} = [s_1 \ s_2 \ \cdots]^T$ is called *irreducible* if its elements are coprime (i.e., the greatest common divisor of all $\{ s_i \} = 1$).

Design Example: Matrix-Vector Multiplication The system dynamics of the retrieving phase of neural nets can all be formulated as a consecutive matrix-vector multiplication problem interleaved with the nonlinear activation function:

$$
\begin{aligned}
\mathbf{u}(k+1) &= \mathbf{W}(k)\mathbf{a}(k) + \theta(k) \\
\mathbf{a}(k+1) &= F[\mathbf{u}(k+1), \mathbf{u}(k), \mathbf{a}(k)]
\end{aligned}
\tag{10.1}
$$

where the $F[\cdot]$ operator performs the nonlinear activation function f. The vectors and matrices used are

$$
\mathbf{u} = [u_1, \ u_2, \ \cdots, \ u_N]^T
$$

$$
\mathbf{a} = [a_1, \ a_2, \ \cdots, \ a_N]^T
$$

$$
\theta = [\theta_1, \ \theta_2, \ \cdots, \ \theta_N]^T
$$

$$
\mathbf{W} = \begin{bmatrix}
w_{11} & w_{12} & \cdots & w_{1N} \\
w_{21} & w_{22} & \cdots & w_{2N} \\
\vdots & \vdots & \ddots & \vdots \\
w_{N1} & w_{N2} & \cdots & w_{NN}
\end{bmatrix}
$$

Let us consider the systolic array design for the matrix-vector multiplication problem, that is,

$$
\mathbf{u} = \mathbf{W}\,\mathbf{a}
$$

By viewing each dependence relation as an arc between the corresponding variables located in the index space, the DG shown in Figure 10.2(a) can be obtained. In this DG, the operation at each node is specified in Figure 10.2(b). If we select the projection vector as $\vec{d} = [1\ 0]$ and the schedule vector as $\vec{s} = [1\ 1]$, we can obtain a linear systolic array. In this design, all inputs $\{a_i\}$ are residing in each PE and outputs $\{u_i\}$ are pumped out sequentially from the boundary PEs; see Figure 10.2(c). On the other hand, if we select the projection vector to be $\vec{d} = [0\ 1]$ and the schedule vector to be $\vec{s} = [1\ 1]$, we can get another linear systolic design. In this array, inputs $\{a_i\}$ are fed one by one into the array and outputs $\{u_i\}$ have to be fetched from each PE; see Figure 10.2(d).

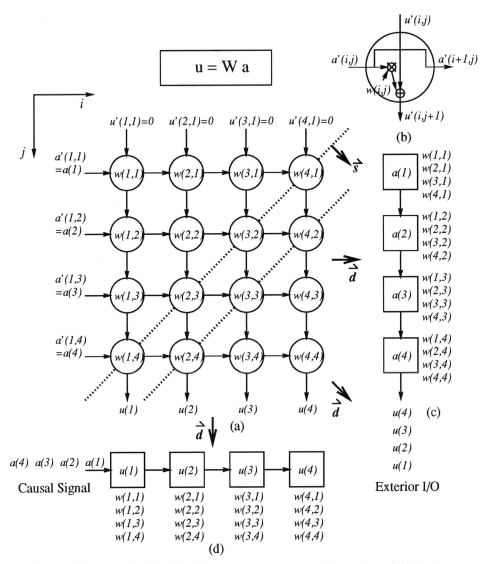

Figure 10.2: (a) Localized DG for matrix-vector multiplication. (b) The functional operation at each node of the DG. (c) A systolic array obtained by selecting $\vec{\mathbf{d}} = [1\ 0]$ and $\vec{\mathbf{s}} = [1\ 1]$. (d) A systolic array obtained by selecting $\vec{\mathbf{d}} = [0\ 1]$ and $\vec{\mathbf{s}} = [1\ 1]$.

Design Parameters in Array Processors There are many design criteria for systolic arrays; some of them are explained in what follows:

- *Computation Time:* This is the time interval between starting the first computation and finishing the last computation of a problem. Given a coprime schedule vector $\vec{s}$, the computation time of a systolic array can be computed as

$$T = \max_{\vec{p},\vec{q} \in L} \{\vec{s}^T (\vec{p} - \vec{q})\} + 1$$

  where L is the index set of the nodes in the DG.

- *Pipelining Period:* This is the time interval between two successive computations in a processor. As previously discussed, If both $\vec{s}$ and $\vec{d}$ are *irreducible*, then the pipelining period $\alpha = \vec{s}^T \vec{d}$.

- *Block Period:* This is the time interval between the initiation of two successive blocks.

- *Processor Utilization Rate:* Define the speed-up factor as the ratio between the sequential computation time and the array computation time, then the utilization rate is the ratio between the speed-up factor and the number of processors.

- *Array Processor Size:* The array size cannot be unlimited. Sometimes, the size of the array is much smaller than the full problem size. In another situation, a one-dimensional array is used in place of an idealistic two-dimensional array. This incurs the so-called *partitioning* problem.

- *Local Memory:* Local memory can be used to expand the physical array to a much larger virtual array size.

10.2.2 Design for Multilayer Networks: Retrieving Phase

We now concentrate our discussion on the most popular neural model, that is, a two-layer back propagation (BP) network. A two-layer network is labeled an N-K-L network, if there are N nodes in the input layer, K nodes in the hidden layer, and L nodes in the output layer.

From Eq. 5.10 and Eq. 5.11, the dynamic equations for a two-layer network are

$$\underline{u}_i = \sum_{j=1}^{N} \underline{w}_{ij} x_j + \underline{\theta}_i$$

$$a_i = f(\underline{u}_i) \quad 1 \le i \le K$$

$$\overline{u}_i = \sum_{j=1}^{K} \overline{w}_{ij} a_j + \overline{\theta}_i$$

$$y_i = f(\overline{u}_i) \quad 1 \le i \le L \tag{10.2}$$

The dynamics of the retrieving phase can be rewritten in matrix form:

$$\underline{u} = \underline{W}x + \underline{\theta}$$

$$a = F[\underline{u}]$$

$$\overline{u} = \overline{W}a + \overline{\theta}$$

$$y = F[\overline{u}]$$

$$\tag{10.3}$$

where $\underline{W}$ and $\overline{W}$ represent the lower weight matrix and the upper weight matrix, respectively, and the operator $F[\cdot]$ performs the nonlinear activation function f on each of the elements of the vector.

10.2.2.1   Linear Systolic Arrays for Retrieving One Pattern

First, let us discuss the simple situation where only a single pattern needs to be retrieved. The retrieving phase of a two-layer network can be implemented in terms of two consecutive matrix-vector multiplications, interleaved with two strips of nonlinear processing units. The rectangular dependence graph (DG) for the matrix-vector multiplication (MVM) is depicted in Figure 10.3(a). If we choose the projection vector as $\vec{d} = [\,1\ 0\,]^T$ and the schedule vector as $\vec{s} = [\,1\ 1\,]^T$, then the resulting linear systolic array is as shown in Figure 10.3(b).

Data Movements in Linear Systolic Design

- **The lower-layer net**

    1. The data $x_j^{(m)}$ are input sequentially into the first PE in the original natural order. They are subsequently propagated downward to all other PEs.

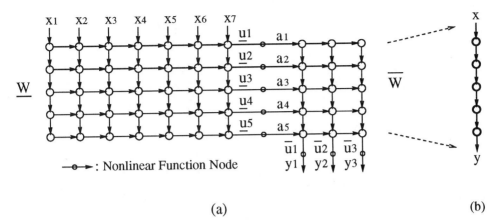

(a)   (b)

Figure 10.3: Retrieving phase design for retrieving a single pattern: (a) Rectangular DGs for MVM, and (b) mapping onto a linear systolic array.

2. The data $\{\underline{w}_{ij}^{(m)}\}$ are stored (row by row) in the PEs.

3. When the value $x_j^{(m)}$ arrives at the i-th PE (from the top), it is multiplied with the stored data $\{\underline{w}_{ij}^{(m)}\}$ to yield a partial sum to be accumulated in the same PE.

4. After N active clocks, the final partial sum $\underline{u}_i^{(m)}$ is generated in each PE. Immediately after this, $a_i^{(m)}$ is computed by applying nonlinear processing f to $\underline{u}_i^{(m)}$.

5. The PE changes mode (by the control unit) to be ready for the next (upper-layer) phase.

• **The upper-layer net**

1. The data $a_i^{(m)}$ stays in the i-th PE and need not be propagated to other PEs. The data $\{\overline{w}_{ki}^{(m)}\}$ are stored (column by column) in the PEs.

2. Multiply values $a_i^{(m)}$ and $\{\overline{w}_{ki}^{(m)}\}$, and add the product to the partial sum received from the upper PE. The new partial sum is then propagated to the lower PE.

3. As soon as a final partial sum $\overline{u}_k^{(m)}$ is computed at the last PE, the activation value $y_k^{(m)}$ can be produced (by a nonlinear processing unit).

Processor Element Design Requirements One design example for an interior PE is shown in Figure 10.4. It takes $N + L$ time units to complete one pattern retrieval, with the time unit defined as the time needed to execute one multiply-and-add and one nonlinear function $f(\cdot)$. (See Problem 10.3.) The processor elements comprise the following key components:

- *Memory:* Each PE should store a row of the lower-layer weight matrix and a column of the upper-layer weight matrix. For example, the synaptic weights $[\underline{w}_{i1}, \ \underline{w}_{i2}, \ \ldots, \underline{w}_{i7}]$ and $[\overline{w}_{1i}, \ \overline{w}_{2i}, \overline{w}_{3i}]$ stored in the RAM in the i-th PE.

- *Communication:* Data are transmitted in one direction between two neighboring PEs.

- *Arithmetic Processing:* Each PE should support all the arithmetic processing capabilities including the MAC (multiply-and-accumulate) operation and the nonlinear function. For the retrieving phase, the nonlinear function f($\cdot$) is needed. (In the learning phase, function f'($\cdot$) is also required, as discussed in Section 10.2.3.) It can be implemented in one of two forms:

  1. By an arithmetic processing approach — suitable only for very special activation functions. A dedicated arithmetic unit usually gives better precision, but it incurs more hardware cost.

  2. By a lookup table approach — suitable for a broader class of nonlinear activation functions. Although more memory space is needed to store the lookup table, it still can be attractive because it obviates complex arithmetic hardware and delivers a reasonable computation time.

10.2.2.2 Rectangular Systolic Arrays for Retrieving Multiple Patterns

For the situation when there are multiple patterns to be retrieved, a cubic DG for matrix-matrix multiplication (MMM) is required, as shown in Figure 10.5, where the third dimension is introduced due to the multiplicity of the retrieving patterns. Now the projection vector is chosen as $\vec{d} = [\ 0\ 0\ 1\ ]^T$ and the schedule vector as $\vec{s} = [\ 1\ 1\ 1\ ]^T$. The resulting two-dimensional systolic array is shown in Figure 10.5(b).

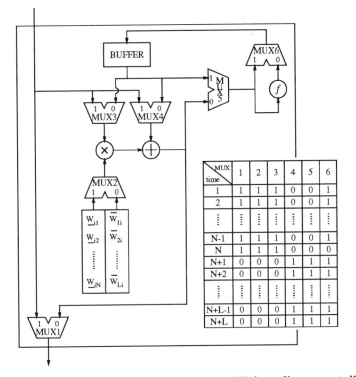

The table in the figure:

MUX time	1	2	3	4	5	6
1	1	1	1	0	0	1
2	1	1	1	0	0	1
⋮	⋮	⋮	⋮	⋮	⋮	⋮
N-1	1	1	1	0	0	1
N	1	1	1	0	0	0
N+1	0	0	0	1	1	1
N+2	0	0	0	1	1	1
⋮	⋮	⋮	⋮	⋮	⋮	⋮
N+L-1	0	0	0	1	1	1
N+L	0	0	0	1	1	1

Figure 10.4: A design sketch of the interior PE in a linear systolic array: retrieving phase.

The data movement in the rectangular systolic array should be quite obvious. The data $x_j^{(m)}$ are input from the top of the array in a time-skewed order. They are propagated downward to the other PEs along the same column.

Processor Element Design Requirements   The design requirements for each processor element are as follows:

- *Memory:* There is one synaptic weight in each PE.

- *Communication:* Each PE requires four channels to communicate with its four neighbors.

- *Arithmetic Processing:* The interior PEs execute MAC operations only. In contrast, the boundary PEs must also support nonlinear operations.

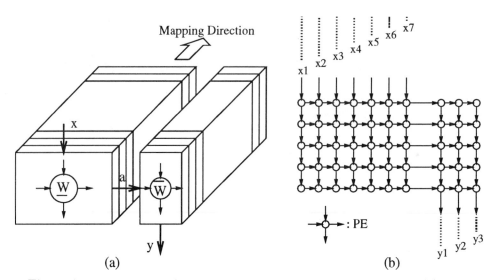

Figure 10.5: Retrieving phase design for retrieving multiple patterns: (a) cubic DGs for MMM and (b) mapping onto a two-dimensional systolic array.

10.2.3 Design for Multilayer Networks: Training Phase

First, the BP learning rule of a two-layer network is briefly reviewed:

Upper Layer Upon the arrival of the m-th training pattern, the updating formula for the upper weight matrix is

$$
\Delta \overline{w}_{ij}^{(m)} = -\eta \, \frac{\partial E}{\partial \overline{w}_{ij}^{(m)}}
$$
$$
= \eta \, \overline{\delta}_i^{(m)} \, f'(\overline{u}_i^{(m)}) \, a_j^{(m)} \tag{10.4}
$$

where $E = \sum_i (t_i^{(m)} - y_i^{(m)})^2$ is the energy function, and $\delta_i^{(m)}$ is the error signal that can be computed by the BP technique.

For the recursion, the initial value (of the upper layer), $\overline{\delta}_i^{(m)}$, can be easily obtained as follows:

$$
\overline{\delta}_i^{(m)} \equiv -\frac{\partial E}{\partial y_i^{(m)}}
$$
$$
= t_i^{(m)} - y_i^{(m)}
$$

Lower Layer The updating formula for the lower weight matrix is

$$
\Delta \underline{w}_{ij}^{(m)} = -\eta \, \frac{\partial E}{\partial \underline{w}_{ij}^{(m)}}
$$

$$= \eta \, \underline{\delta}_i^{(m)} \, f'(\underline{u}_i^{(m)}) \, x_j^{(m)} \tag{10.5}$$

where the error signal $\underline{\delta}_i^{(m)}$ can be derived as follows:

$$\underline{\delta}_i^{(m)} \equiv -\frac{\partial E}{\partial a_i^{(m)}}$$

$$= -\sum_j \frac{\partial E}{\partial \overline{u}_j^{(m)}} \frac{\partial \overline{u}_j^{(m)}}{\partial a_i^{(m)}}$$

$$= \sum_j \overline{\delta}_j^{(m)} \, f'(\overline{u}_j^{(m)}) \, \overline{w}_{ji}^{(m)}$$

Three basic components in the learning phase are: (1) MVM, (2) VMM, and (3) OPU.

1. **MVM (Retrieving Computation in the Forward Step)**

   This is the same as the retrieving phase described in Eq. 10.3. At the very beginning of the learning phase, the retrieving operations have to be executed to obtain the output response of the input training pattern. *The systolic design for the forward step is the same as the retrieving phase in Section 10.2.2.*

2. **VMM (Back-Propagation Step)**

   Denote vectors **g** and **h** as error-signal vectors derived by the back-propagation rule described in what follows. Vector **g** has elements

   $$g_i \equiv f'(\overline{u}_i)\overline{\delta}_i$$
   $$= f'(f^{-1}(y_i))(t_i - y_i) \tag{10.6}$$

   The vector **h** is the error signal derived by the BP rule:

   $$h_j \equiv f'(\underline{u}_j)\underline{\delta}_j$$
   $$= f'(f^{-1}(a_j))\underline{\delta}_j \tag{10.7}$$

   where

   $$\underline{\delta}_j = \sum_i \overline{w}_{ij} g_i$$

Stages	Input	Output
MVM	x, W	a
VMM	$-$	$-$
OPU	$h, x, \underline{W}$	$\underline{W}_{new}$

(a)

Stages	Input	Output
MVM	$a, \overline{W}$	y
VMM	$t, y, a, \overline{W}$	g, h
OPU	g, a, W	$\overline{W}_{new}$

(b)

Table 10.1: The operands and the results in the three stages of the learning phase for the (a) lower layer and (b) upper layer.

which can be expressed by vector-matrix multiplication:

$$\underline{\delta} = \overline{\mathbf{W}}^T \mathbf{g}$$

3. **OPU (Updating Step)**

The actual updating procedure uses an outer-product formulation:

$$\Delta \overline{\mathbf{W}} = \eta \mathbf{g} \mathbf{a}^T$$

$$\Delta \underline{\mathbf{W}} = \eta \mathbf{h} \mathbf{x}^T$$

10.2.3.1   Dependence Graph for the Back-Propagation Algorithm

To facilitate our illustration of the design of the dependence graph, Table 10.1 lists the detailed input operands and output results of each of the three stages of operations for the lower-layer and upper-layer networks. In addition to the DG for MVM (which was shown in Figure 10.3), the DGs for VMM and OPU are shown in Figures 10.6(a) and 10.6(b).

We use the following strategies to facilitate a pipelined design:

- First, the dependency arcs are designed to flow in the same direction shown in Figure 10.3(a) and Figure 10.6. If the dependency arcs had a reverse direction, the pipelining would be hampered.

- According to Table 10.1, we note that $\mathbf{g}$ is used as an operand for both the VMM and OPU steps for the upper layer. Also, for the computation of h_j, we use a_j to derive $f'(\underline{u}_j)$. So, to simplify the subsequent

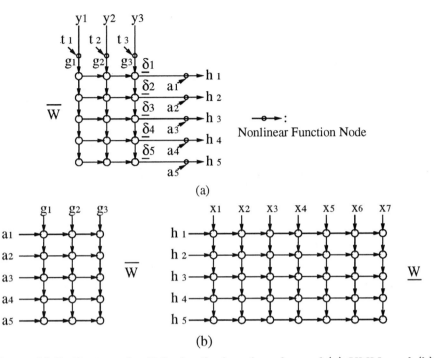

Figure 10.6: Rectangular DGs for the learning phase of (a) VMM, and (b) OPU.

mapping, we adopted an **interleaved DG** design for the VMM/OPU DG here. The interleaved VMM/OPU DG is shown in Figure 10.7.

- Also, a NOP block is artificially inserted in Figure 10.8. Its purpose is to delay the internal data stream long enough to be properly synchronized with the data stream routed from the torus connections.

10.2.3.2   Linear Array Design for Data-Adaptive BP Method

Let us use the 7-5-3 network as an example. We use $\vec{d} = [1\ 0]$ and $\vec{s} = [1\ 1]$. The DG and corresponding systolic array design are illustrated in Figure 10.8 and Figure 10.9, respectively.

Data Movements in Linear Systolic Design

- **Forward Step (MVM)**

    The forward MVM step in the learning phase follows the same data movements as the retrieving operations described in Section 10.2.2.

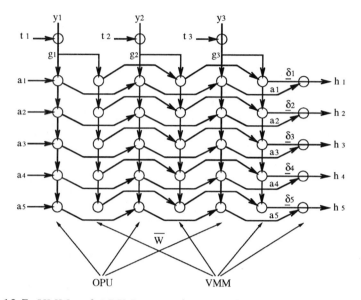

Figure 10.7: VMM and OPU DGs can be merged into one DG by interleaving.

However, it is now necessary to store the input values $x_j^{(m)}$ in the first PE so that they can be reused in a later (OPU) step.

- **Backward Step for the Upper-Layer Net (VMM and OPU)**

In the backward step, both the BP algorithm (VMM) and the training (OPU) are executed.

1. Value $y_k^{(m)}$ is routed by the feedback link to a special processor above the first PE. At the special processor, the value $(t_k^{(m)} - y_k^{(m)})$ and then $g_k^{(m)}$ are produced.

2. After error value $g_k^{(m)}$ is produced, it is propagated downward to all the other PEs.

3. Data $\{\overline{w}_{ki}^{(m)}\}$ and $a_i^{(m)}$ are stored in the i-th PE.

4. When value $g_k^{(m)}$ arrives at the i-th PE (from the top):

    - It is multiplied with the stored data $\{\overline{w}_{ki}^{(m)}\}$, and the product is added to the partial sum being accumulated in the same PE. (After L active clocks, all the final partial sums $\underline{\delta}_i^{(m)}$ are generated.)

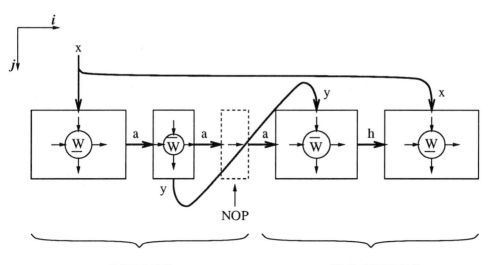

MVM DG VMM/OPU DG

Figure 10.8: Cascaded rectangular DG for MVM/VMM/OPU. To facilitate a pipelined design, the flow directions of the DGs are kept in the same direction. The natural choice of the projection vector is $\vec{\mathbf{d}} = [1\ 0]^T$. The most preferred schedule vector is $\vec{\mathbf{s}} = [1\ 1]^T$. If $K > L$, the output of $\mathbf{a}$ will arrive earlier than the output of $\mathbf{y}$. To make the schedule feasible, a NOP DG is inserted between the MVM DG and the VMM/OPU DG for the upper layer. Its purpose is to introduce enough delay such that the schedule vector $\vec{\mathbf{s}} = [1\ 1]^T$ becomes permissible.

- It is also multiplied by value $a_i^{(m)}$ to yield $\triangle \overline{w}_{ki}^{(m)}$, which is then used to update the new $\overline{w}_{ki}^{(m+1)}$ at the i-th PE.

5. The back-propagated error functions $h_i^{(m)}$ can be derived from $\underline{\delta}_i^{(m)}$ and $a_i^{(m)}$ based on Eq. 10.7.

- **Training Step for the Lower-Layer Weights (OPU)**

1. Recall that value $x_j^{(m)}$ was stored in the first PE during the forward MVM step; now it can be propagated again downward to all the other PEs.

2. When the $x_j^{(m)}$ arrives at the i-th PE, it is multiplied with the value $h_i^{(m)}$ to yield $\triangle \underline{w}_{ij}^{(m)}$, which is in turn used to update the new $\underline{w}_{ij}^{(m+1)}$ in the i-th PE.

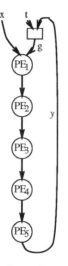

Figure 10.9: The systolic array design of a 7-5-3 two-layer BP network. There is a FIFO hidden in the first PE, which is needed to recycle the x data for processing.

Processor Element Design Requirements   The processor elements comprise basically the same components as are required for the retrieving phase. The PEs should be programmable due to the varying functionalities involved. Some other differences are discussed in what follows:

- *Memory:* This is the same as the retrieving phase. Each PE should store a row of the lower-layer weights and a column of the upper-layer weights. In addition, in the first PE, an extra FIFO is required to recycle the x data for processing. (See Problem 10.8.)

- *Communication:* This is the same as the retrieving phase. Data are transmitted uni-directionally between two neighboring PEs, and a circular link between the first PE and the last PE is added to facilitate pipelining.

- *Arithmetic Processing:* Arithmetic processing includes MAC operations and nonlinear processing operations. However, for the training phase, there are two nonlinear functions involved: $f(\cdot)$ and $f'(\cdot)$.

Performance   The architectural choice hinges upon several key performance measures, including cost effectiveness of the number of processors, utilization rate, and speed-up factor. We use a 7-5-3 network example to illustrate this point. For simplicity, the time calculated in what follows does not include the time delay incurred for nonlinearity processing (i.e., $f(\cdot)$ and $f'(\cdot)$) and multiplication time incurred in Eq. 10.6 and Eq. 10.7. (In a more precise estimate, these computations would each consume some time unit(s).)

According to the DG displayed in Figure 10.6, for each training pattern, the total sequential time = $N \times K + K \times L + 2 \times K \times L + N \times K = 7 \times 5 + 5 \times 3 + 2 \times 5 \times 3 + 7 \times 5 = 115$. The latency in Figure 10.8 can now be computed: latency = $N + \max(K,L) + 2 \times L + N + K - 1 = 7 + 5 + 6 + 7 + 5 - 1 = 29$. Here $\max(K,L)$ is used because the NOP block is necessary only when $K > L$.

In practice, the number of training patterns M is very large. This means that M copies of the DG trio will have to be repeated. Therefore, the through-put rate depends on the average time per pattern (ATPP). The ATPP can be regarded as the pipelining period for each pattern. Figure 10.8 shows that the next pattern training can start before the previous one is finished. Actually, when data $x_N^{(m)}$ leaves the first PE, the PE can be immediately available for processing the next training pattern $x_1^{(m+1)}$. (Because of this, latency is not really critical to speed performance.)

The ATPP can be computed as ATPP = $N + \max(K,L) + 2 \times L + N = 7 + 5 + 6 + 7 = 25$. Therefore, for this linear array, the

$$\text{Speed-up factor} \quad = \quad \frac{2NK + 3KL}{2N + K + 2L} = \frac{115}{25} = 4.6 \qquad (10.8)$$

$$\text{Utilization rate} \quad = \quad \frac{2NK + 3KL}{(2N + K + 2L)K} = \frac{4.6}{5} = 92\%$$

Note that if K= L in the N-K-L two-layer network, then the utilization rate becomes 100%. In general, this design provides very favorable utilization rates while achieving a respectable speed-up factor. However, this estimate is somewhat too optimistic because it is assumed that all the nodes in the DG have the same computation time. In fact, those nodes have different functions and computation times. The block period is determined by the critical path, that is, the path that has the longest computation time in DG. Note that there are a total of 241 floating-point operations in the DG in Figure 10.8. It can also be verified that the number of floating-point operations on the critical path is 57. (See Problem 10.13). The new speed-up factor is now modified as

$$\text{Speed-up factor} \quad = \quad \frac{\text{total number of FPs in the DG}}{\text{number of FPs at the critical path}} \quad (10.9)$$

$$= \quad \frac{241}{57} = 4.23 \quad (10.10)$$

10.2.3.3   Rectangular Array Design for Block-Adaptive BP Method

In order to more effectively design rectangular systolic arrays, we resort to the block-adaptive method, as opposed to the data-adaptive method discussed previously. Based on Eq. 5.26, the block gradient method for a two-layer network is

$$\Delta \underline{\mathbf{w}} \quad = \quad \sum_{m=1}^{M} \Delta \underline{w}^{(m)}$$

$$\Delta \overline{\mathbf{w}} \quad = \quad \sum_{m=1}^{M} \Delta \overline{w}^{(m)} \quad (10.11)$$

In the block-adaptive method, there is no updating for each training pattern; instead, $\Delta \mathbf{w}$ is accumulated through the entire sweep of training patterns. Only at the end of the sweep are the weights updated by $\Delta \mathbf{w}$.

Three-Dimensional Dependence Graph   In Figure 10.10, a 3-D DG is used to display the block-adaptive computation. The DG is just a replica of those in Figure 10.8, with the depth of the third dimension being M, the number of training patterns. However, it is important to note that the OPU cubic DG is used to compute the values of $\Delta w^{(m)}$, which are accumulated over time to obtain Δw.

The main feature distinguishing the block-adaptive method from the data-adaptive one is that the actual updating of the weights is deferred to the end of each block. This implies that there is no need to wait for the OPU DG of the previous pattern to finish before the MVM operations for the new pattern are started. This feature can be exploited to obtain a much greater degree of parallel/pipelined processing.

The interleaved VMM/OPU DG for the block-adaptive method is shown in Figure 10.7. The design in the figure allows VMM and OPU to be executed simultaneously, while the communication load remains the same. The pipelining of the rectangular array is now fairly straightforward, because the cubic DGs are largely homogeneous.

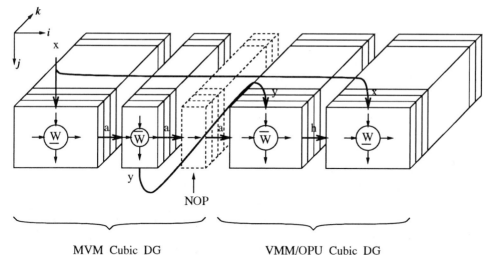

MVM Cubic DG   VMM/OPU Cubic DG

Figure 10.10: A cascaded three-dimensional DG for the block-adaptive BP algorithm. Note that this DG is obtained by repeating the DGs shown in Figure 10.8.

Design of Rectangular Array Structures We use $\vec{d} = [0\ 0\ 1]$ to project the DG in the k direction on a rectangular array. It is easy to verify that schedule vector $\vec{s} = [1\ 1\ 1]$ yields a permissible systolic array design. If the projection direction $\vec{d} = [0\ 0\ 1]$ is used, we will obtain an array processor with four rectangular blocks. The PEs in the upper-layer rectangular array for VMM and OPU operations can perform the VMM and OPU operations concurrently. This is a favorable design because it has maximum parallel processing capability.

Processor Element Design Requirements The design requirements are same as those for the retrieving phase of the rectangular array

Data Movements in Rectangular Systolic Arrays Data $x_j^{(m)}$ are input from the top of the array in skewed order, cf. Figure 10.11. They are propagated downward to the other PEs along the same column. The rest of the actions basically follow what is depicted in the DGs in Figure 10.10. We note that, due to the presence of the NOP block in Figure 10.10, some storage is required to store the intermediate data $a_i^{(m)}$. Only a very brief description is really required, because each subarray has its own functionality and there is no need to change the mode of operations (unlike what is in the linear array

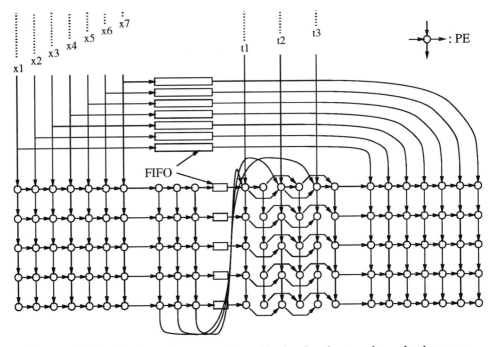

Figure 10.11: Rectangular arrays for a block-adaptive two-layer back propagation ANN.

design.) In fact, the DG itself provides a very direct and clear description of data movements.

Performance   Again, we use an example with a 7-5-3 network and M = 100 patterns. According to the cubic DG in Figure 10.10, the sequential time for the entire block is T_{seq} = (N×K + K×L + 2×K×L + N×K) ×M = (7×5 + 5×3 + 2×5×3 + 7×5)×100 = 11,500. The throughput rate depends on the average time per block (ATPB), which can be computed as ATPB = N + max(K,L) + L + M = 7 + 5 + 3 + 100 = 115. It follows that the speed-up factor = T_{seq} /ATPB.

Note that the number of processors = N×K + K×L + 2×K×L + N×K = 7×5 + 5×3 + 2×5×3 + 7×5 = 115. Therefore, the computed performance is then

$$\text{Speed-up factor} \quad = \quad \frac{(2NK + 3KL)M}{N + K + L + M}$$

$$= \frac{11500}{115} = 100 \qquad (10.12)$$

$$\text{Utilization rate} = \frac{(2NK + 3KL)M}{(N + K + L + M)(2NK + 3KL)}$$

$$= \frac{M}{N + K + L + M} = \frac{100}{115} = 87\%$$

In order to get a more realistic estimate of the speed-up factor, Eq. 10.9 is adopted again. In this case, there are a total of 24,100 operations in the cubic DG, and the number of operations on the critical path is 419 per sweep. (See Problem 10.13.) The modified speed-up factor becomes

$$\text{Speed-up factor} = \frac{24100}{419} = 57.52 \qquad (10.13)$$

Compared with the linear array design, we note that the rectangular array has a clear advantage in the speed-up factor, and the linear design has a higher utilization rate. More precisely, with a ratio of $57.52/4.23$, the speed-up factor can be increased by more than 13 times. The utilization rate of 50% ($57.52/115$) is considered reasonable for massively parallel processing. In fact, the utilization rate can be further improved if the block period can be shortened. This can be accomplished by adding some extra processors to share the floating-point operations on the critical path. This effectively reduces the length of the critical path. It can be shown that if 8 more processors are used on the critical path, the utilization rate can increase to 88.6%. (See Problem 10.14.)

There are still some practical concerns. One concern is that the rectangular array design is good only for the block-adaptive scheme. (The linear array design is good for both data-adaptive and block-adaptive schemes.) Another practical constraint is that the number of processors in a rectangular array for a large-size neural net is often too excessive to be affordable.

When the hardware cost for constructing two-dimensional arrays becomes too high, as is very often the case, one has to opt for a design with less parallelism. One approach is to partition large problems into a manageable size. To do so, extra memory space is required to store weights and intermediate results. Also, it is important to provide hardware and/or software support for an efficient partitioning scheme. Another approach is to revert to a less demanding one-dimensional architecture (e.g., linear or ring arrays) [113, 165].

10.2.4   System Design and Simulation

Generally speaking, in an array system design, one seeks to maximize the following performance indicators: effective array configuration, programmability for different networks, flexibility of problem partitioning, fault tolerance to improve system reliability, word-length effect in fixed/floating-point arithmetic, and efficient memory utilization [152]. Here we focus on partitioning and reconfigurability. In addition, we address the issues of software environment and high-level simulation, which are essential for overall system design considerations.

10.2.4.1   Partitioning and Reconfigurability

Partitioning   The *partitioning* problem is mapping a large size network onto a smaller size processor array. It involves a divide-and-conquer procedure: First, a large problem is partitioned into subproblems to be executed by the smaller array. Afterwards, the partial solutions are integrated together for a total system solution. This can be done by assigning the tasks of several neurons to share the same PE without incurring a major change on the computation/communication strategy and parallel/pipeline processing efficiency. The important issue is to provide hardware and/or software support to facilitate an efficient partitioning scheme.

An example is provided to illustrate the partitioning scheme for a large network. It can be shown that a linear array with 5 PEs can be used to implement the retrieving/learning phase of a 14-10-6 network. (In Figure 10.12, the design for the retrieving phase is shown.) By assigning the tasks of an equal number of neurons from the same layer to one PE, the computational load of each layer can be more uniformly distributed to the PEs even though the number of units on different layers is distinct. If the number of units is not a multiple of the number of PEs (5 for this case), it is always possible to pad some NOP (no-operation) units to help match the size. (For another example, cf. [113].)

Reconfigurability and Fault Tolerance   It is often desirable for the digital implementation to be reconfigurable. Occasionally, it is necessary to switch back and forth between the learning and retrieving phases, possibly on-line. A general-purpose neurocomputer should support a good variety of neural models, already making reconfigurability fairly desirable. An array processor is usually very large scale, and it is highly likely that transient or

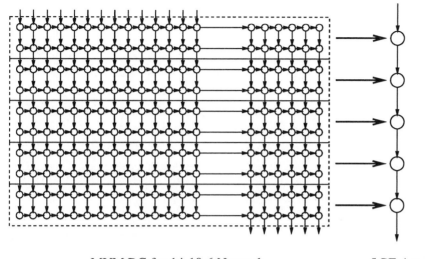

MVM DG for 14-10-6 Network   5-PE Array

Figure 10.12: The linear array architecture with 5 PEs can be used to implement the consecutive MVM in the retrieving phase of a 14-10-6 network.

permanent failure of one or more PEs will occur. For example, a fault at any node of a linear (or ring) array architecture results in discontinuity of the originally smooth data flow. In this case, array reconfigurability can be exploited to enhance system reliability. Redundant paths and spare PEs can be useful in providing some degree of fault tolerance [310]. Algorithm-based fault-tolerance (ABFT) techniques [121] use minimum hardware overhead and incur no penalty on throughput. These are good techniques for transient or permanent fault detection for special-purpose architectures.

An example of a fault-tolerant ring systolic array design is shown in Figure 10.13. In the presence of a permanent fault detected at the i-th PE, a simple reconfiguration scheme can be adopted by using extra multiplexers (MUXs), so that the faulty PE_i is bypassed and the memory M_i is connected to PE_{i+1}. All the necessary connections are shown by dashed lines in Figure 10.13. This scheme is similar to that of [310].

10.2.4.2   Software Environment

A good software environment is critical for a programmable neurocomputer. In a user-friendly environment, the user should be allowed to concentrate on the problem at hand instead of worrying about managing the hardware

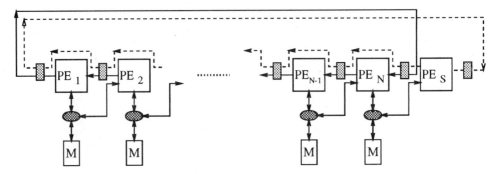

Figure 10.13: Fault tolerance in a ring array. Note that the dashed lines correspond to redundant paths.

resources of a parallel system. Some operating-system support is therefore necessary (e.g., languages, memory management, and communications).

With a microprogrammable PE, a user has the option of defining custom microcodes implementing specific algorithms, provided they can be expressed in terms of inner and outer products. Moreover, microprogramming is very tedious and not appealing for real-time applications. To make the system a friendly tool for neural network research, a software environment is desirable.

With the support of such an environment, the user is able to specify an algorithm as a sequence of predefined operations in a high-level language and execute it without having to know details of underlying hardware. Consequently, the programming effort can be significantly simplified. Such a software environment would consist of the following:

1. *Graphical User Interface:* Facilitates the display of input and output values and network performance.

2. *High-Level Language:* Supports programming systolic/wavefront algorithms by using, for example, matrices and vectors as principal data types.

3. *Algorithm Mapper:* Maps the cascade of basic operations into a virtual systolic array. This tool is possible for the class of basic matrix arithmetic operations. A library of basic matrix-type operations is desired to facilitate rapid prototyping of algorithms.

4. *Array Partitioning Software:* Partitions a large virtual array into a smaller-size physical array To facilitate effective partitioning, more memory space is needed to store extra weights and intermediate results.

5. *High-Level Simulator:* Facilitates system-level design, simulation, and verification.

10.2.4.3 High-Level Simulation Tool

Prior to any implementation attempt, it is advisable that a more accurate estimate of the performance be known. In this regard, simulation tools are indispensable. Also, the mapping methodology only treats idealistic situations. In real-world design, many basic system design constraints, for example, limitations on array size, must be taken into account.

High-Level Timing Simulations by *SISim* Note that the speed-up factors given in Eq. 10.8 and Eq. 10.12 are under idealistic and unrealistic assumptions. Therefore, a more precise simulation tool is required in order to obtain an estimate closer to the real world. In order to get accurate information about the behavior of a system, both the hardware and the software must be specified precisely. This is supported by a simulation tool, *SISim*. The *SISim* simulator is a system-level interactive simulator developed at Princeton [51]. The key application of *SISim* is to accurately estimate the computation time and predict the performance of several variants of an array architecture.

An overview of *SISim* is provided in Figure 10.14. There are two input file modules for *SISim* processing: the hardware description module and software description module. Figure 10.15 illustrates a description of a matrix-vector multiplication on a 5-processor array. The *SISim* itself consists of three components (cf. Figure 10.14): *PARSER*, *DRIVER*, and *ISIM*. The *PARSER* reads the hardware and software description modules and creates an internal data structure that is used as the base of the next (*DRIVER*) simulation stage. The *DRIVER*, based on a time-table, is used to simulate the behavior of the target system. When *SISim* is used in an interactive mode, *ISIM* is also invoked, which works together with *PARSER* and *DRIVER*. *ISIM* allows the user to check the status of any system component at any time during the simulation period. The final statistics concerning the real execution time for each processor are stored in the "rst" file.

Simulations on BP Networks *SISim* can be applied to the BP network to determine more realistic speed-up factors for the linear array or the rectangular array implementations. It also provides a more exact analysis of how the different parameters (e.g., computation time, communication time, buffer size, and memory fetch) affect the overall performance of the array processors.

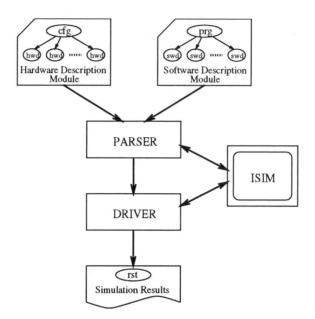

Figure 10.14: An overview of *SISim*

We discuss a simulation example based on a 7-5-3 BP network implemented on (1) a single processor, (2) a linear array processor (Figure 10.9),
and (3) a rectangular array processor (Figure 10.11). For each of the three
implementations, simulations are performed on the entire sweep of 100 training patterns. For the completeness of simulation, the key parameters are
systematically adjusted in order to test their effects on performance.

The simulation results are briefly summarized in what follows. Figure
10.16(a) shows the speed-up factor of linear array processor implementation
with respect to single processor implementation. The coordinates of the base
grid are the communication time and memory-access time. The computation
time is fixed in each of the figures. (The simulations on the rectangular array
processor indicate a similar trend.)

Note that with fixed computation time, the speed-up factor changes about
linearly with respect to communication and memory-access time parameters.
Therefore, the surface in Figure 10.16(a) can be approximated by a plane
expressed by

$$\text{Speed-up factor} = a + b \times t_{comm} + c \times t_{mem} \qquad (10.14)$$

where values a, b, and c are functions of t_{comp}. They can be derived by a
least-squares-error method based on the four corner points in Figure 10.16(a).

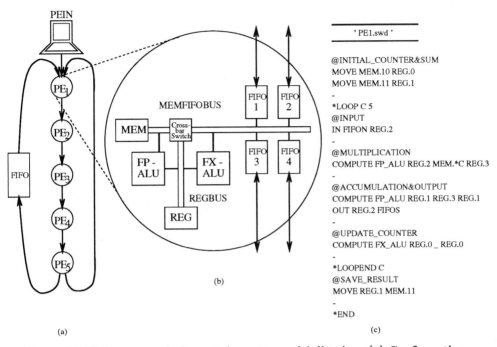

```
' PE1.swd '

@INITIAL_COUNTER&SUM
MOVE MEM.10 REG.0
MOVE MEM.11 REG.1
-
*LOOP C 5
@INPUT
IN FIFON REG.2
-
@MULTIPLICATION
COMPUTE FP_ALU REG.2 MEM.*C REG.3

@ACCUMULATION&OUTPUT
COMPUTE FP_ALU REG.1 REG.3 REG.1
OUT REG.2 FIFOS
-
@UPDATE_COUNTER
COMPUTE FX_ALU REG.0 _ REG.0
-
*LOOPEND C
@SAVE_RESULT
MOVE REG.1 MEM.11
-
*END
```

Figure 10.15: An example for matrix-vector multiplication. (a) Configuration description for the whole system. (b) Hardware description for a single processor. (c) Software description for the program executed by a single processor.

Figure 10.16(b) shows the four curves corresponding to the four corner points (of the communication and memory parameters). Based on these, the interpolation formula of Eq. 10.14 can then be used to derive an approximate speed-up.

From Figure 10.16, the following observations and possible explanations can be offered.

1. *The speed-up factors so obtained are, in general, noticeably lower than what is idealistically derived in Eq. 10.8 and Eq. 10.12.* The discrepancy is due to ignorance of the communication and memory-access times in the idealistic formula. Thus, as verified by the simulation, the longer the communication time, the lower the speed-up factor.

2. *In special cases with long memory-access time, the speed-up factor may even exceed the total number of PEs.* The effect of memory-access time is due to the difference between the time needed by on-chip memory (cache or register) access and the time needed by off-chip memory

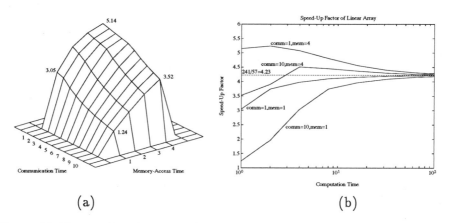

(a)   (b)

Figure 10.16: Speed-up factors of the linear array processor with respect to the single processor. (a) With the fixed computation time = 1 unit. One axis of the base represents memory-access time and the other represents communication time. (b) With respect to computation time.

(RAM or ROM) access. In the single-processor case, most intermediate data must be written into, and read from, the off-chip memory. In an array processor, in contrast, the job for each single processor is simple, and the processor can exploit on-chip register/memory for the intermediate data. When the communication time in a multiprocessor is much shorter than the access time of off-chip memory, it is not unreasonable to expect a speed-up-factor higher than the number of processors, cf. Figure 10.16(a).

3. *When computation time dominates the other time parameters, the speed-up factors approach constant rates.* Figure 10.16 shows that the speed-up factor would asymptotically approach a constant rate that is close to the theoretical value (i.e., 4.23 in the linear case, and 57.52 in the rectangular case). The *SISim* confirms the modified speed-up-factor in Eq. 10.9.

10.3   Dedicated Neural Processing Circuits

Dedicated neural implementation is aimed at high performance for special applications. Consequently, they are tailored to the architectures of specific neural models. *Existing dedicated neural processors emphasize on-chip implementation (instead of system building).* In many preprocessing applications, for example, early vision processing, dedicated neural circuits are more attractive. However, their main weakness lies in the lack of total system-design considerations.

Biological vs. Connectionist Types The dedicated and direct design approach can be divided into two types.

- **Biological Type.** The first type is dedicated implementation for *biological-type* neural networks, which encompass networks mimicking biological neural systems, audio (cochlea) functions, or early vision (retina) functions. The objective is mainly to develop a synthetic element for verifying hypotheses concerning biological systems. Most of the chips are implemented in analog CMOS VLSI devices.

- **Connectionist Type.** The second type is dedicated implementation for *connectionist-type* networks. It is to a greater degree inspired by the connectionist models, as opposed to true biological evidence. The connection networks are used to implement some of the high-level neural functions such as recognition or classification, which are only loosely related to biological reality. In connectionist models, the information storage/retrieval process is accomplished by *altering the pattern of connections among a large number of primitive cells,* and/or by *modifying certain weighting parameters associated with each connection.* The useful technologies are digital or hybrid CMOS, CCD, and optical devices.

Due to the maturity of design tools and the very large-scale integration, complementary metal-oxide semiconductors(CMOS) circuits are now widely adopted in many analog, digital, and hybrid devices.

Analog vs. Digital Designs Both analog and digital techniques have demonstrated a high degree of success in their own application domains. The selection between digital and analog circuits depends on many factors, for example, speed, precision, adaptiveness, programmability, and transfer/storage of signals.

- **Pros and Cons of Analog Circuits**

  In dedicated analog devices , a neuron is basically a differential amplifier with synaptic weights implemented by resistors. Thus many neurons can fit on a single chip. Analog circuits can process more than 1 bit per transistor with a very high speed. The asynchronous updating property of analog devices offers qualitatively different computations from those offered by digital devices [106]. For real-time early vision processing, dedicated analog processing chips offer arguably the most appealing alternative. For example, analog circuits offer inherent advantages on (1) the computation of the sum of weighted inputs by currents or charge packets, and (2) the nonlinear effects of the devices facilitating realization of sigmoid-type functions. Because the vital integration between analog sensors and information preprocessing/postprocessing, analog circuits will continue to have a major impact on dedicated neuron processing designs.

Although analog circuits are more attractive for biological-type neural networks, their suitability for connectionist-type networks remains very questionable. For example, compared with digital circuits, analog circuits are more susceptible to noise, crosstalk, temperature effects, and power supply variations. Although nonvolatile storage of analog weights provides high synaptic density, they are not easily programmable. In fact, the higher the precision, the more chip area is required. Thus, analog precision is usually limited to no more than 8 bits. In resistor-capacitor circuitry, low current consumption calls for high-resistance resistors. In switch-capacitor and resistor-capacitor circuitry, the low-noise constraint limits the minimal transistor surfaces and capacitors. In short, the combined factors of precision, noise, and current consumption lead to a larger chip area.

- **Pros and Cons of Digital Circuits**

For connectionist networks, digital technology offers very desirable features such as design flexibility, learning, expandable size, and accuracy. Digital designs have an overall advantage in terms of system-level performance. Dynamic range and precision are critical for many complex connectionist models. Digital implementation offers much greater flexibility of precision than its analog counterpart. Design of digital VLSI circuits is supported by mature and powerful CAD technology, as well as convenient building-block modular design. Digital circuits also have advantage in access to commercial design softwares and fast turnaround silicon fabrication. The disadvantages of digital circuits are, for example, bulky chip areas and (sometimes) relatively slow speeds.

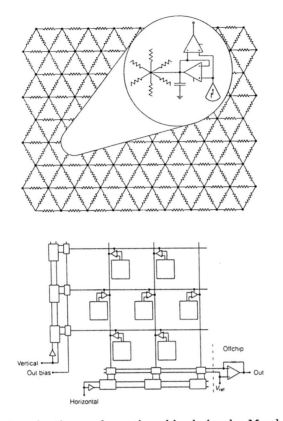

Figure 10.17: An adaptive analog retina chip design by Mead. (a) Diagram of the silicon retina. (b) Chip layout.

10.3.1 Analog Electronic Circuits

Features of analog designs are fast speed, low precision, and resulting small-scale systems. Although analog designs are always continuous-valued, they can be implemented in continuous-time circuits (e.g., RC circuits) or in discrete-time circuits (e.g., analog switch-capacitor circuits and CCD).

10.3.1.1 Analog VLSI CMOS Circuits

An excellent discussion on analog design of neural networks is found in Mead [193]. For a description of the implementation projects, see [58]. Due to space limitations, we describe only a few examples.

Biological Driven Neural Processing Chips

Analog VLSI is often adopted to implement biological driven neural processing chips. A continuous-time analog electronic real-time **electronic retinal chip** was developed by Mead and his co-workers [261], implemented on a $3\text{-}\mu$ CMOS VLSI chip. The chip contains an array of pixel cells from 48×48 to 88×88 cells. Each cell includes a photoreceptor, a data-processing circuit, and a off-chip data transmission circuit. The data-processing circuits produce time and spatial derivatives, with the latter generated in a hexagonal resistive network. Some adaptive learning capability has been incorporated into the design of analog circuits, cf. Figure 10.17. Up to 400K pixels per second were displayed to demonstrate a successful retinal processing of image of vanes. A large fraction of retina processing is dedicated to extracting motion features (e.g., edges), which involves extensive lateral and temporal inhibitory computation. In an demonstration, when the artificial retina was looking at a stationary set of vanes, there was barely any image on the screen. When the vanes started to rotate, the retina exploded in response to the edges of the vanes, clearly outlining the edges.

A continuous-time analog **electronic cochlea chip** was developed by Lyon and Mead [183]. It is implemented on a single CMOS VLSI chip, offering real-time processing speed. Each chip contains a 100-filter stage. The building blocks are transconductance amplifiers and capacitors. Both are implemented by transistors. The transistors operating above threshold are used as capacitors and those below threshold, as active devices.

Connectionist Learning Chip: Mitsubishi Neurochip

Mitsubishi Electric has announced a fast and large-scale learning neurochip. The Mitsubishi chip contains 336 neurons (units) and 28,000 synapses (connections). Synapse weights are controlled by the amount of electricity stored in capacitors, and learning takes place through changes in these amounts. The chip calculates and updates the weights in an analog fashion, as opposed to the more conventional all-digital synapse circuits, making it possible to hold the area needed for a single synapse to 70 square microns. The execution speed is 1 Tera CPS (connections per second) in the retrieving phase (without learning) and 28 Giga CUPS (connection updates per second) in the learning phase. Evaluation tests with connection of several chips indicate that it has a potential of integrating up to 200 chips. Thus, theoretically, a neural network can be created containing 3000 neurons and 5,600,000 synapses with performance of 200 Tera CPS or 5.6 Tera CUPS.

10.3.1.2   Analog CCD Circuits

A CCD works as a delay line, where the charge packets are kept within a potential well for a certain time. By this property, CCD has been very suitable in many signal/image-filtering applications. In a neural network, the output of the neurons is a function of the weighted sum on all inputs. By CCD technology, summation in the charge domain can be performed in a single transfer. Thus the CCD device can be used to produce a fast online analog multiply-and-add operation. The input signal and weights are preloaded into the device, and the output signal must be immediately retrieved after the operation.

In addition to the advantage of parallel computation of the weighted sum of inputs enjoyed by all analog circuits, CCD offers the key features of (1) reducing of wiring by using transport of charges through silicon device channels, and (2) having the suitability to support pulse-coded neural models [100]. CCD is also suitable for (bit-level) systolic design, making it a very viable candidate for neural processor implementation [5, 48, 100, 102, 249].

One promising approach to real-time recognition is to use a hierarchical, distributed computation and information neural network architecture. At the first processing level, processors are used for signal conditioning such as noise removal, enhancing, and/or skeletonizing an input image or Fourier transforming incoming speech. At the next level, neural networks with local connections and replicated weights are used to generate feature maps of the processed input. Finally, the extracted feature map is passed to higher-level fully connected neural networks for object classification. Each of the previously mentioned processing levels requires neural processors with large numbers of neurons, interconnections, and interconnection computations per second. It poses a difficult VLSI design problem, especially if the system is constrained by limited power and weight.

MIT CCD Neural Processor   Since 1987, the MIT Lincoln Laboratory has been developing high-speed, low-power, CCD-based neural network modules based on a time-multiplexed parallel-computation architecture. These modules share common features such as large numbers of time-multiplexed parallel CCD computation elements, digitally stored connection weights, and serial I/O buffers to support either multi-module ring-type or multilevel parallel, pipelined system architecture. A CCD neural module consisting of 224 neurons, providing 1.9 billion connections/s and 6K interconnection storage, has been developed. Currently under development is a single-chip reconfigurable multi-layer neural chip, consisting of 500 neurons and providing 5 billion connections/s and 64K interconnection storage. The chip can be used in implementing a multi-layer net, with programmable numbers of layers and hidden nodes.

The weighted-sum operation of the output neurons has been successfully implemented in a single-chip programmable CCD neural network processor at the MIT Lincoln Laboratory [48]. The analog input values are serially stored in a tapped delay line, and the digital weights are serially preloaded over a broadcast bus. The network is based on parallel CCD structures, which are connected, by a floating gate, to the analog input port of corresponding multiplying D/A converters (MDACs). Each MDAC uses a 32-stage 6-bit wide digital shift register. Thus, 32 sets of 192-word connection weights can be stored by 192 MDACs. In other words, it has 6144 programmable synaptic weights connecting 192 input nodes and 32 output nodes. Physically, the outputs of the MDACs (which are charge packets proportional to the products of the analog inputs and the digital weights) are summed together in the charge domain.

Figure 10.18 shows part of the block diagram. The synaptic weights are preloaded into the 32×192 digital memories, and the 192 analog inputs are loaded online. Each of the 32, 192-word bit-parallel, CCD digital memory vectors is sequentially applied to the MDACs. First, the total summed charge from the first output node is computed; then, that of the second output node, and so on.

The CCD chip delivers a peak speed of 3×10^9 weights/sec, with accuracy of 6 bits and 6144 programmable synapses [48]. As a comparison, the JPL CCD chip [102] (with 1-μ technology) has the speed of 10^{10} weights/sec, accuracy ≈ 4 bits, and 10,000 programmable synapses. In another design by [5], with 1-μ technology, it delivers 10^{10} weights/sec, accuracy ≈ 8 bits, and 64,000 programmable synapses. Several real-time CCD neural information processing applications have been reported [47].

10.3.2   Digital (or Mostly Digital) ASIC Chips

Digital VLSI implementation is suitable for dedicated connectionist-type neural nets. By definition, a digital network implies both discrete-time and discrete-value design. Digital approach provides a high-speed, accurate and yet flexible, implementation for neural networks. A digital design allows a

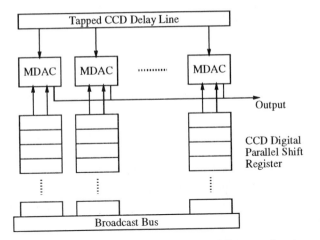

Figure 10.18: Block diagram of a part of a CCD neural net processor.

flexible choice of structure and precision. A possible winning approach is a hybrid design combining digital and analog circuits. In a comparative study in [235], digital CMOS is claimed to be superior to CCD in several key aspects.

JPL Neural Processor   The synaptic matrix developed at JPL (Jet Propulsion Laboratory) consists of an array of 32×32 interconnections and contains 1024 synapses [274]. The synapses are bistable (on/off) and can be controlled individually by external signals. The setting of the synaptic weights has to be determined a priori. The limited adaptability offered by the hardware is not able to support general learning rules.

Bell Labs Analog Chip   An example for mostly digital design is represented by the configurable CMOS neural network chip developed at Bell Laboratories [86, 87]. It is a single hybrid chip (using 1.25-μ CMOS) for synaptic matrix processing. The matrix connects 50 inputs with 24 outputs using 1200 (externally adjustable) synapses. The chip provides 256 blocks. Each block consists of 128 binary synapses. The training and calculations are done at a rate of 10 MHz. Barring the analog comparator, all other functional components are digital. The outputs of the multipliers are summed up in analog fashion. The resulting value is presented to 4 comparators, whose threshold is preset according to the corresponding bit level. In terms of low-level image-recognition applications, the chip's computational performance appears to be very adequate. The chip can be used to implement associative memory based on a discrete-state Hopfield neural net. In order to solve the limited memory-capacity problem encountered in Hopfield-type neural nets, the analog circuit system is modified to be a grandmother cell circuit with differential dynamics used in the winner-take-all mechanism.

Bellcore Neural Processor Bell Communications Research (Bellcore) has designed and implemented a single analog VLSI chip for the Boltzmann machine, as shown in Figure 10.19 [11, 12, 13]. It incorporates both the simulated annealing technique and a stochastic learning mechanism. The chip is implemented in 2-μ CMOS with combined analog and digital circuits. The neurons are based on differential amplifiers with two complementary outputs, cf. Figure 10.19(a). The digital dendrites and synapses are implemented by pass transistors. The weights are adjustable for a wide range of positive and negative values (up to 8 bits). Initial weights can be preset. The Boltzmann machine learning algorithm, which needs only local information and no differentiation, is implemented in the chip. The required probability computation can be replaced by the physical behavior of an analog VLSI circuit. There is an up/down counter used in the processor to accumulate the number of co-occurrences of the "on" and "off" states in the neurons on both sides of a given connection, cf. Figure 10.19(b). The system uses electronic noise to implement the simulated annealing process used in the setting of the system to a stable state during both learning and retrieval. In other words, the temperature-cooling and random decision mechanisms required by the Boltzmann machine are realized by amplified thermal noise.

10.3.3   Digital Design Based on FPGA Chips

Field programmable gate arrays (FPGAs) offer a way of very rapid prototyping. The density of FPGAs is in the range of 1000 to 20,000 equivalent gates. (They use the same CMOS process used in the implementation of gate arrays.) Their density is lower than ASIC; however, this is offset by the convenience that the configuration of the device can be easily programmed by the user. In short, FPGAs are distinguished by their convenience of user programmability.

There are two major programmable subcomponents in an FPGA chip: basic cells and switch lattices.

- **Basic Cells:** The CLBs are replicated as an array over the entire chip. In the Xilinx chip, the basic cell is called a configurable logic block (CLB). The basic cell must be able to support a multitude of logic

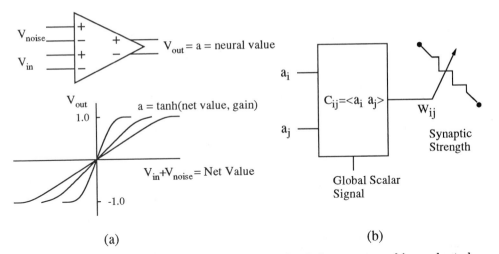

Figure 10.19: A sketch of a VLSI chip for the Boltzmann machine, adapted from [11]. (a) An electronic analog neuron, and (b) the correlations between the neurons connected via the synapse are measured as $C_{ij} = <a_i a_j> = \int a_i a_j \, dt$.

functions and information storage in internal registers. Also, it must be simple and fast and use minimum chip area.

- **Switch Lattices:** Most area between CLBs is taken by the interconnection structure to which each cell can be connected in a fairly flexible manner. (A relatively small area of the chip is consumed by the I/O blocks, which appear only on the border area.) In the case of the Xilinx FPGA, the switch lattices are defined by a switch matrix determined by the content of internal static memory. Normally, the utilization factor is considerably lower than total "raw" capacity in terms of total gate count. Switch lattices play a very important role in logic utilization and the efficiency of connecting cells, which in turn determine the number of "usable" gates.

FPGAs usually come together with supporting CAD tools that offer automatic schematic entry and simulation [4]. When a design is finished and successfully simulated, the configuration codes will be loaded into the FPGA device. This configuration can be either *permanent*, if antifuse technology is used (e.g., the Actel chip), or *alterable* as in the case of electrically reprogrammable interconnections (e.g., the Xilinx chip). The latter is more attractive because reprogrammability allows the design to be easily "loaded", debugged, and modified in milliseconds. Also, it permits dynamically reconfigurable computational structures. These merits have been successfully demonstrated by a programmable active memory (PAM), implemented at DEC Research Labs, Paris. PAM is a memory array interleaved with computing elements. The structure of computing elements is changed according to the computational task, exploiting the reprogrammability feature of the Xilinx FPGAs.

In another example, Xilinx FPGAs are used for the communication hardware design in an array processor called RAP [202], which is elaborated in Section 10.4.3.4. It is based on a ring architecture with processors connected by a data-distribution ring. DSP (TMS320C30) chips are used as basic processors in RAP, and the control circuits of the dedicated high-speed communication channel for the ring structure are implemented with FPGAs. The reprogrammability of Xilinx FPGAs permits easy modification of low-level-register transfer logic to provide flexibility without sacrificing speed. Furthermore, use of FPGAs as glue logic very much simplifies implementation.

10.3.4   Optical Implementation of Neural Nets

Optical processors have been proposed for the implementation of neural networks [62, 65, 184]. Optical systems have potential for global interconnectivity, massive storage, and high-speed processing [93, 190]. Overall, compared with digital technology, optical processing is limited in terms of flexibility, programmability, and precision. Therefore, it represents only a complementary approach to VLSI [84].

Optical computers process information encoded in light beams. Thus, optical computing presents potential computational speeds far beyond the perceived limits for VLSI, GaAs, or other electronic technologies. Optical systems can handle the connectivity problem more gracefully than electronic ones but are more limited for computation. Optical lenses can perform certain special mathematical calculations much more effectively than their electronic counterparts. Algebraic optical array processors have proven to be technically sound. The properties of a lens can be utilized to perform Fourier transforms, convolutions, and advanced mathematics such as matrix-matrix multiplication in linear algebra. High-density, three-dimensional information storage can be achieved through optical holography. Optical processing also offers the unique feature of radiation hardness. It has limited programmability: uploading/downloading and updating of synaptic weights can be implemented with existing space-variant holographic elements and liquid-crystal-display spatial light modulators.

It is not practical yet to construct a neurocomputer based on purely optical PEs and synaptic weights. One of the main reasons is that cost-effective optical technology (e.g., bistable optical material) that can perform high-speed optical logic and nonlinear operations in high-density arrays is not generally available. An example of promising technological progress is the GaAs S-SEED devices from AT&T. The devices have 30,000 pixel pairs, potentially capable of switching at picoseconds with picojoule switching energies. (Earlier results [195] indicated 3.5 pJ at 14 ns, 22 pJ at less than 1 ns, a 64×32 array of 10-μm square pixels switched in less than 2.5 pJ.)

Optical implementations of content-addressable associative memory based on the discrete-state Hopfield neural net have been proposed [65, 175]. They perform associative recall (a matrix-vector multiplication operation) by means of the outer-product technique. The synaptic weights are implemented as a photographic transparency (i.e., a mask), and the neuron output is sent into, and passed through, the weight mask (e.g., Bragg cells) via parallel planar laser beams. The weighted sums are collected by converging the attenuated beams onto a linear detector array.

In addition, a modular electro-optical neural system capable of pattern learning has been proposed [66]. Each module is a complete associative memory that adapts as it is exposed to associated information patterns. All these modules can be optically cascadable, with all inputs and outputs in the form of 1D or 2D image beams or intensity arrays. Various learning modules have been proposed, for example, delta learning, Hebbian learning, and differential learning.

A new approach to learning in multilayer optical neural nets based on holographically interconnected nonlinear photorefractive crystals has also been proposed [294]. This optical net uses self-aligning volume holograms to bidirectionally interconnected nonlinear devices that act as the bidirectional optical neurons. To produce a powerful and flexible parallel optical neural network, This architecture combines (1) the back-propagation learning procedure, (2) the robustness of the distributed neural computation, (3) the self-aligning ability of phase-conjugate mirrors, and (4) the massive storage capacity of volume holograms.

Hybrid VLSI and optical technology represents a very plausible new dimension. A hybrid system can incorporate the advantages of the complementary capabilities of *optics* (efficient linear operations and communications) and *electronics* (efficient nonlinear operations). Some hybrid designs use systolic arrays to allow parallel processing of digital and analog data. Optical/VLSI pattern-recognition systems also utilize the inherent ability of optical systems to perform transforms for computing high-speed correlations.

In the future, microlasers will be available to pass information off GaAs chips with less power and higher bandwidth than by pins. Porous silicon, when stimulated electronically, emits sufficiently visible luminescence; therefore, it should be possible to use this approach with silicon. Chips that perform electronic computations in regular arrays between optical array inputs and outputs are called *smart pixel arrays* [99]. These are candidates for neural network architectures. A variation of the smart pixel, known as *amacronics*, is now appearing in commercial products. *Amacronics* refers to optically and competitively coupled focal-plane structures with local electronic processing cells. The difference, relative to smart pixels, is that the device does not convert back to optics at the output. For example, Sony camera model SSC-M350 is believed to use lithographically produced (or possibly e-beam) diffractive lenses that image light directly to CCD pixels having local electronic processing. This could become a popular approach for vision-related neural networks.

In summary, hybrid systems offer a significant improvement in cost, size, weight, power consumption, and reliability. The domain of their potential applications is very broad, including Fourier transform, feature extraction, correlation systems, scene classification, image analysis, machine vision, pattern recognition, and SAR processing.

10.4   General-Purpose Digital Neurocomputers

Neural computing requires a huge number of computations and communications. Therefore, multiprocessors and massively parallel processors are the most appealing architectures for neurocomputer design. There are several alternatives for the actual implementation of a neurocomputer:

- **Implement neural net algorithms in existing parallel machines.** Many neural net algorithms can be ported to existing machines. The SIMD architecture, for example, can support most neural models. There are, however, restrictions imposed by the machine architecture.

- **Construct new neurocomputers from commercially available chips.** The constraints in existing machines prompt the search for other systems that are more tailored to the desired application. The use of commercially available components usually keeps the cost more affordable; thus, this approach is suitable for experimental systems and even some real systems. As an example, the transputer or TMS320C40 chips are designed with enhanced communication capability ready for the construction of array processors. Sometimes array processors based on commercial chips have either inadequate floating-point performance (e.g., Transputer) or limited interconnectivity (e.g., i860). For these cases, a plausible design strategy is to adopt commercial chips for the floating-point arithmetic unit and the memory unit, and attach additional chips for the communication unit. Because it is often very difficult to identify well-suited commercial chips for the desired communication unit, custom-designed communication chips should be considered.

- **Construct new prototypes from custom ASIC or FPGA chips.** Although it allows optimal design of both PE and array architectures, it often involves an expensive and time-consuming process. Therefore, this should be attempted only after a careful feasibility study of all the specifications pertaining to the given applications. Field-programmable gate arrays (FPGAs) may represent a good compromise for rapid prototyping.

Most existing digital neurocomputers are built with off-the-shelf components. However, the ultimate high-speed neurocomputer must be constructed from full-custom VLSI circuits.

10.4.1 Overall System Configuration

Depicted in Figure 10.20 is a possible overall system configuration [152]. It consists of a *host computer*, an *interface unit*, *interconnection networks*, and *PE arrays*.

- The **host computer** should provide batch data storage, management, and data formatting; determine the schedule program that controls the interface system and interconnection network; and generate and load object codes to the PEs. The host provides interaction between the user and the hardware. It initializes or changes network topology and monitors the overall progress. A convenient choice for the host can be a workstation (enhanced with a special interface bus) with adequate graphics and operating-system capabilities.

- The **interface unit**, connected to the host via the host bus, facilitates the function of downloading and uploading data. Based on the

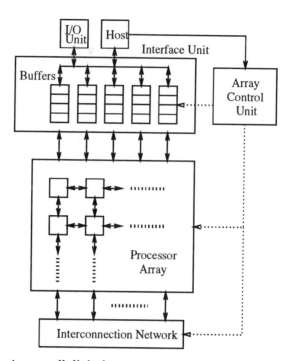

Figure 10.20: An overall digital neurocomputer system consists of a host computer, an interface unit, an interconnection network, and a processor array.

schedule program, the control unit monitors the interface system and interconnection network. The functions that are common in interfaces are DMA, buffering, (cache memory, if necessary), interrupt handling, and data and sequence control.

- The **interconnection networks** provide a set of mappings between processors and processors or between processors and memory modules to accommodate certain common global communication needs. Incorporating certain structured interconnections can significantly enhance the speed performance of the parallel processing systems. For data transfer and message passing in locally interconnected array processors, a special communication unit (i.e., routing hardware) must be included in the processor architecture. In this way, global interconnectivity inherent in some neural networks can be implemented on a locally interconnected mesh array [10].

The following array configurations can be considered for neural information processing, cf. Figure 10.21.

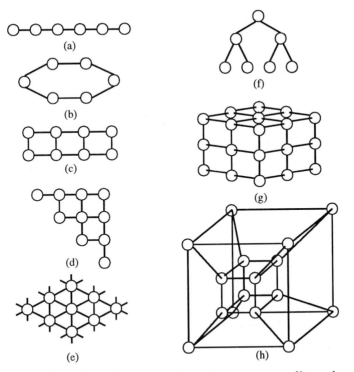

Figure 10.21: Samples of array configurations are one-dimensional architectures: (a) linear array, (b) ring array; two-dimensional architectures: (c) square/rectangular array, (d) triangular array, (e) hexagonal array, (f) tree array; and high-dimensional architectures: (g) 3D array, (h) hypercube array.

- One-dimensional architectures:
  - (a) linear arrays
  - (b) ring arrays
- Two-dimensional architectures:
  - (c) square/rectangular arrays
  - (d) triangular arrays
  - (e) hexagonal arrays
  - (f) tree arrays
- High-dimensional architectures:
  - (g) 3D arrays
  - (h) hypercube arrays

- The **processor element arrays** comprise a number of processor elements (PE) with local memory. The arrays are roughly divided into three groups: those with the number of processors on the order of (1) tens, (2) thousands, and (3) millions. The processors in the first and the second groups are usually *single-chip*, based on either custom-made or commercially available microprocessors. Processors in the third group are usually bit-serial and custom-made, with *many per chip*. This classification is displayed in Figure 10.22. The granularity of a PE is closely related to the number of PEs in the array. At the massively parallel end are fine-grain machines, such as the Connection Machine and MPP, where bit-serial processors are used. The neurons can be mapped one to one onto the processors, but routing units are required to support the desired links. Simple processor primitives are often preferred in many low-precision image-processing applications. However, as the level of parallelism increases, and the processing power and memory of processors increase, the interconnection and routing problems become more complicated. Many neural processing applications require fast multiply-and-accumulate, high-speed RAM, and fast coefficient table addressing. In coarser-grain PEs, more powerful arithmetic units can be accommodated. Two prominent examples of large granularity are TI's TMS320C40 and INMOS's transputer. They belong to the range of the microcomputer array in Figure 10.22.

10.4.2 Processor Element Architecture

There are extremely high demands on all the digital computing components: *computations*, *memories*, and *communications*. Neurocomputer design must ensure a balance of these components. The basic arithmetic building blocks are a nonlinear processing unit, floating-point/fixed-point MACs, and probabilistic processors. The nonlinear unit is used for the activation function. It can be built by using a lookup table. The MACs support matrix operations such as MVM, VMM, and OPU. The probabilistic processor is meant for stochastic neural models such as the Boltzmann machine. The memory units include program memory and data memory. The storage mechanisms include registers, cache, external local memory, and shared memory. A special communication unit is required to support the array processing environment.

High processing speed is the most important goal of any PE design. Dynamic logic is, in general, slower than static logic but requires much less area.

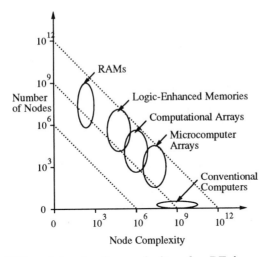

Figure 10.22: Different levels of granularity of a PE in an array processor system. (Adapted from [254].)

For memory design, dynamic logic can provide one transistor per bit storage, and static logic requires 3 to 6 transistors per cell. Design time, yield, and power consumption are directly influenced by the size of a chip. We should use CMOS logic in our chip because it provides low power consumption. The complexity of internal buses should be kept at a minimum because they require a large percentage of the chip area and dissipate a lot of power.

The chip should be programmable and independent of the specific algorithm and configuration. In order to program the control of the floating-point unit (FPU) to suit specific application need, it is preferable to use a microprogrammable controller over one based on random logic. The chip design should support the expandability of the array system. The regularity of operations can, and should, be exploited. Special hardware must be incorporated to support the partitioning of large problems.

A generic block diagram for the processing element is shown in Figure 10.23. (A more elaborated description of a PE prototype is provided in Figure 10.26.) It consists of the controller, address generator, three memory banks, I/O subsystem, and floating-point unit containing a multiplier and an adder. Each block is accompanied by a set of registers. In order to provide fast execution, several buses are provided to permit simultaneous data movement from different sources to different destinations. In the following discussion, we detail how this generic architecture can be realized.

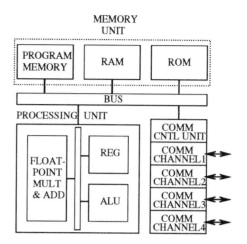

Figure 10.23: Schematic diagram for a *complete* PE design. The actual implementation could involve a subset of the components.

10.4.2.1   Arithmetic Unit

Arithmetic processing units need to support the multiplication, addition, and nonlinear operations with their required precision. A good majority of connectionist networks need floating-point arithmetic capability. The word length must be made adequate for the dynamic range of the weight and activation calculations. Word length of 32-bit floating-point unit is often required in signal-processing applications. However, word length of 8- to 16-bit fixed-point unit would suffice for many image-processing applications.

The multiply-and-accumulate (MAC), or equivalently the multiply-and-add, is the most important arithmetic unit. It is advisable to route the output of the multiplier to the input of the adder such that the multiply-and-add operations can be pipelined. Registers store some intermediate data during the operations. This facilitates a concurrent execution among several independent instructions. In the retrieving phase, the adder input is the output of the adder during the previous cycle. Temporary registers can be used to hold the accumulator value.

Pipelining can increase the throughput of the processing unit. Beside a floating-point arithmetic unit, a fixed-point arithmetic unit is also needed to calculate the addresses and other control data. As mentioned before, the nonlinear function can be implemented by using a lookup table.

10.4.2.2   Memory Unit

A proper balance and trade-off must be made between on-chip and off-chip storage, including cache, local memory, and global memory. There are many ways to store synaptic weights. One is to distribute the weights over many neural chips; another is to store the weights off-chip in DRAMs. Unless carefully designed in advance, repeated reloading of new sets of weights into local memory in the neural chip may become necessary. Note that the reloading of weights can be very time-consuming due to the communication bottleneck [235]. As an example, for the Bell Labs chip [86], it takes 256 clock cycles to reload, whereas the multiplication time (for all the stored weights) takes only one cycle.

Because the chip area is constant, the trade-off between functionality and storage is inevitable: If storage is vital, then a good fraction of the chip area has to be allocated to on-chip weight storage. If functionality cannot be compromised, however, then chip area must be reserved for arithmetic processing and the weights are stored off-chip in cheaper DRAMs. With new submicron ULSI technology, it should be feasible to simultaneously meet on-chip arithmetic and memory requirements.

The program code is stored in program memory, which does not change during a specific application. For a special-purpose network, PROM or ROM can be used to store the code when the array is built. For a general-purpose network, programs for different applications can be loaded to a RAM. It is desirable to have simultaneous program fetches and other memory accesses. The weight and training data are often stored in fast RAMs. This memory can be implemented using two-level hierarchy with a (smaller and faster) cache built within the processor and a (larger and slower) external local memory.

Nonlinear functions (e.g., the sigmoid function) play a very important role in many neural algorithms. Most neurocomputers, for example, the Princeton Engine, do not directly support either the exponential function or floating-point arithmetic operations, and the indirect arithmetic procedures are very time-consuming. The lookup table is one of the more effective methods of implementing nonlinear functions. The table is prestored in a ROM/PROM/RAM, and the nonlinear function can be implemented by a memory fetch. For example, the Princeton Engine provides large local memory (320K bytes) for each processing unit, which may be exploited to implement lookup tables for any nonlinear functions.

To compare the performances of the (exact) arithmetic and the (approximate) lookup-table approaches, we conducted a simulation study on the

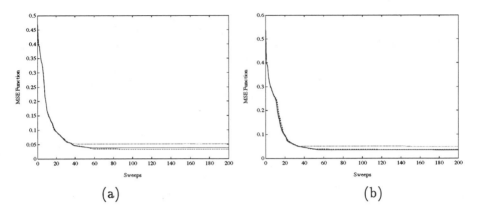

(a)   (b)

Figure 10.24: Both graphs show the convergence curves of the conjugate-gradient method by different approaches from two different initial conditions. The solid line represents the convergence curve by arithmetic method. The dashed line represents the convergence curve by using a 1024-entry(12 bits) lookup table. The dotted line represents the convergence curve by using a 256-entry lookup table.

conjugate-gradient BP method based on Princeton Engine architecture. Some typical simulation results are shown in Figure 10.24. Note that the performance with a 1024-entry lookup table is very close to what is achievable with the floating-point arithmetic method. It is also clear that a smaller-size (256-entry) lookup table will result in degraded performance, although the degradation does not appear to be too severe.

10.4.2.3   Communication Unit

The basic requirement of the interconnection network is to ensure that all messages can be successfully forwarded to their destinations as quickly as possible. The communication unit is critical in supporting the array processing environment. In practice, constructing direct and physical links for all the thousands of synaptic weights is not feasible. Various options and trade-offs exist in selecting communication modules and interconnection networks to support parallel neural processing. In order to support communication in a linear array, two communication channels are needed. To support a rectangular array, four channels are used. The I/O buffer requirements will depend on the application.

In order to satisfy communication channel requirements, a large number of I/O ports can be required. The number of I/O pins on a chip significantly affects the cost because packaging could be as expensive as the actual chip. In addition, driving output pins consume a large percentage of the total power required by the chip. Therefore, it is important to minimize or economize the number of I/O pins.

The communication unit is used to control interprocessor data movement and array reconfiguration. When a PE is to communicate with another PE, a token with a global ID of the destination PE is generated. The communication unit of the destination PE, upon token matching, keeps the data for the arithmetic unit or memory unit. The array structure can be reconfigured by changing the global ID of each PE.

Synchronous versus Asynchronous Architectures   The array architecture can be synchronous or asynchronous. In a synchronous network, all neurons change their state in lockstep under the control of a global clock. In asynchronous networks, the neuron may be self-clocked. The use of a global clocking signal greatly simplifies the processing element control, but it also creates clock distribution problems in large arrays. Given the limited propagation speed of the signals both on a chip and on a board, processors that are far from the clock source will receive the clock pulses with a few nanoseconds delay relative to processors closer to the source (i.e., *clock skew*) [152]. In reality, a global clock can drive up to only several tens of processors of an FPU. Nowadays, many configurations have gone beyond that range. In addition, any flexible architecture must be designed with expandability in mind. Under such circumstances, clock skew will become a problem.

One way to avoid clock skew is to use a multistage clock buffer and minimize the length of the wires. It shortens the length of the wire at each stage, and hence reduces skew. Another alternative involves the use of an *asynchronous* clocking scheme, whereby each processor has its own clock and is synchronized with the others via an *asynchronous communication protocol.*

The architecture of the I/O interface is shown in Figure 10.25. Each processor that needs to communicate with its neighbor issues an OREQ signal and puts its data on the bus, while loading them to the output FIFO. If the corresponding processor is ready to accept the data, it issues an IACK signal and reads the data from the bus. The sending processor uses the IACK signal to clock its output FIFO. If no IACK signal is received, the processor temporarily store the outgoing data in the output FIFO and continues execution. If the FIFO is full, it waits until a slot is available. When the receiving processor receives the OREQ signal, it checks the input FIFO. If the input FIFO

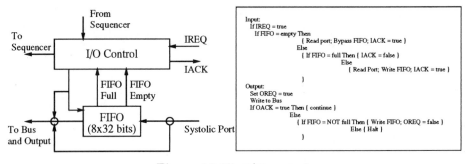

Figure 10.25: I/O control.

is full, it simply ignores the OREQ signal and continues processing. If the FIFO is empty *and* an input instruction is being executed, the data is put directly on the appropriate bus to its eventual destination. If the processor is not ready to process the input data, it admits the data into the FIFO and issues an IACK signal.

10.4.2.4   A Prototype Processor Element Design

A processor element (PE) prototype is proposed in [291]. This is a board-level design, based on microprogrammable, commercially available building blocks. The prototype provides a platform where many hardware and software features can be tested. The design emphasizes flexibility and performance at the expense of cost, size, and power consumption. The block diagram of the processing element is shown in Figure 10.26.

Instruction Set   The design of the processing element is aimed mainly at the implementation of systolic algorithms. Optimized instructions for arithmetic and memory access are provided for initialization and nonpipelineable algorithms. These instructions can be used for rapid prototyping and testing of algorithms. They obviate the need for detailed microprogramming involving multicycle instructions.

The `gen_step` instruction is a generic instruction capable of implementing the three basic algorithms in neural networks. To understand its design, consider the basic algorithmic steps:

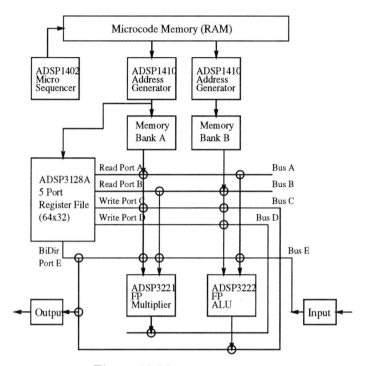

Figure 10.26: A PE prototype.

MVM_step	Input to `treg`, Fetch weight from memory
	Multiply/Accumulate
	Output `treg`, store accumulator (optional)
VMM_step	Input to `areg`, Fetch weight from memory
	Fetch g from memory, Multiply/Accumulate
	Output Accumulator, Store accumulator to memory
OPU_step	Input to `treg`, Fetch ΔW from memory to accumulator
	Fetch g from memory, Multiply/Accumulate
	Output `treg`, Store accumulator to memory

From these steps, we can define the generic step instruction:

Gen_step	Input to `Raddress`, Fetch from `Maddress` to `Raddress`
	Fetch from `Maddress` to `Raddress`, MAC
	Output from `Raddress`, Store `Raddress` to `Maddress`

Here, `Raddress` is a register address and `Maddress` is a memory address.

Microsequencer and Microcode Memory The microsequencer is responsible for generating microcode addresses and handling interrupts occurring when the microprogram RAM is initially loaded, and when the I/O buffers are full during I/O. The microsequencer operates at a speed of 50 *ns*. The microcode memory consists of 512×180 bits and contains a *horizontal* microcode to reduce delays and simplify hardware construction. Its access time is 30 *ns*.

Address Generator and Data Memory   The data memory of the system can be regarded as a large circular buffer. That is, when addressing reaches the end of buffer, it wraps back to the beginning. The operation implementing this function can be described by

$$Y \leftarrow R_n; \text{ IF } (R_n \geq C_i) \text{ THEN } R_n \leftarrow I_k; \text{ ELSE } R_n \leftarrow R_n + B_m$$

where Y is the output address bus, R_n is an address register, C_i is a limit register containing the limit address of the circular buffer, I_k is an initialization register, and B_m is an increment register. The architecture of the address-generator chip used is specially tailored for the execution of this operation. It can generate addresses in 30 *ns*, and the multiplicity of address, limit and increment registers facilitates the implementation of partitioning algorithms that map large problems on a small physical array.

The data memory consists of three banks of fast SRAM (30 *ns*). One bank is addressed independently and the remaining two share the address bus. In neural net simulations, the third memory bank is used to store the change of the weights ΔW_{ij} during learning. Because we read weight W_{ij} in order to calculate ΔW_{ij}, it is not necessary to recompute the address. In addition, the data memory belongs to the controller address space so that data can be loaded directly during the initialization phase.

Arithmetic Unit   A main feature of the board-level PE design is that two floating-point units are used instead of a single multiplier/accumulator. The reason is that most commercially available FPUs have, at most, two input ports. Moreover, for some operations (e.g., OPU updating), three numbers need to be loaded into the execution unit. Two cycles would be needed to complete an operation if a single FPU (with only two ports) is used. With two floating-point units, such operations could be completed in one cycle.

10.4.3   Parallel Array Architectures

Many parallel processing architectures are proposed for neural network implementation. The prominent ones are bus-oriented architectures, SIMD arrays,

MIMD multiprocessors, and pipelined (systolic/wavefront) arrays. Comparisons of the different categories inevitably involve complex trade-offs among various factors, such as programmability, reconfigurability, synchronization, and interprocessor communication. Some key design examples for each of the neurocomputer categories are now discussed.

10.4.3.1 Bus-Oriented Architectures

Single-bus or multiple-bus structures have been widely used for many years in conventional multiprocessor architectures. One of the early examples is the Multimax machine by Encore Computer Corp., which has a speed of 100 Mbyte/s and can be expanded from 2 to 20 microprocessors. The number of processors is often limited by the bandwidth of the buses. In order to enhance the performance of bus-oriented networks, very high-speed buses are required.

Mark III and Mark IV   The Mark III is a bus-oriented architecture, using eight single-board computers. Each single-board computer contains a standard VME bus circuit board. The boards are plugged into a backplane cardcage rack along with a bus master card and an input/output interface card. The neurocomputer is hosted by a Digital Equipment Corporation MicroVAX computer. To allow broadcast operations, all eight single-board computers have their bus addresses set to the same value. Thus, a transmission on the bus to a memory location within this address block would be received by all eight single-board computers simultaneously.

The Mark IV is a neurocomputer that is constructed out of signal-processing building blocks (memories, multiplier, adders, and barrel shifters), TTL logic parts, and memory parts. This computer was designed to be a node of a much larger neurocomputer (which was never constructed). This larger neurocomputer, if constructed, would consist of up to 1000 Mark IV nodes on a fast broadcast bus structure [94].

A Mark IV processing node is capable of emulating as many as 262,144 processing elements and 5.5M connections. It consists of weight-application and weight-update units, a two-plane weight table, a state update table with TMS32020, a state table, and a connection table. The connection table contains the addresses of the processing elements that supply input signals of the network. Weights are updated according to this table. The weight-update units are designed to handle a wide variety of neural algorithms. However, the design suffers from a serious weakness on the low arithmetic accuracy. For example, all processing states are assumed to be 8-bit fixed-point numbers. All weights are coded as 21-bit fixed-point numbers.

Hitachi Neurocomputer This is a single-bus neurocomputer, with approximately 70K synapses and 1K neurons. Because memory is relatively more expensive in gate array technology, each neuron has only 64 synapses. The circuit uses a single bus, and the peak performance is claimed to exceed 2 Giga CUPS (connection updates per second) . The basic technological specifications are as follows: 0.8-micron CMOS gate array; 16-bit synapse weight; 9-bit neuron output; 5-in diameter wafer; 30 cm × 21 cm × 23 cm system size; and 50-watt power consumption. The key architectural specifications of the Hitachi neurocomputer follow. (More details can be found in [308].)

- Neuron circuits: completely digital circuits with learning function.

- Architecture: time-sharing digital bus and dual networks for learning.

- Number of neurons: 1152 neurons in the system, with 144 per wafer.

- Performance of learning circuits: 2.3 Giga CUPS.

10.4.3.2   SIMD Architectures

A single-instruction multiple-data (SIMD) machine is a parallel array of arithmetic processors with local memory. An SIMD array has control (instruction) buses and data buses (in lieu of local instruction codes adopted in systolic or MIMD arrays). Instructions are broadcast from a host, with all processors executing the same instruction simultaneously [152]. Two prominent examples of SIMD architectures suitable for neural processing are the *Connection Machine* [36, 96, 275] and the *Princeton Engine* [49].

Connection Machine The Connection Machine is an SIMD architecture developed by Thinking Machines Corporation. It provides a large number of tiny processor/memory cells connected by a programmable communications network. (The assembly-level REL-2 programming language and the higher-level C and LISP programming languages are provided.) The current Connection Machine contains 64K processor cells interconnected in a hypertorus structure, each with 4K-bit memory and a simple serial arithmetic logic unit. The basic building blocks are custom CMOS chips, each containing 16 processor cells and one router unit. The router is responsible for routing messages between chips. The chips are physically connected as a 12-dimensional hypercube. Within a chip, the processors are connected in a 4 × 4 grid. Each processor cell can communicate directly with its North, East, West and South (NEWS) neighbors without involving the router. This two-dimensional grid pattern can be extended across multiple chips. All processors execute instructions from a single stream generated by a microcontroller under the direction of a conventional host. The machine has a peak instruction rate (32-bit addition) of about 1000 MIPS. The block of the connection machine with host, processor/memory cells, communications network, and input/output is shown in Figure 10.27(a).

A Connection Machine cell is a bit-serial processor comprising a few registers, an ALU, a message buffer, and a finite-state machine, cf. Figure 10.27(b). Each cell is "intelligent". Based on the incoming message and its internal state, it can execute a sequence of steps such as arithmetic or storage operations on the contents of the message and the registers, adjusting the internal state, and sending out new messages. It can be applied not only to connectionist networks in neural processing, but also to semantic networks representing a knowledge base in AI systems.

In the Connection Machine, each cell is sufficiently small so that it is incapable of performing meaningful computations on its own. Instead, multiple cells are connected together into data-dependent patterns, called **active data structures**, that both represent and process data. Their activities are controlled by a conventional host computer. The Connection Machine is connected to a conventional computer much like a conventional memory, but it differs from conventional memory in three respects. First, associated with each cell of storage is a processing cell that can perform local computations based on the information stored in that cell. Second, there exists a general intercommunication network that can connect all the cells in an arbitrary pattern. Third, there is a high-bandwidth input/output channel that can transfer data between the Connection Machine and peripheral devices at a much higher rate than would be possible through the host.

The hypercube connection of the *Connection machine* is not natural to most neural connectivities. Therefore, software routing is needed to modify the communication scheme and better support the data flow. This seriously affects its real-time performance in many highly demanding applications. For example, real-time processing speed for 256 × 256 images is not attainable by the current Connection Machine. Very recently, however, it was reported that the newest Thinking Machines computer CM-200, which could cost as

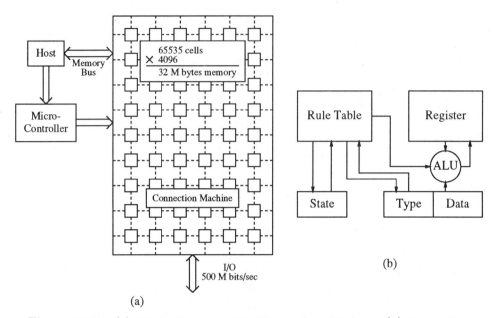

(a)

(b)

Figure 10.27: (a) Block diagram of the Connection Machine. (b) Connection Machine's "intelligent" cell. (Adapted from [239].)

much as $10 million, is capable of 9 Giga operations per second.

Princeton Engine: A Video Supercomputer The Princeton Engine is a 29.3-GIPS image-processing system capable of simulating in real-time video rate signals, including NTSC and HDTV video [49]. It consists of a massively parallel arrangement of up to 2048 processing elements, cf. Figure 10.28. Each processing element contains a 16-bit arithmetic unit and multiplier, a 64-word triple-port register stack, and 650,000 words of local processor memory. These functional units and registers are connected by seven parallel buses supporting up to five simultaneous and independent micro-operations. Local processor memory supports video rate access, providing over 1000 temporal frames of image storage. There are four interprocessor communication operations: *left, right, broadcast* and *receive.* These operate under a processor interconnection pattern such that during any instruction, a processor can be *bypassed* or *connected* to its neighbors. The default pattern connects each processor to its nearest neighbors. A subsequent left or right primitive move causes data to move $p-1$ or $p+1$ processors. When a processor or consecutive string of processors is bypassed, left or right move operations cause data to move $p \pm n$ processors away. A hierarchy of interprocessor communi-

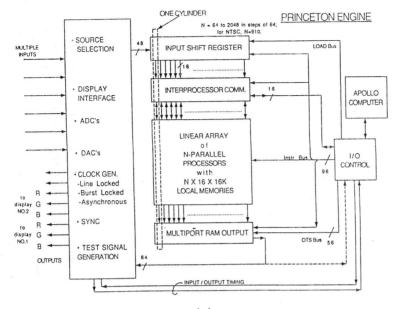

(a)

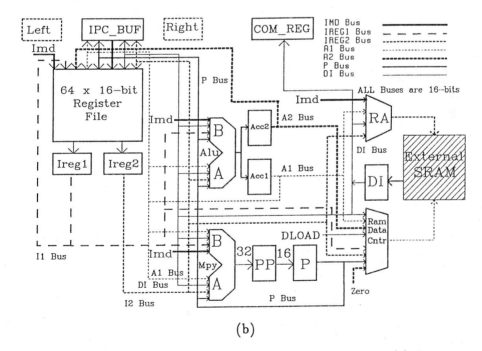

(b)

Figure 10.28: The Princeton Engine: a video supercomputer. (a) Processor element and (b) system configuration. (Courtesy of David Sarnoff Laboratories, Princeton, NJ.)

cation buses guarantees that long strings of processors can be bypassed with
a minor increase in delay. Special hardware is provided for *jumps* of 1, 8,
or 64 processors. (Communication time is 1 cycle when within a region of
less than 64 bypassed processors, with additional cycles for longer jumps, up
to a maximum of 5 instruction cycles between any two processors across the
entire array.) Reduction operations, such as *sum*, *any*, or *all* across the entire
array of processors, can be supported with additional cycles. This model of
interprocessor communication has been labeled *cut-through communication*
by [277]. In terms of SIMD taxonomy, this appears to be unique to the
Princeton Engine. In addition, general broadcast operations are provided.
For this mode, one processor acts as the *transmitter* and any number of en-
abled processors serve as receivers. The global broadcast time is, at worst,
350 ns.

The Princeton Engine also provides a second and independent communication model. A video input bus (*28 MHz × 48 bits*) transfers data into
local processor memory independently from the instruction stream. Similarly,
a video output bus (*28 MHz × 64 bits*) transfers data from local processor
memory to an output stream. Data from the linear array of processors can
be transferred into the output stream in any order under control of an *output timing sequencer* control memory. By frame-delay matching, the original
image with the transposed image, an efficient data structure can be realized
for 2D and 3D image transforms. A *feedback* mechanism, useful for transfer-
ring 32 of the 64 bits from the output channel back into the input channel,
facilitates real-time and transparent image transposes.

X1 SIMD Neurocomputer Architecture   The X1 architecture [90] was
proposed by Adaptive Solutions Inc. The X1 system consists of a single X1
chip, a linear array of X1 chips, or multiple arrays of X1 chips, cf. Figure 10.29. An X1 chip is composed of 64 simple PEs, each a digital signal
processor. The array operates in an SIMD mode: The array is sequenced
by a single controller, which contains a writable control store and a microsequencer; thus, each PE executes the same instruction at each clock. Broadcast interconnection is used in the X1 architecture to create inexpensive,
high-performance communication. In the basic X1 architecture, each neuron
is mapped onto one PE. (It is also possible to assign multiple neurons to a
PE via time-division multiplexing.) In this way, a layer of neuron units is
emulated by a linear array of PEs. The linear array can efficiently perform
matrix-vector multiplication (MVM) and other related matrix operations. At
25 MHz, the maximum performance in the nonlearning mode is 1.6 billion

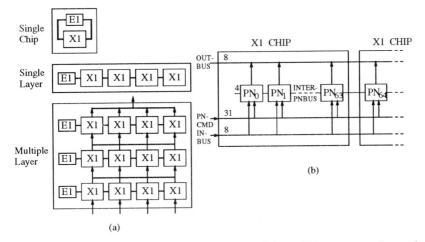

Figure 10.29: (a) An example of X1 system, (b) an X1 array configuration. (Adapted from [90].)

connections computed per second per chip, assuming the weights are 8 bits. For example, the entire NetTalk network (203 input nodes, 64 hidden nodes, and 21 output nodes) can be mapped onto a single X1 chip with high processing speed. A training set with over the 76,800 patterns can be trained with the standard back-propagation algorithm in just 8 seconds.

MUSIC: A DSP Array Processor   The MUSIC system (MUlti Signal processor system with Intelligent Communication) is a parallel distributed memory architecture based on digital signal processors (DSP) [204]. A system with 60 processor elements is operational. It has a peak performance of 3.8 GFlops, an electrical power consumption of less than 800 Watts, and fits into a 19 inch rack. The system software of MUSIC especially supports the implementation of data-parallel algorithms. This means that the same algorithm is executed on several processor elements in parallel, but each of them produces a different part of the resulting data block. This is considered a SPMD (Single Program Multiple Data) architecture.

The MUSIC system can achieve supercomputer performance for neural net simulation with an array of digital signal processors. Two applications (the back-propagation algorithm for neural net learning and molecular dynamics simulations) run approximately 6 times faster than on a CRAY Y-MP and 2 times faster than on an NEC SX-3. A sustained performance of more than 1 GFlops is reached. In summary, at a significantly lower cost, power consumption, and space requirement than conventional supercomputers, MUSIC is well suited to computationally intensive neural network applications.

10.4.3.3 MIMD Architectures

MIMD multiprocessors offer much greater architectural flexibility. The processors communicate either with a shared memory or by a message-passing scheme. In the former case, each of the processors has its own local instruction codes and has access to shared memories. In the latter case, the MIMD computer is equipped with a special hardware routing communication processor to support asynchronous data distribution. Because the interconnections can be easily time-multiplexed, this technique may help alleviate the problem of the stringent limitation on I/O pin count and other interconnection hardware. It also allows self-controlled bypassing of defective processor elements – when necessary – and thus enhances the fault-tolerance capability.

Message-passing techniques in MIMD computers depend on the routing communication processor. The communication processor enables separate processing of communication signals. That is, switching communication and neuro-processing tasks can function simultaneously. It executes local and global communication by routing messages through the network of locally interconnected processor chips. A typical message contains a control field, an address field, and several data fields. (Typical data fields are membrane potential, synapse weight, synaptical delay time, neuron threshold, and model function.)

For example, the interconnection tasks can be handled by an elaborate communication processor that allows message passing through the network [240]. Each processor has a global ID (address). Only when the processor ID matches the ID number on the message will the incoming data be retained for internal processing. Two kinds of address schemes can be hierarchically implemented: one is relative address, and the other is global address. The chip is being fabricated by a 2-μ CMOS/SOI process. There are 4 neurons with 40 synapses in a single chip. As designed, the chip has a size of 94 mm^2 and a total pin count of 64, including internal bus signals. (The size required for a neural processor is 14 mm^2, and that for a communication processor is 10 mm^2, including 6 mm^2 for the 6 serial link ports.)

One of the main applications of the MIMD neurocomputer is parallel image processing [240]. To make the neuro-computer suitable for image-processing applications, it must be able to load and store image data at video frequencies and to process data at rates that are acceptable for most industrial applications. The system is designed to support video interface and three image-processing layers, cf. Figure 10.30(a).

- **Video Bus Interface** The data-distribution network shown in Figure 10.30(b), contains a 10 Mbyte/s video bus interface and a frame buffer. The topmost neural processor serves as the interface chip whose communication processor determines the shortest connection to the target chip. An additional address generator, cf. Figure 10.30(b), has to be adopted to compute a target chip address for each 3-byte video data packet. The remaining 16 neural processors, first used as a frame buffer, are then used to redistribute the image data to the first image-processing layer, cf. Figure 10.30(a). Each neural processor in the image-preprocessing layer will handle a (32×32) segment of the original image. The frame buffer processors first compute the destination pixel and target computer address, and then distribute the buffered data to the neural processing layer.

- **Neural Processing Layers** There are several neural processing layers: preprocessing, feature extraction, and neural classifier layers. All the operations in the preprocessing layer can be executed by a very simple neural model. Several neural algorithms are implemented for feature extraction and classification. The bidirectional links between the different network layers allow us to build specialized network structures such as feedback loops for edge detection, contrast enhancement, and others. Another useful feature is that neural processors can be reprogrammed in less than 2 ms.

  1. *Preprocessing Layer* A two-dimensional 16×16 mesh of neural processors forms the first image-processing layer, holding an entire 512×512 pixel grey-tone image and the algorithmic code. Each neural processor stores at least 1K-byte segment of image data, with a 32×32 segment size. The neural processors are coded to carry out some fixed-weight preprocessing operations such as median filtering and edge detection.

  2. *Feature-Extraction Layer* The second layer performs feature-extraction operations on the preprocessed data. This is a data compression phase. The lower data rate facilitates more sophisticated neuron processing models for the next layer.

3. *Neural Classifier Layer* The third lower layer of neural processors implements trainable and self-organizing classifiers, which are used for different neural recognition experiments.

10.4.3.4   Array Processor Architectures

VLSI pipelined array processors possess the properties of modularity, regularity, local interconnection, and pipelining. Typical examples are systolic and wavefront architectures. These arrays have local instruction codes and external data that are piped into the array concurrently with the processing. A systolic array is a network of processors that rhythmically compute and pass data through the system [148, 149]. A wavefront array [154, 168] is an asynchronous, self-timed, data-driven computation array. Because there is no need to synchronize the entire array, a wavefront array is truly architecturally scalable. More significantly, it employs the asynchronous data-driven capability of dataflow machines and can, therefore, accommodate the critical problem of timing uncertainty in VLSI array systems.

The ring array requires far less complicated routing and a smaller number of processors, thus satisfying economy requirements as well. Ring architectures have been shown to be a good match to a variety of signal-processing and connectionist algorithms. The simple communication ring topology is common to several other proposed and realized machines. Similar examples are RAP [202], NeuroTurbo [117], and Intel's iWarp [27, 224].

The **RAP** [202] is a multi-DSP system targeted at the work in continuous speech recognition using connectionist algorithms. Four boards, each with 4 Texas Instruments TMS 320C30 DSPs, serve as an array processor for a 68020-based host running a real-time operating system. The overall system is controlled by a Sun workstation via Ethernet. The RAP transfers a word between DSP nodes within a single 62.5-ns cycle using FPGA design for communication hardware. In addition, it provides the ability to customize this array for different low-level communication protocols without sacrificing performance. Program development is simplified by the use of custom matrix and vector library routines. The RAP software environment provides a debugger interface that simplifies program building as well as several options for performing simulations. **Neuro-Turbo** [117] uses dual-port memories between pairs of processors to implement the communication ring. The dual-port memory approach provides no hardware communication interlock, but it presents a simple model for user-designed software management of the ring.

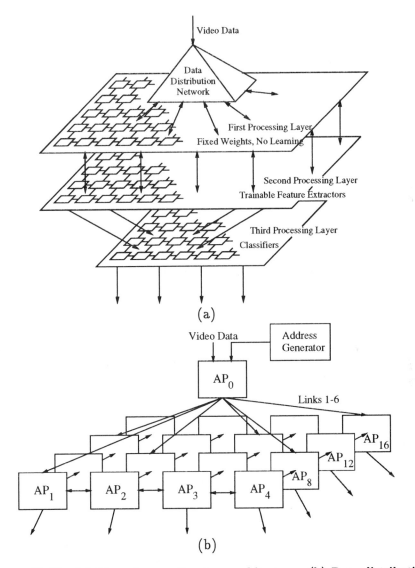

Figure 10.30: (a) Three layers of system architecture. (b) Data-distribution network. (Adapted from [240].)

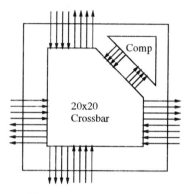

Figure 10.31: An iWarp chip consists of a computation agent and a communication agent. (Adapted from [32].)

The iWarp Array Processor   WARP, a programmable linear systolic array, consists of 10 processors. A more advanced version of WARP is the iWarp VLSI chip by Intel [27, 224]. The iWarp is a scalable parallel computing system, aimed at supporting both systolic (in a wavefront-processing fashion) and message-passing applications. The iWarp processor consists of two essentially independent agents: a computation agent and a communication agent, cf. Figure 10.31. The computation agent contains integer core hardware, floating-point hardware, memory interface, and a 128-word Register File (RF). There is an integer arithmetic unit, featuring 8/16/32-bit data operations in one clock cycle. In addition, there are floating-point adder and multiplier units (32/64-bit IEEE754 Floating Point Standard). For memory operations, internal 256-word instruction cache and 2K-word instruction ROM are included. The peak performance of iWarp consists of 20 MFLOPs, 20 MIPs, 160 Mbytes/sec memory operations, 80 Mbytes/sec data transfer (send), and 80 Mbytes/sec data transfer (receive).

Systolic computations involve few (typically < 10) calculations per data element, so a balance between I/O, memory, and CPU performance is as critical as raw CPU MFLOPs. For this purpose, the versatile communication agent is used to handle all pathway traffic and manipulation of the virtual channel buffers. The communication agent consists of 4 bidirectional pathways, each 8 bits (+control) wide and 40 Mbytes/sec per bus (320 Mbytes/sec aggregate). This allows 20 simultaneous connections through/to/from the cell. It performs asynchronous (handshaking) data transfers between computing nodes with a latency of 100 to 150 ns per word. *The versatility of the communication agents makes the iWARP favorable for consideration in constructing high-level complex systems.*

On a Warp array with 10 processors, the NETtalk neural network benchmark (based on the back-propagation algorithms) runs at 16.5 million connections per second and 70 MFLOPS. For comparison, the same benchmark runs at 36 million connections per second and 153 MFLOPS on an iWarp array of 10 processors [32].

Siemens Neurocomputer Siemens has recently developed a Neurocomputer called Synapse-1 [237]. It has a 2-D systolic array architecture, which is designed to support neural algorithms. The interface hardware with real world (namely image acquisition) is included to support an input image data rate up to 80 MByte/sec. The array consists of 4×2 MA16 ASIC chips, each representing a specific VLSI neural signal processor chip. Each chip contains a small systolic array of 16 fixed-point (16-bit $\times$ 16-bit) multipliers. (It can also be reprogrammed to perform 16-bit block floating-point operations by the same speed.) Each chip yields a performance for the retrieving phase of 640 MC/sec, (MC = $10^6 \times 16bit$ connections). In the first performance measurement for the retrieving phase, it reported 8000 folds of speed improvement over SUN IPX Sparc Workstation.

10.5 Concluding Remarks

Most neural processing algorithms are computationally iterative and intensive, and they demand very high throughput. From an architectural perspective, the main concern is to systematically derive parallel processing architectures that optimize performance. Multiprocessors, array processors, or massively parallel processors provide a natural solution. Depicted in Table 1.4 are Various neural models, presented in a unified framework. Based on this framework, neural algorithms can be expressed as basic matrix operations (such as inner-product, outer-product, and matrix multiplications). These operations, in turn, can be mapped to basic processor arrays. Detailed procedures mapping the BP multilayer network to array architectures are discussed. Performance analyses are also provided. The focus is placed on systolic/wavefront designs, because they fully harness the parallel processing potential offered by VLSI/ULSI technologies. A simulation tool covering multiple levels of simulations is needed in order to obtain an estimate closer to the real world. The development of *SISim* represents a plausible starting point.

Most existing dedicated neural processors are still limited to single-chip implementation instead of system building. General-purpose neurocomputers are necessary to support a broad range of neural networks. Multiprocessors, array processors, or massively parallel processors are appealing architectures. Neurocomputers must be based on a balanced design of *computations, memories,* and *communications.* Additional emphasis should be placed upon ease of systems integration. Therefore, a neurocomputer must be general-purpose, embracing a broad set of connectionist networks.

The goal of the digital neurocomputer is to provide a low-cost, high-speed, and flexible platform for neural processing techniques. Therefore, its development represents a total system approach to application-driven supercomputers. It should ultimately lead to real-time and intelligent supercomputing systems for future information processing.

10.6 Problems

Exercise 10.1 (a) Show that a vector-matrix multiplication $\mathbf{c}^T = \mathbf{b}^T \mathbf{A}$ can be represented by the following recursive equation.

$$c_i^{(j+1)} = c_i^{(j)} + b_i^{(j)} a_i^{(j)}$$

where j is the recursion index, $j = 1, 2, \cdots, N$, and

$$
\begin{aligned}
c_i^{(1)} &= 0 \\
a_i^{(j)} &= \mathbf{A}(j, i) \\
b_i^{(j)} &= \mathbf{b}(j)
\end{aligned}
$$

After N iterations, $\mathbf{c}$ is obtained as

$$\mathbf{c}(i) = c_i^{(N+1)}$$

(b) Derive a two-dimensional DG for the vector-matrix multiplication with $N = 4$.

(c) Find a permissible schedule vector $\vec{s}$ and projection vector $\vec{d}$ that map the DG onto a linear systolic SFG. Complete the systolic array design. What are the computation time, the pipelining period, and the block pipelining period?

Exercise 10.2 When there are multiple patterns to be retrieved, then a cubic DG for MMM in Figure 10.5(a) is considered. Design a linear systolic array with full size, that is, with 5 PEs.

Exercise 10.3 Examine the design sketch shown in Figure 10.4 and, more specifically, verify the correctness of the multiplexer control table.

Exercise 10.4 For the retrieving phase, based on Figure 10.6, give a design sketch of (a) the first PE and (b) an interior PE for the linear systolic array. (Hint: Compare with Figure 10.4.)

Exercise 10.5 For the training phase, based on Figure 10.6, give a design sketch of the first PE for the linear systolic array. (Hint: Compare with Figure 10.9.)

Exercise 10.6 Compare the area-time product performance between the linear array and the rectangular array for BP networks.

Exercise 10.7 Propose a different interleaved DG design, replacing the DG in Figure 10.7, so that the g data can be used twice in two consecutive DG nodes and, therefore, save off-chip communication.

Exercise 10.8 A different DG than that in Figure 10.8 can be obtained by routing the x data from bottom to top, as depicted in Figure 10.32(a).
(a) Show that the linear systolic array will be Figure 10.32(b).
(b) Show that the length of the FIFO in Figure 10.32(b) is shorter than that of the FIFO hidden in the first PE in Figure 10.9.
(c) Which design is more preferable, and why?

Exercise 10.9 Refer to Figure 10.11 for the block-adaptive rectangular array design. Show that it is possible to use a time-interleaved design (e.g., the same multiplier will be used to execute both the VMM and OPU operations in a time-divided fashion). Show that as many as 15 multipliers can be saved in the 7-5-3 network. However, also show that it needs more complex control and incurs much more computation time.

Exercise 10.10 Show that for the system of rectangular arrays in Figure 10.11, the latency for the entire block of M patterns can be computed as Latency = N + max(K,L) + L + N + (K-1) + (M-1). What is the latency for the 10-5-2 network with 50 patterns?

Exercise 10.11 Extend the systolic array designs (both linear and rectangular) to the *conjugate-gradient BP algorithm* on a 2-layer network. Again use a 7-5-3 structure to illustrate your design.

Exercise 10.12 Extend the rectangular-array design to a 3-layer network. Use a 6-7-5-3 structure to illustrate your design.

Exercise 10.13 The following is a pseudo program for the 7-5-3 BP neural network trained by 100 patterns. (Note that for simplicity, the multiply operation associated with η is now hidden in the nonlinear function.)

for k=1,100

```
(* MVM for lower layer *)           for j=1,5
for j=1,5                               d[j]=0;
    ul[j]=0;                            for i=1,3
    for i=1,7                               temp=g[i]*wu[i,j];
        temp=x[i]*wl[j,i];                  d[j]=d[j]+temp;
        ul[j]=ul[j]+temp;                   h[j]=nonlinearF'(a[j])*d[j];
    a[j]=nonlinearF(ul[j]);
                                        (* OPU for upper layer *)
(* MVM for upper layer *)            for i=1,3
for i=1,3                               for j=1,5
    uu[i]=0;                                temp=g[i]*a[j];
    for j=1,5                               wu[i,j]=wu[i,j]+temp;
        temp=a[j]*wu[i,j];
        uu[i]=uu[i]+temp;            (* OPU for lower layer *)
    y[i]=nonlinearF(uu[i]);          for i=1,7
                                        for j=1,5
(* VMM *)                                   temp=h[j]*x[i];
for i=1,3                                   wl[j,i]=wl[j,i]+temp;
    temp=t[i]-y[i];
    g[i]=nonlinearF'(y[i])*temp;
```

(a) For each training pattern, how many floating-point operations (*, +, -) will be executed by this program?

(b) What is the critical path in the DG, and what is the number of floating-point operations on the critical path? (Hint: Based on the this program, find the number of floating-point operations assigned to each node in Figure 10.8. Utilize the "hidden parallelism". For example, the multiplication in MVM does not have to wait until the partial sum is generated by the previous processor.)

Exercise 10.14 (a) There are 115 processors in Figure 10.11. Show that putting 3 extra processors between MVM block and VMM/OPU block to do the following operations:

$$temp=t[i]-y[i];$$
$$g[i]=nonlinearF'(y[i])*temp;$$

will change the critical path and, in effect, reduce the number of floating-point operations on the critical path. Therefore, the utilization rate can be increased.

(b) Show that it is possible to use 5 more processors between the VMM block and OPU block for the lower layer to increase the utilization rate to 88.6%. (The number of processors now totals 123.)

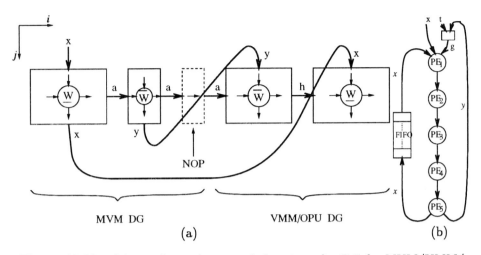

Figure 10.32: (a) An alternative cascaded rectangular DG for MVM/VMM/ OPU. (b) The corresponding systolic array design.

Exercise 10.15 (Ring Systolic Design for Hopfield Feedback Networks)
The systolic design for the retrieving phase in Section 10.2.2 can be adapted for the Hopfield model. This will naturally lead to a linear ring array. The important feature for any feedback neural network is that the same DGs will be repeated for many iterations. This necessitates a modification of the DG design described in the following discussion. To facilitate data arrangement, a proper modification is useful on the MVM DG: The data ordering of the $\{w_{ij}\}$ elements can be rearranged so that the direction of the inputs $\{a_i(k)\}$ in the DG becomes aligned with that of the outputs $\{a_i(k + 1)\}$ [152], as depicted in Figure 10.33(a).

(a) Based on this new cascaded DG, mapping by a linear projection and a linear schedule can lead to a ring systolic architecture, as shown in Figure 10.33(b). What is the projection vector $\vec{d}$ and the schedule vector $\vec{s}$?

(b) Show that the pipelining period of this design is 1, which implies 100% utilization efficiency.

(c) This design leads to a ring architecture with a (global) spiral communication link. What is the number of delays on that link?

(d) Give a brief description of the data operations and movements in the ring systolic design.

(e) Verify the schematic diagrams for the logic-level PE design in Figure 10.34. Describe the basic processor element design requirements.

Exercise 10.16 (Ring Systolic Design for BAM) Show that the previous design in Problem 10.15 can be adapted for Kosko's BAM. The basic structure of BAM is a two-layer network, with the upper and lower layers having symmetric weights. Thus, one set of weights would suffice. The Hopfield model can be regarded

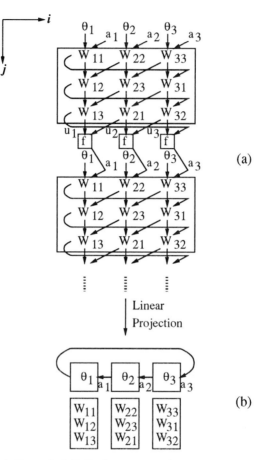

(a)

(b)

Figure 10.33: (a) Cascaded DGs for consecutive matrix-vector multiplication formulation. (b) The corresponding ring systolic array. In this DG, the i-th row of the $\mathbf{W}$ matrix is placed on the i-th column of the $\{w_{ij}\}$ data array in DG; and for $i = 1, 2, \ldots, N$, the i-th column of the $\{w_{ij}\}$ data array is circularly shifted up by $i - 1$ positions. Because the input (from the top) and the output (at the bottom) are now aligned in the same direction, many copies of such DGs can be cascaded top-down, with input and output data perfectly interfaced.

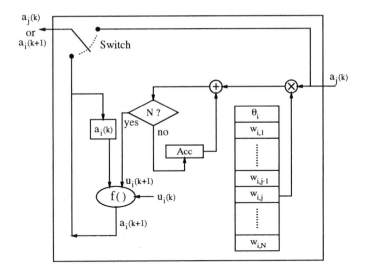

Figure 10.34: A simple sketch of a PE design for the retrieving phase in a ring array.

as a special case of BAM, therefore, the same systolic design for the Hopfield models can be carried through to BAM.

Exercise 10.17 Map the APEX network for principal-component extraction (Chapter 8) onto a full-size ring systolic array.

Exercise 10.18 Design linear systolic arrays for the supervised learning vector quantization (LVQ) algorithm.

Exercise 10.19 Suppose you have a two-layer back-propagation network (8 inputs/8 hidden neurons/2 outputs) to be implemented by a 4-PE ring systolic array. Work out a partitioning scheme for (1) the retrieving phase and (2) the training phase.

Exercise 10.20 Discuss two application examples when one would want to use (1) the analog approach, and (2) the digital approach.

Exercise 10.21 By the partitioning scheme, design a linear systolic array with only 3 PEs for the cubic DG in Figure 10.5(a).

Exercise 10.22 Map a two-layer back-propagation algorithm to a hypercube-connected parallel processor like the Connection Machine. Evaluate the performance. What is the potential bottleneck?

Exercise 10.23 (Neural Processing Units Based on CORDIC Processors)
A CORDIC scheme is an iterative method based on a bit-level shift-and-add operation. It is especially suitable for computing a specific set of functions, including rotations of two-dimensional vectors, trigonometric functions, logarithms, multiplications, and divisions [7, 59, 152, 292]. For example, by using a rotation operator R_m^α, a 2-dimensional vector $\mathbf{v} = [x, y]$ can be rotated by an angle α:

$$\mathbf{v}' = R_m^\alpha \mathbf{v}$$

where

$$R_m^\alpha = \begin{bmatrix} \cos\sqrt{m}\alpha & -\sqrt{m}\sin\sqrt{m}\alpha \\ \frac{1}{\sqrt{m}}\sin\sqrt{m}\alpha & \cos\sqrt{m}\alpha \end{bmatrix}$$

$$= K \begin{bmatrix} 1 & -\sqrt{m}\tan\sqrt{m}\alpha \\ \frac{1}{\sqrt{m}}\tan\sqrt{m}\alpha & 1 \end{bmatrix}$$

and the scaling constant $K = \cos\sqrt{m}\alpha$. Parameter m characterizes three possible arithmetic operations, namely, the circular ($m = 1$), the linear ($m = 0$) and the hyperbolic ($m = -1$) operations [7, 59, 152, 292].

(a) Show that, in the linear coordinate system ($m = 0$), a CORDIC can be used for MAC operations. Note that the rotation operator can be simplified as

$$R_0^\alpha = \begin{bmatrix} 1 & 0 \\ \alpha & 1 \end{bmatrix}$$

Given x, y, and α, we can get the CORDIC output $y + x\alpha$ [7], which is very useful for propagation-rule operations in neural processing units.

(b) Show that, in the hyperbolic coordinate system ($m = -1$), the rotation operator can be simplified to

$$R_{-1}^\alpha = K \begin{bmatrix} 1 & \tanh\alpha \\ \tanh\alpha & 1 \end{bmatrix} \tag{10.15}$$

Note that the nonlinear sigmoid activation function bears the form

$$f(u) = \frac{1}{1 + e^{-u}} = (1/2)(1 + \tanh(u/2)) \tag{10.16}$$

where u is the net input of the neuron. By comparing Eq. 10.15 and Eq. 10.16, it is easily seen that the sigmoid activation function can be implemented by setting $m = -1$, $\mathbf{v} = [1, 1]$, and $\alpha = u/2$ [7]. (The scaling operation K is not necessary here.)

(c) Perform a general feasibility study on using CORDIC processors as neural arithmetic units. Show that a CORDIC (coordinate rotation digital computer) requires much less silicon area than an array multiplier for the same number of bits. If speed is more critical than area, show that bit-level pipelined CORDIC designs can be implemented [59, 278].

Bibliography

[1] E. Aarts and J. Korst. *Simulated Annealing and Boltzmann Machine*. John Wiley, New York, 1989. (*pp.* 331,336)

[2] N. I. Achieser. *Theory of Approximation*. C. J. Hyman (Transl.), Ungar, N.Y., 1956. (*p.* 170)

[3] D. H. Ackley, G. E. Hinton, and T. J. Sejnowski. A learning algorithm for Boltzmann machines. *Cognitive Science*, 9:147–169, 1985. (*pp.* 329,333)

[4] M. Ade, R. Lauwereins, and J. Peperstraete. A fast simulator for neural networks on DSPs or FPGAs. In S. Y. Kung, F. Fallside, J. A. Sorensen, and C. A. Kamm, editors, *Neural Networks for Signal Processing, II*. Proceedings of the 1992 IEEE Workshop, Helsingoer, Denmark, 1992. (*p.* 377)

[5] A. J. Agranat et al. A CCD based neural network integrated circuit with 64k analog programmable synapses. In *Proceedings, International Joint Conference on Neural Networks*, volume II, pages 551–555, San Diego, June 1990. (*pp.* 339,373,374)

[6] S. C. Ahalt, P. Chen, and A. K. Krishnamurthy. Performance analysis of two image vector quantization techniques. In *Proceedings, International Joint Conference on Neural Networks*, pages I 169– I 175, Washington, D.C., 1989. (*p.* 88)

[7] H. M. Ahmed. Alternative arithmetic unit architectures for VLSI digital signal processors. In S. Y. Kung, H. J. Whitehouse, and T. Kailath, editors, *VLSI and Modern Signal Processing*, chapter 16, pages 277–306. Prentice Hall, Englewood Cliffs, NJ, 1985. (*p.* 412)

[8] H. Akaike. Fitting autoregressive models for prediction. *Annals of Institute of Statistical Mathematics*, 21, 1969. (*pp.* 10,172)

[9] H. Akaike. A new look at the statistical model identification. *IEEE Transactions on Automatic Control*, 19:716–723, 1974. (*p.* 10)

[10] L. A. Akers, M. R. Walker, D. K. Ferry, and R. O. Grondin. Limited interconnectivity in synthetic systems. In R. Eckmiller and C. V. D. Malsburg, editors, *Neural Computers, Computer and Systems Science Series*, pages 407–416. Springer-Verlag, New York, 1988. (*pp.* 14,76,339,382)

413

[11] J. Alspector and R. B. Allen. A neuromorphic VLSI learning systems. In P. Losleben, editor, *Advanced Research on VLSI*, pages 313–349. MIT Press, Cambridge, MA, 1987. (*pp.* 14,339,376)

[12] J. Alspector, R. B. Allen, V. Hu, and S. Satyanarayana. Stochastic learning networks and their electronic implementation. In *Proceedings, IEEE, Conference on Neural Information Processing Systems — Natural and Synthetic*, pages 9–21, Denver, November 1987. (*p.* 376)

[13] J. Alspector, A. Jayakumar, and B. Ngo. An electronic parallel neural CAM for decoding. In S. Y. Kung, F. Fallside, J. A. Sorensen, and C. A. Kamm, editors, *Neural Networks for Signal Processing, II*, pages 581–587. Proceedings of the 1992 IEEE Workshop, Helsingoer, Denmark, 1992. (*p.* 376)

[14] S. I. Amari. Characteristics of randomly connected threshold-element network systems. *Proceedings of the IEEE*, 59:35–47, January 1971. (*p.* 43)

[15] J. A. Anderson. A simple neural network generating an interactive memory. *Mathematical Biosciences*, 14:197–220, 1972. (*p.* 43)

[16] J. A. Anderson. *Neurocomputing — Paper Collections*. MIT Press, Cambridge, MA, 1988. (*pp.* 2,76)

[17] T. Ash. Dynamic node creation in backpropagation networks. *Connection Science*, 1:365–376, 1989. (*p.* 183)

[18] L. R. Bahl, F. Jelinek, and R. L. Mercer. A maximum likelihood approach to continuous speech recognition. *IEEE Transactions on Pattern Analysis and Machine Intelligence*, 5(2):179–190, March 1983. (*pp.* 243,258)

[19] P. Baldi and K. Hornik. Neural networks for principal component analysis : Learning from examples without local minima. *Neural Networks*, 2:53–58, 1989. (*pp.* 289,290)

[20] D. H. Ballard, G. E. Hinton, and T. J. Sejnowski. Parallel visual computation. *Nature*, 306:21–26, 1983. (*p.* 316)

[21] A. Barr and E. Feigenbaum. *The Handbook of Artificial Intelligence*. W. Kaufmann, San Mateo, CA, 1981. (*p.* 259)

[22] A. Barron. Universal approximation bounds for superpositions of a sigmoidal function. 1991. Also in Proceedings, IEEE International Symposium on Information Theory, Budapest, June, 1991. (*p.* 171)

[23] E. B. Baum and D. Haussler. What size net gives valid generalization? In D. S. Touretzky, editor, *Advances in Neural Information Processing Systems*, volume 1, pages 81–90. Morgan Kaufmann, San Mateo, CA, 1989. (*p.* 10)

[24] L. E. Baum. A maximization technique occurring in the statistical analysis of probabilistic functions of Markov chains. *Annals of Mathematical Statistics*, 41:164–171, 1970. (*p.* 268)

[25] L. E. Baum and J. A. Eagon. An inequality with applications to statistical estimation for probabilistic function of Markov processes and a model for ecology. *American Mathematics Society Bulletin*, 73:360–363, May 1967. (*pp.* 249,252)

[26] L. E. Baum, T. Petrie, G. Soules, and N. Weiss. A maximization technique occurring in the statistical analysis of probabilistic functions of Markov chains. *Annals of Mathematical Statistics*, 41:164–171, 1970. (*p.* 252)

[27] B. Baxter et al. Building blocks for a new generation of application-specific computing systems. In S. Y. Kung et al., editor, *Application-Specific Array Processors*, pages 190–201. IEEE Computer Society Press, Los Almitos, CA, 1990. (*pp.* 402,404)

[28] J. Besag. Spatial interaction and statistical analysis of lattice system (with discussion). *Journal of Royal Statistics Society, series B*, 36:192–236, 1974. (*p.* 325)

[29] J. Besag. On the statistical analysis of dirty pictures. *Journal of Royal Statistics Society, series B*, 48(3):192–236, 1986. (*pp.* 325,326)

[30] E. L. Bienenstock, L. N. Cooper, and P. W. Munro. Theory for the development of neuron selectivity: orientation specificity and binocular interaction in visual cortex. *Journal of Neuroscience*, 2:32–48, 1982. (*p.* 87)

[31] R. R. Bitmead and B. D. O. Anderson. Exponentially convergent behavior of simple stochastic adaptive estimation algorithms. In *Proceedings, 17-th IEEE Conference on Decision and Control*, pages 580–585, Fort Lauderdale, FL, December 1979. (*p.* 151)

[32] S. Borkar et al. iWarp: An integrated solution to high speed parallel processing. In *Proceedings, Supercomputing*, pages 300–339. IEEE Computer Society Press, Washington, D.C., 1988. (*pp.* 404,405)

[33] H. Bourlard and Y. Kamp. Auto-association by multilayer perceptrons and singular value decomposition. *Biological Cybernetics*, 59:291–294, 1988. (*pp.* 289,291)

[34] H. Bourlard and C. J. Wellekens. Multilayer perceptrons and automatic speech recognition. In *Proceedings, First IEEE International Conference on Neural Networks*, pages IV407–IV416, San Diego, June 1987. (*p.* 266)

[35] H. Bourlard and C. J. Wellekens. Speech pattern discrimination and multilayer perceptrons. *Computer Speech and Language*, pages 1–19, 1989. (*p.* 217)

[36] N. H. Brown. Neural network implementation approaches for the connection machine. In *Proceedings, IEEE, Conference on Neural Information Processing Systems — Natural and Synthetic*, Denver, November 1987. (*pp.* 14,339,394)

[37] J. P. Burg. Maximum entropy spectral analysis. Ph.D. thesis, Department of Electrical Engineering, Stanford University, 1975. (*p.* 233)

[38] Jr. C. R. Johnson. Adaptive IIR filtering: current results and open issues. *IEEE Transactions on Information Theory*, Vol. IT-30(2):237–250, 1984. (*p.* 214)

[39] D. Callaerts, J. Vandewalle, W. Sansen, and M. Moonen. On-line algorithm for signal separation based on SVD. In E. F. Deprettere, editor, *SVD and Signal Processing*, pages 269–276. Elsevier - North Holland, New York, 1988. (*p.* 298)

[40] S. M. Caroll and B. W. Dickinson. Construction of neural nets using the Radon transform. In *Proceedings, International Joint Conference Neural Networks*, pages 607–611, Washington, D.C., 1989. (*p.* 171)

[41] G. A. Carpenter and S. Grossberg. Art2: Self-organization of stable category recognition codes for analog input patterns. In *Proceedings, IEEE International Conference on Neural Networks*, pages II 727– II 736, San Diego, 1987. (*p.* 79)

[42] Y. Censor. Row-action methods for huge and sparse systems and their applications. *SIAM Review*, 23:444–466, October 1981. (*p.* 150)

[43] P. C. Chang and B. H. Juang. Discriminative template training for dynamic programming speech recognition. *IEEE Transactions on Signal Processing*, in press. (*p.* 139)

[44] T. S. Chang and K. Abdel-Ghaffar. A universal neural net with guaranteed convergence to zero system error. *IEEE Transactions on Signal Processing*, in press. (*p.* 183)

[45] Y. Chauvin. A back-propagation algorithm with optimal use of hidden units. In David S. Touretzky, editor, *Advances in Neural Information Processing Systems*, volume 1, pages 519–526. Morgan Kaufmann, 1989. (*p.* 180)

[46] H. Chen and R. Liu. An alternative proof of convergence for Kung-Diamantaras APEX algorithm. In B. H. Juang, S. Y. Kung, and C. A. Kamm, editors, *Neural Networks for Signal Processing*. Proceedings of the 1991 IEEE Workshop, Princeton, NJ, 1991. (*p.* 308)

[47] A. Chiang. CCDs for pattern recognition. In S. Y. Kung, F. Fallside, J. A. Sorensen, and C. A. Kamm, editors, *Neural Networks for Signal Processing, II*, pages 606–616. Proceedings of the 1992 IEEE Workshop, Helsingoer, Denmark, 1992. (*p.* 374)

[48] A. Chiang, R. Mountain, J. Reinold, J. LaFranchise, and G. Lincoln. A programmable CCD signal processor. In *Proceedings, IEEE International Solid-State Circuits Conference, ISSCC90*, pages 146–148, San Francisco, 1990. (*pp.* 339,373,374)

[49] D. Chin et al. The princeton engine: A real-time video system simulator. In *IEEE Transactions on Consumer Electronics*, volume 34, pages 285–298, 1988. (*pp.* 394,396)

[50] P. A. Chou. The capacity of the Kanerva associative memory. *IEEE Transactions on Information Theory*, IT-35:281–298, 1989. (*p.* 60)

[51] W. H. Chou. SISim: A System-level Interactive Simulator. Technical Report, Computer Engineering Group, Department of Electrical Engineering, Princeton University, 1991. (*p.* 365)

[52] L. O. Chua and L. Yang. Cellular neural networks: theory and applications. *IEEE Transactions on Circuits and Systems*, 35(10):1257–1290, 1988. (*pp.* 215,224)

[53] J. Connor, L. E. Atlas, and D. R. Martin. Recurrent networks and NARMA modeling. In J. E. Moody, S. J. Hanson, and R. P. Lippman, editors, *Advances*

in Neural Information Processing Systems, volume 4, pages 301–308. Morgan Kaufmann, San Mateo, CA, 1992. (*p.* 232)

[54] N. E. Cotter. The Stone-Weierstrass theorem and its application to neural networks. *IEEE Transactions on Neural Networks*, 1(4):290–295, December 1990. (*p.* 170)

[55] J. D. Cowan and D. H. Sharp. Neural nets. Technical Report, Mathematics Department, University of Chicago, 1987. (*pp.* 2)

[56] Y. Le Cun, J. S. Denker, and S. A. Solla. Optimal brain damage. In David S. Touretzky, editor, *Advances in Neural Information Processing Systems*, volume II, pages 599–605. Morgan Kaufmann, San Mateo, CA, 1990. (*pp.* 167,180)

[57] G. Cybenko. Approximation by superpositions of a sigmoidal function. *Mathematics of Control, Signals and Systems*, 2:303–314, 1989. (*p.* 169)

[58] *DARPA Neural Network Study*. AFCEA International Press, 1988. (*pp.* 4,18,371)

[59] E. Deprettere, P. Dewilde, and P. Udo. Pipelined cordic architecture for fast VLSI filtering and array processing. In *Proceedings, IEEE International Conference on Acoustics, Speech, and Signal Processing*, pages 41.A.6.1 – 41.A.6.4, San Diego, 1984. (*pp.* 412)

[60] P. Dewilde and E. Deprettere. Singular value decomposition: An introduction. In E. Deprettere, editor, *SVD and Signal Processing*, pages 3–41. Elsevier - North Holland, New York, 1988. (*p.* 296)

[61] R. O. Duda and P. E. Hart. *Pattern Classification and Scene Analysis*. John Wiley, New York, 1973. (*pp.* 114,129,140,190,303)

[62] G. Eichmann and H. J. Caulfield. Optical learning (inference) machines. *Applied Optics*, 24, 1985. (*p.* 378)

[63] Y. Epharaim, D. Malah, and B. H. Juang. Application of hidden Markov models for enhancing noisy speech. *IEEE Transactions on Acoustics, Speech, and Signal Processing*, 37(12):1846–1856, December 1989. (*p.* 258)

[64] S. E. Fahlman and C. Lebiere. The cascade-correlation learning architecture. In D. Touretzky, editor, *Advances in Neural Information Processing Systems*, volume II, pages 524–532. Morgan Kaufmann, San Mateo, CA, 1990. (*pp.* 183,304)

[65] N. H. Farhat, D. Psaltis, A. Prata, and E. Paek. Optical implementation of the Hopfield model. *Applied Optics*, 24:1469–1475, May 1985. (*pp.* 14,339,378,379)

[66] A. D. Fisher and J. N. Lee. Optical associative processing elements with versatile adaptive learning capability. In *Proceedings, IEEE, COMPCOM Meeting*, volume 137-140, 1985. (*pp.* 14,339,379)

[67] J. L. Flanagan. Computers that talk and listen: Man-machine communication by voice. *Proceedings, IEEE*, 4:416–432, April 1976. (*p.* 21)

[68] P. Foldiak. Adaptive network for optimal linear feature extraction. In *Proceedings, International Joint Conference on Neural Networks*, pages I 401 – I 406, Washington, D.C., 1989. (*p.* 283)

[69] G. D. Forney. The Viterbi algorithm. *Proceedings of the IEEE*, 61:268–278, Mar 1973. (*p.* 263)

[70] P. W. Frey and D. J. Slate. Letter recognition using holland-style adaptive classifier. *Machine Learning*, 6(2):161–182, March 1991. (*pp.* 133)

[71] K. S. Fu. *Syntactical Pattern Recognition and Applications*. Prentice Hall, Englewood Cliffs, NJ, 1982. (*p.* 24)

[72] K. Fukunaga and W. C. G. Koontz. Applications of the Karhunen Loeve expansion to feature extraction and ordering. In *IEEE Transactions on Computers*, volume C-19, pages 311–318, 1970. (*p.* 302)

[73] K. Fukushima. Cognitron: A self-organizing multilayered neural network. *Biological Cybernetics*, 20:121–136, 1975. (*pp.* 73,91)

[74] K. Fukushima. A neural network for visual pattern recognition. *IEEE Computer Magazine*, 21(3):65–76, March 1988. (*pp.* 91,92,93)

[75] K. Fukushima, S. Miyaki, and T. Ito. Neocognitron: A neural network model for a mechanism for visual pattern recognition. *IEEE Transaction on Systems, Man and Cybernetics*, SMC-13:826–834, 1983. (*p.* 91)

[76] K. Funahashi. On the approximate realization of continuous mappings by neural networks. *Neural Networks*, pages 183–192, 1989. (*p.* 169)

[77] D. Geiger and A. Yuille. A common framework for image segmentation. In *International Journal of Computer Vision*, volume 6:3, pages 227–243, 1991. (*p.* 327)

[78] S. Geman, E. Bienenstock, and R. Doursat. Neural networks and the bias/variance dilemma. *Neural Computation*, 4:1–58, 1992. (*p.* 175)

[79] S. Geman and D. Geman. Stochastic relaxation, Gibbs distributions, and the Bayesian restoration of images. *IEEE Transactions on Pattern Analysis and Machine Intelligence*, Vol. 6:721–741, November 1984. (*pp.* 316,326)

[80] G. Golub and C. F. Van Loan. *Matrix Computations, 2nd ed.* Johns Hopkins University Press, Baltimore, MD, 1989. (*p.* 283)

[81] G. H. Golub, M. Health, and G. Wahba. Generalized cross-validation as a method for choosing a good ridge parameter. *Technometric*, 21(2):215–223, 1979. (*p.* 173)

[82] G. H. Golub and C. Reinsch. Singular value decomposition and least squares solutions. *Numerische Mathematik*, 14:403–420, 1970. (*p.* 304)

[83] R. C. Gonzalez and P. Wintz. *Digital Image Processing*. Addison-Wesley, Reading, MA, 1977. (*pp.* 296,297)

[84] J. W. Goodman, F. J. Leonberger, S. Y. Kung, and R. A. Athale. Optical interconnections for VLSI systems. *Proceedings, IEEE*, 72:850–866, July 1984. (*p.* 378)

[85] A. R. Gourlay and G. A. Watson. *Computational Methods for Matrix Eigenproblems*. John Wiley, New York, 1973. (*pp.* 305,307)

[86] H. P. Graf and P. deVegvar. A CMOS implementation of a neural network model. In P. Losleben, editor, *Advanced Research on VLSI*, pages 351–367. MIT Press, Cambridge, MA, 1987. (*pp. 14,339,375,387*)

[87] H. P. Graf, W. Hubbard, L. D. Jackel, and P. G. N. DeVegvar. A CMOS associative memory chip. In *Proceedings, First IEEE International Conference on Neural Networks*, volume III, pages 461–468, San Diego, 1987. (*p. 375*)

[88] S. Grossberg. Adaptive pattern classification and universal recoding: Part 1. parallel development and coding of neural feature detectors. *Biological Cybernetics*, 23:121–134, 1976. (*pp. 27,73,79*)

[89] C. L. Giles, C. B. Miller, D. Chen, H. H. Chen, G.Z. Sun, and Y. C. Lee. Learning and extracting finite state automata with second-order recurrent neural networks. *Neural Computation*, 4(3):393, 1992. See also "Inserting rules into recurrent neural networks", C. L. Giles and C. W. Omlin, in Proceedings of the 1992 IEEE Workshop, Helsingoer, Denmark. (*p. 233*)

[90] D. Hammerstrom. A VLSI architecture for high-performance, low-cost, on-chip learning. In *Proceedings, International Joint Conference on Neural Networks*, pages II 537 – 543, San Diego, 1990. (*pp. 398,399*)

[91] S. J. Hanson and L. Y. Pratt. Comparing biases for minimal network construction with back-propagation. In David S. Touretzky, editor, *Advances in Neural Information Processing Systems*, volume 1, pages 177–185. Morgan Kaufmann, San Mateo, CA, 1989. (*p. 180*)

[92] D. O. Hebb. *The Organization of Behavior*. John Wiley, New York, 1949. (*p. 27*)

[93] R. Hecht-Nielsen. Performance limits of optics, electro-optics, and electronic neurocomputers. In *Proceedings, SPIE, Optical and Hybrid Computing*, volume 634, 1987. (*pp. 14,378*)

[94] R. Hecht-Nielsen. *Neurocomputing*. Addison-Wesley, Reading, MA, 1990. (*p. 393*)

[95] J. Hertz, A. Krogh, and R. G. Palmer. *Introduction to the Theory of Neural Computation*. Addison-Wesley, Reading, MA, 1991. (*p. 317*)

[96] W. D. Hillis. *The Connection Machine*. The MIT Press, Cambridge, MA, 1985. (*p. 394*)

[97] G. E. Hinton. Connectionist learning procedure. Technical Report CMU-CS-87-115, Carnegie Mellon University, September 1987. (*pp. 75,159,235*)

[98] G. E. Hinton and T. J. Sejnowski. Learning and relearning in Boltzmann machine. In D. E. Rumelhart, J. L. McClelland, and the PDP Research Group, editors, *Parallel Distributed Processing (PDP): Exploration in the Microstructure of Cognition*, volume 1, chapter 7, pages 282–317. The MIT Press, Cambridge, MA, 1986. (*pp. 314,316,328,329,333*)

[99] H. S. Hinton. Architectural considerations for photonic switching networks. *IEEE Journal on Selected Areas of Communication*, 6(7):1209–1226, 1988. (*p. 380*)

[100] J. Hoekstra. (Junction) charge-coupled device technology for artificial neural networks. In U. Ramacher and U. Ruckert, editors, *VLSI Design of Neural Networks*, chapter 2, pages 19–45. Kluwer, Norwell, MA, 1991. (*pp.* 339,373)

[101] R. M. Holdaway. Enhancing supervised learning algorithms via self-organization. In *IEEE International Joint Conference on Neural Networks*, volume II, pages 523–530, Washington, D.C., 1989. (*p.* 179)

[102] M. Holler et al. An electrically trainable artificial neural network (ETANN) with 10240 floating gate synapses. In *Proceedings, International Joint Conference on Neural Networks*, pages 11–191, Washington, D.C., June 1989. (*pp.* 339,373,374)

[103] V. Honavar and L. Uhr. A network of neuron-like units that learns to perceive by generation as well as reweighting of its links. Computer Science Technical Report 793, University of Wisconsin, Madison, 1988. (*p.* 183)

[104] J. J. Hopfield. Neural network and physical systems with emergent collective computational abilities. *Proceedings of the National Academy of Science*, 79:2554–2558, 1982. (*pp.* 44,51)

[105] J. J. Hopfield. Neurons with graded response have collective computational properties like those of two-state neurons. *Proceedings of the National Academy of Science*, 81:3088–3092, 1984. (*pp.* 44,51,52,54,65)

[106] J. J. Hopfield and D. W. Tank. Neural computation of decision in optimization problems. *Biological Cybernetics*, 52:141–152, 1985. (*pp.* 14,44,51,52,311,339,370)

[107] Y. H. Hu, W. J. Tompkins, and Q. Xue. Artificial neural networks for ECG arryhthmia monitoring. In S. Y. Kung, F. Fallside, J. A. Sorensen, and C. A. Kamm, editors, *Neural Networks for Signal Processing, II*, pages 350–359. Proceedings of the 1992 IEEE Workshop, Helsingoer, Denmark, 1992. (*p.* 231)

[108] Y. H. Hu, Qiuzhen Xue, and W. J. Tompkins. Structural simplification of a feed-forward, multi-layer perceptron artificial neural network. Proceedings, IEEE International Conference on Acoustics, Speech, and Signal Processing, May 1991. (*pp.* 180,183)

[109] W. Huang and R. Lippmann. Comparison between neural network and conventional classifiers. In *Proceedings, First IEEE International Conference on Neural Networks*, San Diego, 1987. (*pp.* 242,258)

[110] J. N. Hwang and H. Li. A surface reconstruction neural network for absolute orientation problems. In B. H. Juang, S. Y. Kung, and C. A. Kamm, editors, *Neural Networks for Signal Processing, I*, pages 513–522. Proceedings of the 1991 IEEE Workshop, Princeton, NJ, 1991. (*p.* 186)

[111] J. N. Hwang and Hang Li. Interactive query learning for isolated speech recognition. In S. Y. Kung, F. Fallside, J. A. Sorensen, and C. A. Kamm, editors, *Neural Networks for Signal Processing, II*, pages 93–102. Proceedings of the 1992 IEEE Workshop, Helsingoer, Denmark, 1992. (*pp.* 189,217)

[112] J. N. Hwang, J. A. Vlontzos, and S. Y. Kung. Systolic architectures for hidden Markov models. In *Proceedings, SPIE Visual Comm. and Image Processing III, Cambridge, Massachusetts*, pages 328–335, November 1988. (*pp.* 238,247)

[113] J. N. Hwang, J. A. Vlontzos, and S. Y. Kung. A systolic neural network architecture for hidden Markov models. *IEEE Transactions on Acoustics, Speech and Signal Processing*, 37(12):1967–1979, December 1989. (*pp.* 238,247,361,362)

[114] J.N. Hwang and Y. H. Tseng. 3d motion estimation using single perspective sparse range data via surface reconstruction neural networks. In *Submitted to International Joint Conference on Neural Networks*, San Francisco, CA, March 1993. (*p.* 186)

[115] K. Hwang and J. Ghosh. Hypernets for parallel processing with connectionist architectures. Technical Report CRI-87-03, University of Southern California, January 1987. (*pp.* 12,339)

[116] INMOS. *Transputer Development System*. Prentice Hall, Englewood Cliffs, NJ, 1988. (*p.* 381)

[117] A. Iwata et al. An artificial neural network accelerator using general purpose floating point digital signal processors. In *Proceedings, International Joint Conference on Neural Networks*, pages 171–175. Washington, D.C., June 1989. (*p.* 402)

[118] A. K. Jain. *Fundamentals of Digital Image Processing*. Prentice Hall, Englewood Cliffs, NJ, 1989. (*pp.* 22,208,273,296)

[119] F. Jelinek. The development of an experimental discrete dictation recognizer. *Proceedings, IEEE*, 73(11):1616–1624, November 1985. (*pp.* 242,258)

[120] I. C. Jou, Y. J. Tsay, S. C. Tsay, Q. Z. Wu, and S. S. Yu. Parallel distributed processing with multiple one-output back-propagation neural networks. In *Proceedings, International Symposium on Circuits and Systems, Singapore*, pages 1408–1411, 1991. (*p.* 187)

[121] J. Y. Jou and J. A. Abraham. Fault-tolerant matrix arithmetic and signal processing on highly concurrent computing structures. *Proceedings of the IEEE*, 74:732–741, May 1986. (*p.* 363)

[122] B. H. Juang. On the hidden Markov model and dynamic time warping for speech recognition — a unified view. *AT&T Bell Laboratories Technical Journal*, 63(7):1213–1243, September 1984. (*p.* 255)

[123] B. H. Juang and S. Katagiri. Discriminative learning for minimum error classification. *IEEE Transactions on Signal Processing*, in press. (*p.* 127)

[124] B. H. Juang, S. Y. Kung, and C. A. Kamm (Editors). *Neural Networks for Signal Processing*. Proceedings of the 1991 IEEE Workshop, Princeton, NJ, 1991. (*pp.* 7,185)

[125] B. H. Juang and L. R. Rabiner. Mixture autoregressive hidden Markov models for speech signals. *IEEE Transactions on Acoustics, Speech and Signal Processing*, ASSP-33(6):1404–1413, December 1985. (*pp.* 242,258,266,268)

[126] T. Kailath. *Linear Systems*. Prentice Hall, Englewood Cliffs, NJ, 1980. (*pp.* 40,210)

[127] R. E. Kalman. A new approach to linear filtering and prediction problems. *Journal of Basic Engineering*, 82:35–45, 1960. (*p.* 233)

[128] S. Katagiri, C. H. Lee, and B. H. Juang. A generalized probabilistic decent method. In *Proceedings, Acous. Sco. of Japan, pages 141-142, Nagoya*, Sep. 1990. (*pp.* 126,127)

[129] S. Katagiri, C. H. Lee, and B. H. Juang. Discriminative multi-layer feedforward networks. In B. H. Juang, S. Y. Kung, and C. A. Kamm, editors, *Neural Networks for Signal Processing, I*. Proceedings of the 1991 IEEE Workshop, Princeton, NJ, 1991. (*p.* 127)

[130] M. Kawato, Y. Uno, and M. Isobe. A hierarchical model for voluntary movement and its application to robotics. In *Proceedings, First IEEE International Conference on Neural Networks*, volume IV, pages 573–582, San Diego, June 1987. (*p.* 191)

[131] S. Kayalar and H. L. Weinert. Error bounds for the method of alternating projections. *Mathematics of Control, Signals, and Systems*, 1:43–59, 1988. (*p.* 151)

[132] S. Kirkpatrick, C. D. Gelatt Jr., and M. P. Vecci. Optimization by simulated annealing. *Science*, 220(4598):671–680, May 1983. (*p.* 316)

[133] J. Kittler. The subspace approach to pattern recognition. In R. Trappl, G. J. Klir, and L. Ricciardi, editors, *Progress in Cybernetics and Systems Research*. Hemisphere, Washington, D.C., 1978. (*p.* 302)

[134] C. Koch, J. Marroquin, and A. Yuille. Analog neuronal networks in early vision. *Proceedings, National Academy Science*, 83:4263–4267, 1986. (*p.* 311)

[135] T. Kohonen. Correlation matrix memories. *IEEE Transactions on Computers*, C-21:353–359, 1972. (*p.* 43)

[136] T. Kohonen. Self-organized formation of topologically correct feature map. *Biological Cybernetics*, 43:59–69, 1982. (*pp.* 74,85)

[137] T. Kohonen. *Self-Organization and Associative Memory, Series in Information Science*, volume 8. Springer-Verlag, New York, 1984. (*pp.* 73,74,85,116,117,122)

[138] T. Kohonen. Workstation-based phonetic typewriter. In B. H. Juang, S. Y. Kung, and C. A. Kamm, editors, *Neural Networks for Signal Processing, I*, pages 279–288. Proceedings of the 1991 IEEE Workshop, Princeton, NJ, 1991. (*p.* 258)

[139] J. Komlos and R. Paturi. Convergence results in an associative memory model. *Neural Networks*, 1:239–250, 1988. (*p.* 60)

[140] G. A. Korn and T. M. Korn. *Mathematical Handbook for Scientists and Engineers*. McGraw-Hill, New York, 1961. (*p.* 223)

[141] B. Kosko. Adaptive bidirectional associative memories. *Applied Optics*, 26(23):4952, December 1987. (*p.* 63)

[142] B. Kosko. *Neural Networks and Fuzzy Systems*. Prentice Hall, Englewood Cliffs, NJ, 1992. (*pp.* 63,64)

[143] J. K. Kruschke. Improving generalization in back-propagation networks with distributed bottlenecks. In *Proceedings, International Joint Conference on Neural Networks*, volume I, pages 443–447, Washington, D.C., 1989. (*p.* 180)

[144] J. K. Kruschke and J. R. Movellan. Benefits of gain: Speeded learning and minimal hidden layers in back propagation networks. *IEEE Transactions on Systems, Man, and Cybernetics*, 21(1), January 1991. (*p.* 180)

[145] A. Kuh and B. W. Dickinson. Information capacity of associative memories. *IEEE Transactions on Information Theory*, IT-35:59–68, 1989. (*p.* 60)

[146] G. Kuhn. Recurrence, context, state, and stack. Paper presented at Speech Research Symposium X, Linthicum, MD, 1990. (*p.* 224)

[147] S. Kullback. *Information theory and statistics*. John Wiley, New York, 1959. (*p.* 328)

[148] H. T. Kung. Why systolic architectures? *IEEE Computer Magazine*, 15(1):37–46, January 1982. (*p.* 402)

[149] H. T. Kung and C. E. Leiserson. Systolic arrays (for VLSI). In *Proceedings, Sparse Matrix Symposium*, pages 256–282. SIAM, 1978. (*pp.* 16,402)

[150] S. Y. Kung. A Toeplitz approximation method and some applications. In *Proceedings, International Symposium on Mathematical Theory of Networks and Systems*, pages 262–266. Western Periodicals Company, North Hollywood, CA, 1981. (*p.* 300)

[151] S. Y. Kung. On supercomputing with systolic/wavefront array processors. *Proceedings of the IEEE*, 72(7), July 1984. (*pp.* 15,305)

[152] S. Y. Kung. *VLSI Array Processors*. Prentice Hall, Englewood Cliffs, NJ, 1988. (*pp.* 15,16,340,341,342,362,381,389,394,409,412)

[153] S. Y. Kung. Adaptive principal component analysis via an orthogonal learning network. In *Proceedings, International Symposium on Circuits and Systems*, pages 719–722, New Orleans, May 1990. (*pp.* 281,285,288)

[154] S. Y. Kung, K. S. Arun, R. J. Gal-Ezer, and D. V. Bhaskar Rao. Wavefront array processor: Language, architecture, and applications. *IEEE Transactions on Computers, Special Issue on Parallel and Distributed Computers*, C-31(11):1054–1066, November 1982. (*p.* 402)

[155] S. Y. Kung, K. S. Arun, and D. V. Bhaskar Rao. State-space and Singular-value Decomposition-based Approximation Methods for the Harmonic Retrieval Problem. *Journal of Optics Society of America*, 73:1799–1811, 1983. (*pp.* 296,300)

[156] S. Y. Kung and W. H. Chou. Mapping Neural Networks onto VLSI Array Processors. In K. W. Przytula and V. K. Prasanna, editors, *Digital Parallel Implementations of Neural Networks*. Prentice Hall, Englewood Cliffs, NJ, 1992. (*p.* 185)

[157] S. Y. Kung, K. Diamantaras, and J. S. Taur. On principal components type networks. In R. Vaccaro, editor, *SVD and Signal Processing*. Elsevier - North Holland, New York, 1990. (*pp.* 296,302)

[158] S. Y. Kung and K. I. Diamantaras. A neural network learning algorithm for adaptive principal component extraction (APEX). In *Proceedings, IEEE International Conference on Acoustics, Speech, and Signal Processing*, pages 861–864, Albuquerque, NM, April 1990. (*pp.* 183,281,283,285)

[159] S. Y. Kung, F. Fallside, J. A. Sorensen, and C. A. Kamm (Editors). *Neural Networks for Signal Processing, II*. Proceedings of the 1992 IEEE Workshop, Helsingoer, Denmark, 1992. (*p.* 7)

[160] S. Y. Kung and Y. H. Hu. A Frobenius approximation reduction method (FARM) for determining optimal number of hidden units. In *Proceedings, International Joint Conference on Neural Networks*, Seattle, July 1991. (*pp.* 180,181)

[161] S. Y. Kung and J. N. Hwang. Systolic design for state space models: Kalman filtering and neural networks. In *Proceedings, 26th IEEE Conference on Decision and Control*, pages 1461–1467, Los Angeles, December 1987. (*pp.* 57,339)

[162] S. Y. Kung and J. N. Hwang. An algebraic projection analysis for optimal hidden units size and learning rate in back-propagation learning. In *IEEE, International Conference on Neural Networks*, volume 1, pages 363–370, San Diego, July 1988. (*p.* 159)

[163] S. Y. Kung and J. N. Hwang. Neural network architectures for robotic applications. IEEE Journal of Robotics and Automation, special issue on Computational Algorithms and Architectures in Robotics and Automation, October 1988. (*p.* 339)

[164] S. Y. Kung and J. N. Hwang. Parallel architectures for artificial neural nets. In *IEEE, International Conference on Neural Networks*, volume 2, pages 165–172, San Diego, July 1988. (*p.* 339)

[165] S. Y. Kung and J. N. Hwang. A unified systolic architecture for artificial neural networks. *Journal of Parallel and Distributed Computing, Special Issue on Neural Networks*, 6(2), April 1989. (*pp.* 40,361)

[166] S. Y. Kung and J. S. Taur. Decision based neural networks with signal/image classification applications. *In press, IEEE Transactions on Neural Networks*, 1993. Also in Proceedings of 1992 IEEE Workshop on Neural Networks for Signal Processing, Helsingoer, Denmark. (*p.* 116)

[167] S. Y. Kung and H. K. Liu. An optical inner-product array processor for associative retrieval. In *Proceedings, SPIE*, Los Angeles, January 1986. (*pp.* 14,59,339)

[168] S. Y. Kung, S. C. Lo, S. N. Jean, and J. N. Hwang. Wavefront array processors: from concept to implementation. *IEEE Computer Magazine*, pages 18–33, July 1987. (*p.* 402)

[169] K. J. Lang and G. E. Hinton. Dimensionality reduction and prior knowledge in e-set recognition. In David S. Touretzky, editor, *Advances in Neural Information Processing Systems*, volume 1, pages 179–185. Morgan Kaufmann, San Mateo, CA, 1990. (*p.* 180)

[170] J. Larsen. A generalization error estimate for nonlinear systems. In S. Y. Kung, F. Fallside, J. A. Sorensen, and C. A. Kamm, editors, *Neural Networks for Signal Processing, II*, pages 29–38. Proceedings of the 1992 IEEE Workshop, Helsingoer, Denmark, 1992. (*p.* 174)

[171] S. E. Levinson, L. R. Rabiner, and M. M. Sondhi. An introduction to the application of the theory of probabilistic functions of a Markov process to automatic speech recognition. *The Bell System Technical Journal*, 62:1035–1074, April 1983. (*pp.* 266,268)

[172] Y. Linde, A. Buzo, and R. M. Gray. An algorithm for vector quantizer design. *IEEE Transactions on Communications*, COM-28(1):84–95, 1980. (*p.* 123)

[173] R. Linsker. Self-organization in a perceptual network. *IEEE Computer Magazine*, 21:105–117, March 1988. (*p.* 296)

[174] R. P. Lippmann. An introduction to computing with neural nets. *IEEE ASSP magazine*, 4:4–22, 1987. (*p.* 153)

[175] H. K. Liu, S. Y. Kung, and J. A. Davis. Real-time optical associative retrieval techniques. *Optical Engineering*, 25:853–856, 1986. (*p.* 379)

[176] L. Ljung. Convergence analysis of parametric identification methods. *IEEE Transactions on Automatic Control*, AC-23:770–783, 1978. (*p.* 310)

[177] L. Ljung. *System Identification: Theory for the User*. Prentice Hall, Englewood Cliffs, NJ, 1987. (*pp.* 40,172)

[178] L. Ljung and J. Sjoberg. A system identification perspective on neural nets. In S. Y. Kung, F. Fallside, J. A. Sorensen, and C. A. Kamm, editors, *Neural Networks for Signal Processing, II*. Proceedings of the 1992 IEEE Workshop, Helsingoer, Denmark, 1992. (*pp.* 10,173,174)

[179] L. Ljung and T. Soderstrom. *Theory and Practice of Recursive Identification*. The MIT Press, Cambridge, MA, 1987. (*p.* 288)

[180] James T. Lo. Finite-dimensional sensor orbits and optimal nonlinear filtering. *IEEE Transactions on Information Theory*, Vol. IT-18(No. 5):583–588, September 1972. (*p.* 170)

[181] D. G. Lowe. *Perceptual Organization and Visual Recognition*. Kluwer, Norwell, MA, 1985. (*p.* 24)

[182] D. G. Luenberger. *Linear and Nonlinear Programming, 2nd ed.* Addison-Wesley, Reading, MA, 1984. (*pp.* 157,163,164,167,311)

[183] R. F. Lyon and C. Mead. An analog electronic cochlea. *IEEE Transactions on Acoustics, Speech, and Signal Processing*, 36(7):1119–1134, July 1988. (*p.* 372)

[184] H. Mada. Architecture for optical computing using holographic associative memories. *Applied Optics*, 24, 1985. (*p.* 378)

[185] W. D. Mao. Neural network algorithms and VLSI architectures for pattern classification. Ph.D. thesis, Princeton University, December 1990. (*p.* 179)

[186] J. D. Markel and A. H. Gray. *Linear Prediction of Speech.* Spring-Verlag, 1976. (*pp.* 207,208,211)

[187] D. Marr and H. K. Nishihara. Representation and recognition of the spatial organization of three-dimensional shapes. In *Proceedings, Roy. Society B.,* pages 269–291, 1978. (*p.* 24)

[188] J. T. Marti. On the convergence of the discrete art algorithm for the reconstruction of digital pictures from their projections. *Computing, Springer-Verlag,* 21:105–111, 1979. (*p.* 151)

[189] S. Mayrargue and J. P. Jouveau. A new application of SVD to harmonic retrieval. In E. F. Deprettere, editor, *SVD and Signal Processing,* pages 467–472. Elsevier - North Holland, New York, 1988. (*pp.* 300,301)

[190] A. D. McAulay. *Optical Computer Architectures.* John Wiley, New York, 1991. (*p.* 378)

[191] J. L. McClelland and D. E. Rumelhart. Distributed memory and the representation of general and specific information. *Journal of Experimental Psychology: General,* 114:158–188, 1985. (*p.* 31)

[192] R. J. McEliece, E. C. Posner, and S. S. Venkatesh. The capacity of the Hopfield associative memory. *IEEE Transactions on Information Theory,* 33:461–482, 1987. (*p.* 59)

[193] C. Mead. *Analog VLSI and Neural Systems.* Addison-Wesley, Reading, MA, 1989. (*pp.* 3,371)

[194] C. Mead and L. Conway. *Introduction to VLSI Systems.* Addison-Wesley, Reading, MA, 1980. (*p.* 15)

[195] D. A. B. Miller. Quantum well self-electro-optic effect devices. *Optical and Quantum Electronics,* 22, 1990. (*p.* 379)

[196] M. Minsky and S. Papert. *Perceptrons: An Introduction to Computational Geometry.* The MIT Press, Cambridge, MA, 1969. (*pp.* 99,152)

[197] G. Mirchandani and Wei Cao. On hidden nodes for neural nets. *IEEE Transactions on Circuits and Systems,* 36, No. 5:661–664, May 1989. (*p.* 194)

[198] J. Moody and C. Darken. Learning with localized receptive fields. Technical Report YALEU/DCS/RR-649, Yale University, New Haven, September 1988. (*p.* 179)

[199] J. E. Moody. Note on generalization, weight decay, and architecture selection in nonlinear learning systems. In B. H. Juang, S. Y. Kung, and C. A. Kamm, editors, *Neural Networks for Signal Processing, I,* pages 1–10. Proceedings of the 1991 IEEE Workshop, Princeton, NJ, 1991. (*p.* 10)

[200] M. Moonen, P. Van Dooren, and J. Vandewalle. Combined Jacobi-type algorithms in signal processing. In R. Vaccaro, editor, *SVD and Signal Processing.* Elsevier - North Holland, New York, 1990. (*p.* 305)

[201] B. De Moor, J. Staar, and J. Vandewalle. Oriented energy and oriented signal to signal ratio concepts in the analysis of vector sequences and time series. In E. F. Deprettere, editor, *SVD and Signal Processing*, pages 209–232. Elsevier - North Holland, New York, 1988. (*p. 296*)

[202] N. Morgan et al. The RAP: A ring array processor for layered network calculations. In S. Y. Kung et al., editor, *Proceedings, Application Specific Array Processors*. IEEE Computer Society Press, Los Almitos, CA, 1990. (*pp. 378,402*)

[203] M. C. Mozer and P. Smolensky. Skeletonization: A technique for trimming the fat from a network via relevance assessment. In David S. Touretzky, editor, *Advances in Neural Information Processing Systems*, volume 1, pages 107–115. Morgan Kaufmann, San Mateo, CA, 1989. (*p. 180*)

[204] U. A. Muller, B. Baumle, P. Kohler, A. Gunzinger, and W. Guggenbuhl. Achieving supercomputer performance for neural net simulation with an array of digital signal processors. *IEEE Micro*, pages 55–65, October 1992. "Acvhieving Super Computer Performance with a DSP Array Processor", A. Gunzinger et al., Proceedings, International Conference on Supercomputing, Minneapolis, 1992. (*p. 399*)

[205] C. Myers, L. R. Rabiner, and A. E. Rosenberg. Performance tradeoffs in dynamic time warping algorithms for isolated word recognition. *IEEE Transactions on Acoustics, Speech, and Signal Processing*, Vol. ASSP-28(No. 6):623–635, December 1980. (*p. 133*)

[206] K. Nakano. Association — a model of associative memory. *IEEE Transactions on Systems, Man and Cybernetics*, SMC-2, 1972. (*p. 43*)

[207] M. Nayeri and W. K. Jenkins. Analysis of alternate realizations of adaptive IIR filters. In *Proceedings, 22nd Asilomar Conference on Signal, Systems, Computers*, pages 2157–2160, Pacific Grove, CA, 1988. (*p. 211*)

[208] H. Nyquist. Certain topics in telegraph transmission theory. *Transactions of the AIEE*, 47:617–644, February 1928. (*p. 22*)

[209] E. Oja. A simplified neuron model as a principal component analyzer. *Journal of Mathematical Biology*, 15:267–273, 1982. (*pp. 280,281,290,296*)

[210] E. Oja. *Subspace Methods for Pattern Recognition*. Research Studies Press, Letchworth, U.K., 1983. (*p. 301*)

[211] E. Oja and J. Parkkinen. *Texture Subspaces*. Springer-Verlag, Berlin, 1987. (*pp. 296,301,303*)

[212] A. Oppenheim and R. Schafer. *Digital Signal Processing*. Prentice-Hall, Englewood Cliffs, NJ, 1975. (*pp. 40,206*)

[213] Y. H. Pao. *Adaptive Pattern Recognition and Neural Networks*. Addison-Wesley, Reading, MA, 1989. (*p. 79*)

[214] C. H. Papadimitriou and K. Steiglitz. *Combinatorial Optimization: Algorithms and Complexity*. Prentice-Hall, Englewood Cliffs, NJ, 1982. (*pp. 321,323,335*)

[215] D. Parikh, N. Ahmed, and S. D. Stearns. An adaptive lattice algorithm for recursive filters. *IEEE Transactions on Acoustics, Speech, and Signal Processing*, Vol. ASSP-33(4):983–996, August 1988. (*p.* 214)

[216] D. Parker. Learning logic. Technical Report TR-47, Center for Computational Research in Economics and Management Science, MIT, Cambridge, 1985. (*pp.* 99,154)

[217] B. N. Parlett. *The Symmetric Eigenvalue Problem*. Prentice-Hall, Englewood Cliffs, NJ, 1980. (*pp.* 282,304)

[218] B. N. Parlett. Remarks on matrix eigenvalue computations. In S. Y. Kung et al., editor, *Signal Processing: Theory and Applications, Part I*, pages 106–120. Prentice Hall, N.J., 1985. (*p.* 304)

[219] E. Parzen. On estimation of a probability density function and mode. *Annals of Mathematical Statistics*, 33:1065–1076, 1962. (*pp.* 170,190)

[220] D. A. Patterson and J. L. Hennessy. *Computer Architecture: A Quantitative Approach*. Morgan Kaufmann Publishers, San Mateo, CA, 1990. (*p.* 15)

[221] T. Pavlidis. *Algorithms for Graphics and Image Processing*. Computer Science Press, 1982. (*p.* 262)

[222] B. A. Pearlmutter. Learning state space trajectories in recurrent neural networks. *Neural Computation*, 1:263–269, 1989. (*pp.* 222,224)

[223] E. Persoon and K. S. Fu. Shape discrimination using Fourier descriptors. *IEEE Transactions on Systems, Man, Cybernetics*, SMC-7:170–179, 1977. (*p.* 42)

[224] C. Peterson, J. Sutton, and P. Wiley. iWarp: A 100-mop LIW microprocessor for multicomputers. In *IEEE Micro*, June 1991. (*p.* 404)

[225] P. J. Pineda. Generalization of backpropagation to recurrent neural networks. *Physics Review Letters*, 18:2229–2232, 1987. (*pp.* 222,224)

[226] V. F. Pisarenko. The retrieval of harmonics from a covariance function. *Geophysical Journal of Royal Astronomical Society*, 33:247–266, 1973. (*p.* 300)

[227] D. C. Plaut and G. E. Hinton. Learning sets of filters using back-propagation. *Computer Speech and Language*, 1987. (*p.* 159)

[228] T. Poggio and F. Girosi. A theory of networks for approximation and learning. Technical Report AI Memo No. 1140, MIT, 1989. (*pp.* 170,173,175,176,178,199)

[229] M. J. D. Powell. Restart procedure for the conjugate gradient method. *Mathematical Programming*, 12:241–254, April 1977. (*pp.* 163,165)

[230] R. W. Prager, T. D. Harrison, and F. Fallside. Boltzmann machines for speech recognition. *Computer Speech and Language*, pages 3–27, 1986. (*p.* 266)

[231] D. Psaltis, A. Sideris, and A. Yamamura. A hierarchical model for voluntary movement and its application to robotics. In *Proceedings, First IEEE International Conference on Neural Networks*, volume IV, pages 551–558, San Diego, June 1987. (*p.* 191)

[232] D. Psaltis, K. Wagner, and D. Brady. Learning in optical neural computers. In *Proceedings, First IEEE International Conference on Neural Networks*, San Diego, June 1987. (*p.* 191)

[233] L. Rabiner, B. H. Juang, S. E. Levinson, and M. M. Sondhi. Recognition of isolated digits using hidden Markov models with continuous mixture densities. *Bell Laboratories Technical Journal*, 64:1211–1234, July 1985. (*p.* 258)

[234] L. R. Rabiner and B. H. Juang. An introduction to hidden Markov models. *IEEE ASSP Magazine*, 3(1):4–16, January 1986. (*pp.* 239,243,247,252,255,258)

[235] U. Ramacher. Guidelines to VLSI design of neural nets. In U. Ramacher and U. Ruckert, editors, *VLSI Design of Neural Networks*, chapter 1, pages 1–17. Kluwer, Norwell, MA, 1991. (*pp.* 375,387)

[236] U. Ramacher. Hamiltonian dynamics of neural networks (I). *Neural Networks*, 1993. (*pp.* 222,224)

[237] U. Ramacher. Synapse — a neurocomputer that synthesizes neural algorithms on a parallel systolic engine. *Journal of Parallel and Distributed Computing*, 9, 1992. (*p.* 405)

[238] R. Rastogi, P. K. Gupta, and R. Kumaresen. Array signal processing with interconnected neuron-like elements. In *Proceedings, IEEE International Conference on Acoustics, Speech, and Signal Processing*, pages 54.8.1–54.8.4, Dallas, 1987. (*p.* 311)

[239] M. Recce and P. C. Treleaven. Parallel architectures for neural computers. In R. Eckmiller and C. von der Malsburg, editors, *Neural Computers*, pages 487–498. Springer-Verlag, New York, 1988. (*p.* 396)

[240] P. Richert et al. Digital neural network architecture and implementation. In U. Ramacher and U. Ruckert, editors, *VLSI Design of Neural Networks*, chapter 7, pages 125–152. Kluwer, Norwell, MA, 1991. (*pp.* 400,403)

[241] Eve A. Riskin, Les E. Atlas, and S. R. Lay. Ordered neural maps and their applications to data compression. In B. H. Juang, S. Y. Kung, and C. A. Kamm, editors, *Neural Networks for Signal Processing, I*, pages 543–551. Proceedings of the 1991 IEEE Workshop, Princeton, NJ, 1991. (*p.* 87)

[242] A. J. Robinson and F. Fallside. Static and dynamic error propagation networks with application to speech coding. In *Proceedings, IEEE Conference on Neural Information Processing Systems*, pages 632–641, Denver, 1988. (*p.* 219)

[243] F. Rosenblatt. The perceptron: A probabilistic model for information storage and organization in the brain. *Psychology Review*, Vol. 65, 1958. (*pp.* 42,99)

[244] F. Rosenblatt. *Principles of neurodynamics: Perceptrons and the theory of brain mechanisms*. Spartan Books, Washington D.C., 1961. (*pp.* 104,116,122)

[245] D. E. Rumelhart, G. E. Hinton, and R. J. Williams. Learning internal representations by error propagation. In D. E. Rumelhart, J. L. McClelland, and the PDP Research Group, editors, *Parallel Distributed Processing (PDP): Exploration in the Microstructure of Cognition*, volume 1, chapter 8, pages 318–362. MIT Press, Cambridge, MA, 1986. (*pp.* 99,235)

[246] D. E. Rumelhart, J. L. McClelland, and the PDP Research Group. *Parallel Distributed Processing (PDP): Exploration in the Microstructure of Cognition*, volume 1. The MIT Press, Cambridge, MA, 1986. (*pp.* 76,77,154,155,219,329)

[247] D. E. Rumelhart and D. Zipser. Feature discovery by competitive learning. *Cognitive Science*, 9:75–112, 1985. (*pp.* 77,78)

[248] S. Saarinen, R. Bramley, and G. Cybenko. Ill-conditioning in neural network training problems. Technical Report CSRD Report No. 1089, Center for Supercomputing Research and Development, University of Illinois at Urbana-Champaign, January 1991. (*p.* 174)

[249] J. P. Sage, K. Thompson, and R. S. Withers. An artificial neural network integrated circuit based on MNOS/CCD principles. In *Proceedings, AIP Conference*, page 151, San Mateo, CA, 1986. Morgan Kaufmann Publishers. (*pp.* 339,373)

[250] H. Sakoe and S. Chiba. Dynamic programming optimization for spoken word recognition. *IEEE Transactions on Acoustics, Speech, and Signal Processing*, 26:43–49, August 1978. (*pp.* 133,135)

[251] T. D. Sanger. Optimal unsupervised learning in a single-layer linear feedforward neural network. *Neural Networks*, 2(6):459–473, 1989. (*p.* 296)

[252] T. D. Sanger. An optimality principle for unsupervised learning. In D. S. Touretzky, editor, *Advances in Neural Information Processing Systems*, volume 1, pages 11–19. Morgan Kaufmann, San Mateo, CA, 1989. (*p.* 283)

[253] L. L. Scharf. The SVD and reduced-rank signal processing. In R. Vaccaro, editor, *SVD and Signal Processing*. Elsevier - North Holland, New York, 1990. (*p.* 277)

[254] C. Seitz. Concurrent VLSI architectures. *IEEE Transactions on Computers*, C-33, December 1984. (*p.* 385)

[255] T. J. Sejnowski. Parallel networks that learn to pronounce English text. *Complex Syst.*, 1:145–168, 1987. (*p.* 215)

[256] T. J. Sejnowski and C. R. Rossenberg. A parallel network that learns to read aloud. Technical Report, JHU/EECS-86/01, Johns Hopkins University, Department of Electrical Engineering and Computer Science, 1986. (*p.* 331)

[257] C. E. Shannon. A mathematical theory of communication. *Bell System Technical Journal*, 27:623–656, October 1968. (*p.* 22)

[258] J. J. Shynk. Performance of alternative adaptive IIR filter realization. In *Proceedings, 21st Asilomar Conference on Signal, Systems, Computers*, pages 144–150, Pacific Grove, CA, 1987. (*p.* 211)

[259] J. J. Shynk. Adaptive IIR filtering. *IEEE ASSP Magazine*, pages 4–21, April 1989. (*p.* 214)

[260] J. Sietsma and R. Dow. Neural net pruning, why and how. In *Proceedings, IEEE International Conference on Neural Networks, Vol. II, San Diego, CA*, pages 205–212, 1988. (*p.* 182)

[261] M. A. Sivilotti, M. A. Mahowald, and C. A. Mead. Real-time visual computations using analog CMOS processing arrays. In P. Losleben, editor, *Advanced Research on VLSI*, pages 295–312. MIT Press, Cambridge, MA, 1987. (*pp.* 14,339,372)

[262] J. Sjoberg and L. Ljung. Overtraining, regularization, and searching for minimum in neural networks. Technical Report LITH-ISY-I-1297, Department of Electrical Engineering, Linkoping University, Sweden, May 1992. (*p.* 173)

[263] P. Smolensky. Information processing for dynamic systems: foundations of harmony theory. In D. E. Rumelhart, J. L. McClelland, and the PDP Research Group, editors, *Parallel Distributed Processing (PDP): Exploration in the Microstructure of Cognition*, volume 1, chapter 6, pages 194–281. The MIT Press, Cambridge, MA, 1986. (*p.* 328)

[264] S. A. Solla. Capacity control in classifiers for pattern recognition. In S. Y. Kung, F. Fallside, J. A. Sorensen, and C. A. Kamm, editors, *Neural Networks for Signal Processing, II*, pages 255–266. Proceedings of the 1992 IEEE Workshop, Helsingoer, Denmark, 1992. (*pp.* 10,175)

[265] N. Sonehara, M. Kawato, S. Miyake, and K. Nakane. Image data compression using a neural network model. In *Proceedings, International Joint Conference on Neural Networks*, volume II, pages 35–42, Washington, D.C., 1989. (*p.* 185)

[266] K. Steinbush. The learning matrix. *Kybernetik (Biological Cybernetics)*, pages 36–45, 1961. (*p.* 43)

[267] M. Takeda and J. W. Goodman. Neural networks for computation: number representations and programming complexity. *Applied Optics*, 25:3033–3046, September 1986. (*pp.* 54,65,311)

[268] K. Tanabe. Projection method for solving a singular system of linear equations and its applications. *Numerische Mathematik*, 17:203–214, 1971. (*p.* 150)

[269] D. W. Tank and J. J. Hopfield. Simple "neural" optimization networks: An a/d converter, signal decision circuit, and a linear programming circuit. *IEEE Transactions on Circuits and Systems*, 33:533–541, 1986. (*pp.* 44,51,311)

[270] G. Taubin. Algebraic nonplanar curve and surface estimation in 3-space with applications to position estimation. Technical Report, LEMS-43, Brown University, Providence, RI, February 1988. (*p.* 186)

[271] J. S. Taur and S. Y. Kung. Comparison of several learning subspace methods for classification. In *Proceedings, IEEE International Conference on Acoustics, Speech, and Signal Processing*, May 1991. (*pp.* 303)

[272] M. F. Tenorio and W. T. Lee. Self organizing neural networks for the identification problem. In David S. Touretzky, editor, *Advances in Neural Information Processing Systems*, volume 1, pages 57–61. Morgan Kaufmann, San Mateo, CA, 1989. (*p.* 183)

[273] G. Tesauro and R. Janssens. Scaling relationship in back-propagation learning: dependence on predicate order. Technical Report, Center for Complex Systems Research, University of Illinois at Urbana-Champaign, February 1988. (*p.* 159)

[274] A. P. Thakoor. Content-addressable, high density memories based on neural network models. Technical Report, JPL D-4166, Jet Propulsion Laboratory, Pasadena, CA, March 1987. (*p.* 375)

[275] S. Tomboulian. Introduction to a system for implementing neural net connections on SIMD architectures. Technical Report, NASA Langley Research Center, Hampton, NASA Contractor Report 181612, January 1988. (*pp.* 14,339,394)

[276] J. R. Treichler, Jr. C. R. Johnson, and M. G. Larimore. *Theory and Design of adaptive filters.* John Wiley, New York, 1987. (*p.* 214)

[277] R. R. Tuck. Porta-SIMD: An optimally portable SIMD programming language. Ph.D. thesis, Department of Computer Science, Duke University, Durham, NC, also published as Technical Report, Duke University CS-1990-12 and University of North Carolina CS TR90-021, 1990. (*p.* 398)

[278] R. Udo and E. Deprettere. On the design of pipelined architecture for the cordic algorithm. Technical Report, Delft, University of Technology, The Netherlands, 1985. (*p.* 412)

[279] S. Ullman. *An Approach to Object Recognition: Aligning Pictorial Descriptions.* Massachusetts Institute of Technology, Artificial Intelligence Laboratory, A. I. Memo No. 931, December 1986. (*p.* 24)

[280] R. J. Vaccaro, D. W. Tufts, and G. F. Boudreuz-Bartels. Advances in principal component signal processing. In E. F. Deprettere, editor, *SVD and Signal Processing*, pages 115–146. Elsevier - North Holland, New York, 1988. (*p.* 296)

[281] R. L. De Valois and K. K. De Valois. *Spatial Vision.* Oxford University Press, New York, 1988. (*p.* 21)

[282] J. Vanderschoot, D. Callaerts, W. Sansen, J. Vandewalle, G. Vantrappen, and J. Janssens. Two methods for optimal MECG elimination and FECG detection from skin electrode signals. *IEEE Transactions on Biomedical Engineering*, BME-34(3):233–242, March 1987. (*p.* 298)

[283] J. Vandewalle and B. De Moor. A variety of applications of singular value decomposition in identification and signal processing. In E. F. Deprettere, editor, *SVD and Signal Processing*, pages 43–91. Elsevier - North Holland, New York, 1988. (*pp.* 296,304)

[284] V. N. Vapnik. *Estimation of dependency based on empirical data.* Springer-Verlag, New York, 1982. (*p.* 200)

[285] V. N. Vapnik. *Private Communication*, 1992. (*p.* 175)

[286] V. N. Vapnik and A. Ya. Chervonenkis. On the uniform convergence of relative frequencies of events to their probabilities. *Theory of Probability and Its Applications*, 16:264–280, 1971. (*pp.* 10,175)

[287] S. S. Venkatesh. *Private Communication*, 1991. (*p.* 61)

[288] A. J. Viterbi. Error bounds for convolution codes and an asymptotically optimal decoding algorithm. *IEEE Transactions on Information Theory*, IT-13:260–269, April 1967. (*p.* 255)

[289] J. A. Vlontzos. Hidden Markov Models for Character Recognition. Ph.D. thesis, Department of Electrical Engineering, University of Southern California, November 1989. (*pp.* 258,259)

[290] J. A. Vlontzos and S. Y. Kung. A hierarchical system for character recognition with stochastic knowledge representation. In *Proceedings, IEEE International Conference on Neural Networks*, volume 1, pages 601–608, San Diego, July 1988. (*pp.* 242,258,259)

[291] J. A. Vlontzos and S. Y. Kung. Digital neural network architecture and implementation. In U. Ramacher and U. Ruckert, editors, *VLSI Design of Neural Networks*, chapter 11, pages 205–227. Kluwer, Norwell, MA, 1991. (*p.* 390)

[292] J. E. Volder. The cordic trigonometric computing technique. *IRE Transactions on Electronic Computer*, EC-8(3):330–334, September 1959. (*p.* 412)

[293] C. von der Malsburg. Self-organization of orientation selective cells in the striate cortex. *Kybernetik*, 14:85–100, 1973. (*p.* 77)

[294] K. Wagner and D. Psaltis. Multilayer optical learning networks. *Applied Optics*, 26:5061–5076, December 1987. (*pp.* 14,339,379)

[295] A. Waibel, T. Hanazawa, G. Hinton, K. Shikano, and K. Lang. Phoneme recognition using time-delay neural networks. *IEEE Transactions on Acoustics, Speech and Signal Processing*, 37:328–339, March 1989. (*p.* 217)

[296] D. Walters. Selection of image primitives for general-purpose visual processing. *Computer Vision, Graphics and Image Processing, 37*, pages 261–298, 1987. (*pp.* 24,208)

[297] Li Wang and Dong-Chen He. Texture classification using texture spectrum. *Pattern Recognition*, 23(8):905–910, 1990. (*p.* 130)

[298] S. Watanabe. *Knowing and Guessing − A Quantitative Study of Inference and Information*. John Wiley, New York, 1969. (*p.* 301)

[299] R. L. Watrous and L. Shastri. Learning phonetic features using connectionist networks: An experiment in speech recognition. In *Proceedings, IEEE International Conference on Neural Networks*, pages 381–388, San Diego, June 1987. (*p.* 219)

[300] A. S. Weigend, B. A. Huberman, and D. E. Rumelhart. Predicting the future: A connectionist approach. Technical Report No. PDP-90-01, Department of Psychology, Stanford University, Palo Alto, CA., 1990. Also in International Journal of Neural Systems, Vol. 1, No. 3, 1990. (*p.* 180)

[301] P. J. Werbos. Beyond regression: New tools for prediction and analysis in the behavior science. Ph.D. thesis, Harvard University, Cambridge, 1974. (*pp.* 99,154)

[302] H. White. Connectionist nonparametric regression: Multilayer feedforward network can learn arbitrary mappings. *Neural Networks*, 3:535–549, 1990. (*p.* 183)

[303] B. Widrow and S.D. Stearns. *Adaptive Signal Processing*. Prentice-Hall, Englewood Cliffs, NJ, 1985. (*pp.* 214,301)

[304] B. Widrow and R. Winter. Neural nets for adaptive filtering and adaptive pattern recognition. *IEEE Computer Magazine*, 21:25–39, 1988. (*p.* 151)

[305] G. Widrow and M. E. Hoff. Adaptive switching circuit. *IRE Western Electronic Show and Convention: Convention Record*, pages 96–104, 1960. (*pp.* 99,149)

[306] R. J. Williams and D. Zipser. A learning algorithm for continually running fully recurrent neural networks. *Neural Computation*, 1(2):270–280, 1989. (*pp.* 219,221,222,224)

[307] D. J. Willshaw, O. P. Buneman, and H. C. Longuet-Higgins. Non-holographic associative memory. *Nature*, 222:960–962, June 1969. (*p.* 43)

[308] M. Yasunaga et al. Design, fabrication and evaluation of a 5-inch wafer scale neural network LSI composed of 576 digital neurons. In *Proceedings, International Joint Conference on Neural Networks*, volume II, page 527, San Diego, 1990. (*p.* 394)

[309] A. L. Yullie and N. M. Grzywacz. The motion coherence theory. In *Proceedings, International Conference on Computer Vision*, pages 344–353, 1988. (*p.* 178)

[310] P. Zafiropulo. Performance evaluation of reliability improvement techniques for single loop communications systems. *IEEE Transactions on Communications*, pages 742–751, June 1974. (*p.* 363)

[311] K. Diamantaras and S. Y. Kung. An unsupervised neural model for oriented principal component extraction. In *Proceedings, IEEE International Conference on Acoustics, Speech, and Signal Processing*, May 1991. (*p.* 303)

[312] K. I. Diamantaras. Principal component learning networks and applications. Ph.D. thesis, Department of Electrical Enginnering, Princeton University, Princeton, NJ, 1990. (*pp.* 296,303)

[313] S. Y. Kung and K. I. Diamantaras. Neural networks for extracting unsymmetric principal components. In B. H. Juang, S. Y. Kung, and C. A. Kamm, editors, *Neural Networks for Signal Processing, I*, pages 50–59. Proceedings, IEEE Workshop, Princeton, NJ, 1991. Also as "Multilayer neural networks for reduced-rank approximation", IEEE Transactions on Neural Networks, 1993. (*p.* 293)

[314] J. S. Taur and S. Y. Kung. Fuzzy-decision neural networks. In *Proceedings, IEEE International Conference on Acoustics, Speech, and Signal Processing, Minneapolis, April*, 1993. (*pp.* 126,129)

[315] J. S. Taur and S. Y. Kung. Prediction-based networks with ecg application. In *Proceedings, IEEE International Conference on Neural Networks, San Francisco*, 1993. (*p.* 225)

[316] K. S. Fu. *Sequential Methods in Pattern Recognition and Machine Learning.* Academic Press, New York, 1968. (*p.* 116)

[317] N. J. Nilsson. *Learning Machines.* McGraw-Hill, New York, 1965. (*p.* 116)

Index